The Evil Doers

D1235982

by Dick Sheppard

9/24/02

To Norman,
I Hope you enjoy The book!
Best Wishes!!
Dick Sheppard

Unlimited Publishing
Bloomington, Indiana

Distributing Publisher:
Unlimited Publishing, LLC
Bloomington, Indiana

www.unlimitedpublishing.com

Distributed electronically by:
BookZone, Inc.
Scottsdale, Arizona

www.bookzone.com

Advancing Publishing

Contributing Publisher:
Dick Sheppard

Cover and Book Design by Charles King
Copyright © 2002 by Unlimited Publishing, LLC
This book was typeset with Adobe® InDesign®, using the Minion® and Willow® typefaces.

Cover photo provided by the National Nuclear Security Administration, Nevada Operations Office.

Unlimited Publishing, LLC ("UP") provides worldwide book design, production, marketing and distribution services for authors and small presses, serving as distributing publisher. BookZone provides worldwide electronic distribution. Neither BookZone nor UP exercises editorial control over books. Sole responsibility for the content of each work rests with the author(s) and/or contributing publisher(s). Information or opinions expressed herein may not be interpreted in any way as originating from nor endorsed by UP, BookZone nor any of their officers, employees, agents or assigns.

Printed copies of this book are available at:
http://www.unlimitedpublishing.com/authors

Electronic copies of this book are available at:
http://www.bookzone.com/bookzone

ISBN: 1-58832-050-2

Unlimited Publishing
Bloomington, Indiana

ACKNOWLEDGMENTS

I am very grateful to many people who have assisted me in the creation and completion of my first novel. In particular I would like to thank my wife for allowing me to remain at work late at night to work on this novel. Many thanks go out to my dad, Barbara, Robin, Chuck, Linda, Nick, Petro, Mark, Mike, Keith, Rich, David, Chris, Jeannine, Peter, Judith, Nivea and Vicki who have given me the use of their names and also for their support, time and proof reading skills, without which, this novel could not have been completed. I would also like to give thanks to Tom Clancy for his books on submarines and aircraft carriers, which provided a wealth of knowledge and technical understanding of military combat procedures and terminology. Finally, I would like to thank all of those countless people that I have met over the last two and one half years that have given me ideas and a sense of direction in areas that needed clarification.

PROLOGUE

Her 883-foot slender body knifed through the dark Atlantic. Her 45,000 tons of steel painted black, with a gold line dividing the hull from the white superstructure glistened in the darkness. Her cabin and navigational lights sparkled across the calm North Atlantic water like a thousand diamonds resembling a floating city crossing the sea. Her four funnels, painted a golden yellow, pointed towards the heavens, three of which spewed forth smoke and grit toward the stars as her boilers consumed tons of coal that produced the steam needed to turn her three giant screws. Majestically, she sailed headlong into the bitter cold darkness at a speed of 23 knots.

This was the age of wonder. Man had made fantastic machines that conquered the air, the sea, and the land. This vessel was the pinnacle of man's maritime achievements. She was the most luxurious vessel ever built, she was heralded to be unsinkable, she was the crown jewel of the White Star Line… she was the Titanic.

The temperature was 31° F. Overhead, the multitude of stars and planets produced a radiant display of God's wonder that shined softly upon the inky black sea. There was no moon. The Atlantic stretched unusually calm before the mighty Titanic as she sliced her way through the darkness, her wake forming a frothy ribbon behind her, glowing softly in the dim light of the stars above. New York lay approximately 1200 miles ahead due East. Captain Smith was off the bridge as his crew kept watch into the night.

Mid-ship, the Marconi headset crackled and buzzed as the radio operator Phillips sent countless, "Having a marvelous time… wish you were here." messages to Cape Race. Suddenly, a strong radio signal blasted into the Phillips' ears. "Another bloody iceberg warning." Phillips thought. His fist jerked the telegraph key sending a reply, "Received, thanks." This message from the Mesaba, gave specific coordinates for an ice field that lay directly in the path of the

Titanic. Perhaps because several ice warnings had been delivered to the bridge earlier that day, perhaps because of the remaining messages Phillips still had to send to Cape Race, or perhaps because it was meant to be, the Mesaba ice warning never made it to Captain Smith, but sat on Phillips desk. At 11:00 PM, Phillips was again interrupted by another iceberg warning from the California, "Say, old man, we are stopped and surrounded by ice." This time Phillips was not as gracious as the time before and snapped back, "Shut up! Shut up! I am busy. I am working Cape Race."

Below decks, passengers for the most part either slept or were preparing to go to sleep. A few remained in the first class lounge, and others in the smoking lounge, while still others strolled on the outside promenade decks taking in the night air before retiring for the night.

High above the bow stood two men in the crow's nest looking into the inky darkness. "Damn. It's as cold as a witches tit." said one. The other replied, "I suppose that this is really going to do some good. They don't even give us any field glasses, there is no moon, and even if we do see something that even resembles a berg, by the time we see it, ring that bloody bell, give then the message, the ship responds to her helm, we are sure to hit it. Besides we are unsinkable aren't we?? So why bother?? Window dressing, that's all we are mate… window dressing. What I wouldn't give to be in my warm bunk with a shot of Irish whisky right now."

"I'd rather be next to a warm Irish lass myself. Now that's something that can really keep you warm on a night like this." he said as his eyes stared into the cold darkness. The wind stung his cheeks; his hands were stuffed into his coat pockets. "Odd." he thought, "it was as if some of the stars seemed to blink. On… Off… On… Off." Again he stared into the darkness as he leaned slightly forward into the wind, holding onto the crow's nest. "What was that?" he thought as he wiped his eyes, "It looks like a waves crashing onto a reef." His eyes strained harder as he now saw why the stars were blinking at him. It was like they were giving him a visual SOS, but the warning was too late. The stars were being hidden from view by the body of the massive iceberg that floated directly in the path of the Titanic. "Jesus, Mary, and Joseph" the man cried as he reached for the rope on the bell. The bell sounded three times and the other seaman cranked at the telephone to the bridge.

Sixth Officer, Moody reached for the phone and said, "Yes." The watchman cried, "Iceberg dead ahead Sir... Iceberg dead ahead!" "Thank you." said Moody as he placed the phone back into the cradle and yelled to Murdoch, "Iceberg right ahead." Murdoch immediately used the telegraph to the engine room to give full speed astern and ordered the helmsmen Hichens, "Hard a' starboard". Putting the helm to starboard would make the vessel turn port (left). Murdoch intended to swing the Titanic around the berg. As the Titanic's bow began to swing, Murdoch ordered Hichens, "Hard a port" to continue to swing the Titanic away from the iceberg.

It was Sunday, April 14, 1912 at 11:40 PM when Murdoch and the rest of the passengers aboard the Titanic felt a shudder and heard a sickening scratching sound. The Titanic was crashing against an underwater spur that was buckling the plates of her hull and flooding the first six of her watertight compartments. Titanic designer Thomas Andrews told Captain Smith the horrible news. The unsinkable Titanic, the ship that God himself could not sink, was sinking and would flounder within two and one half hours taking with her 1,517 men, women, and children to their death. 706 men, women, and children survived and were plucked from the cold Atlantic by the Carpathia at dawn.

Thus began the legend of the Titanic, hypnotic, terrifying, controversial, and a story that would never die in the imaginations of men, women, and children of all ages. It was as if the ghost of the 1,517 people that had perished with the Titanic refused to allow their memory to decay with the passage of time. Countless books were published about the tragedy as well as a Broadway play and several motion pictures were made during the twentieth-century about the sinking of the unsinkable Titanic.

Many of the people who died as well as many of the people who survived the sinking of the Titanic were immortalized. How many of us remember stories told about the orchestra that played, "Nearer My God To Thee" up to the very end, the Unsinkable Molly Brown who wanted to return to the survivors and rescue as many as possible, Mr. and Mrs. John Jacob Astor who chose to die together rather than be separated in life, Captain Smith who piloted his ship into history, Thomas Henry Ismay, the president of White Star Lines who saved his own life by entering a lifeboat reserved for women and children, and Frank "Lucks" Towers, who is reported to have survived the sinking of the Titanic, only to find himself a survivor of sinking of the Empress of Ireland, and the torpedoing of the Lusitania. His reported words, "Now what!" as the torpedo exploded into the side of the Lusitania, had inspired Rod Serling to write an episode for his television series, *The Twilight Zone*®.

As the Titanic sank, she had broken up on her way down to her watery grave, two and one half miles deep in the north Atlantic. Like a toy boat, she had gone down by the bow, filling with water, thus raising her stern high into the air. This was definitely not something that designer Thomas Andrews had designed for her to do.

With gravity tugging at both her water filled bow and still dry stern that was sticking high into the air, the Titanic ripped apart, breaking in two. The bow section descending into the dark abyss first and crashed upright into the ocean floor, hiding forever the icebergs damage.

The stern section had bobbed like a fishing cork for several minutes, thus giving the hundreds of hopeful survivors the false belief that they would simply ride on their new found lifeboat until help arrived.

Horribly, their hopes vanished as the stern section quickly began to follow the bow into the depths of the sea. As the stern disappeared beneath the waves, the cry from the hundreds of doomed people filled the night air like the roar of a sports arena during a world-series game. Minutes later, the numbing cold took its toll as hypothermia blissfully silenced the voices of these lost souls with an eternal sleep. The stern followed the bow to the ocean floor and crashed about a mile from the bow section.

On the way to the ocean floor, the partially air filled stern section was crushed by the rapidly increasing water pressure. The contents of the Titanic had poured out of the ship from both sections. Dishes, boilers, toilets, baggage, furniture, and bodies were strewn across the mile-wide ocean floor that separated the two halves of the Titanic. This is what Dr. Ballard had discovered in 1985. All he had to do was follow the debris back to the Titanic herself.

The first sight of the Titanic sitting upright in the darkness was overpowering. The lights from the submersible Alvin pierced the darkness and lifted the black veil that had hidden the Titanic for almost a century. Her majestic shape was still there. The anchor chains were on her forward deck, the mast that had carried the men in the crow's nest had crashed back against the bridge and brilliant orange columns of rust now shrouded the once neatly painted ship. The grand staircase that was the crown jewel of the Titanic first class section was gone, eaten by wood bores, but the Titanic, the crown jewel of the White Star Line was still there, silent, majestic, and untouched for 74 years.

In 1912, the Titanic disaster quickly turned into a moneymaker as newspapers sold as fast as they could be printed. The disaster would prove to be an economic bonanza seventy-four years later when Dr. Robert Ballard and his crew located the final resting place of the Titanic.

Dr. Ballard only took away with him the memories and the videotapes of the Titanic when he left her side for the last time. A plaque was left by Dr. Ballard on the Titanic near the grand staircase that read, "In recognition of the scientific effort of the American and French explorers who found the R.M.S. Titanic; be it resolved that any who may come hereafter leave undisturbed this ship and her contents as a memorial to deep water exploration."

For Dr. Robert Ballard and his crew, the Titanic represented a tomb for the 1517 people that had died that fateful night. Dr. Ballard wanted the Titanic to rest in peace for all time, but to others, it was to become an object of salvage.

The elusive Titanic had finally been found. For Dr. Ballard, the honors bestowed upon him were richly deserved. For others, the knowledge of the true coordinates that would pinpoint the exact location of the Titanic was like a call to arms. To these people, this was money in the bank.

Soon after the location of the Titanic was made public, a court battle began for exclusive salvage rights for the Titanic remains. Finally, in 1994, the R.M.S. Titanic, Inc. won the battle.

The eternal slumber of the Titanic was now at an end. Deep diving manned submarines poked and prodded the debris field, photographed the entire remains of the Titanic hull, used sonar to see through the mud in the hopes of finding out what did sink the Titanic, and brought hundreds of objects to the surface. The Titanic fever swept the entire planet. A Titanic safe was brought to the surface and opened on public television and objects were placed on display in Long Beach, CA, Memphis, TN., Atlantic City, NJ and elsewhere.

For the first time since the Titanic had disappeared beneath the waves of the North Atlantic, people were able to see actual artifacts of the Titanic. Bottles, dishes, port holes, medical syringes, and other items were made available for public viewing in traveling exhibits, all for the price of admission, of course.

For $25.00, you could mail order a piece of Titanic coal about the size of a pecan nut, receive a certificate of authenticity that the coal was really from the Titanic, and a display case with your name on it.

In 1996, you could have purchased a ticket on a cruise ship, hob knob with the rich and famous, movie stars and the like, and watch the raising of a large piece of the Titanic from ringside. Fortunately or unfortunately, whichever the case may be, the piece never made it to the surface and went crashing back to the sea floor. It was as if the Titanic had said "no" to the world at large, reached up from its watery grave and snatched the artifact back to her bosom.

Countless other entrepreneurs cashed in on the general stampede to buy anything that bore the name Titanic. Broadway show tickets, sweatshirts, paintings that had the unfortunate misprint S. S. Titanic and not R.M.S. Titanic, 1912 coins with a picture of the Titanic in a plastic case sold like hot cakes to a hungry market. Even a new motion picture was made depicting the tragedy and quickly became the highest grossing box-office film in the history of Hollywood. It seemed as if the world had gone mad.

It was no wonder that a group of businessmen began discussing the possibility of building another Titanic. Why not? After all, wouldn't it be great to sail on an exact duplicate of the Titanic, follow the exact course that Captain Smith had taken, and live to tell the story?

Quickly, the idea took form as business plans were drafted and circulated around the investment community. Finally, the dream became a reality and construction began on the R.M.S. Titanic II, an exact replica down to the last bolt. She would sail in the year 2002. For a mere $100,000.00, you could travel 1st class. For $30,000.00 you could go steerage.

During the '90s, the news of the new Titanic hit the wire services with little notice to the general population of the world. There were more important things to worry about. President Clinton, was defending himself from countless women who wanted to "tell all" about their nights in the White House, the word "intern" suddenly had a new meaning, oral sex was not like having real sex and could not be called adultery, Kenneth Star issued subpoenas like New York City parking tickets trying to find something that would stick to the Teflon® president. President Clinton was eventually impeached by the House and tried in the Senate, India and Pakistan were testing nuclear weapons like two kids in a pissing contest, Pfizer, Inc. had introduced a new pill that would cure male impotency. Who cared about this new Titanic II anyway?

There were those that did care about the Titanic. In fact, they had been instrumental in raising the needed investment capital to build the vessel. The investment bankers, who raised the money seemingly overnight, did not realize that over 60% of the funds came from mysterious overseas investors. Carefully, the money had been laundered so that there would be no trace of its origin. Silently these evildoers watched as the investment dollars for the new Titanic grew. Quietly, they began to put the finishing touches on a plan for world domination.

To the evildoers, the Titanic was a means to an end, an end that would assure a final victory over their enemy. It would be an end that would have as its beginning, the sinking of the new Titanic, the death of the Prime Minister of Israel, and ultimately, the death of all of the leaders of the free world. It would be an end that would surely trigger a Jihad and ultimately, Armageddon, their final revenge.

CHAPTER ONE

The sun shown brightly through the window of the Israeli air Force One jet flying at an altitude of 35,000 feet, non-stop from Tel Aviv to Heathrow. Prime Minister, Joshua Cane sat motionless staring out of the window at the clouds that stretched forth beneath him. In is hand; he held a solitaire diamond engagement ring that radiated a fiery glow in the sunlight. Joshua was lost in thought, his mind was reliving the events of his past, he did not move, his breath was regular but shallow, and his eyes were watery.

The sounds of Boston filled his mind as he remembered the warm sun and smell of spring in the air that April morning 1969. He was a student at Harvard University attending law school. His father was the Israeli ambassador to the United Nations. He was 25 years old, his family was independently wealthy, and he did not have a care in the world. He was on his way back to his fraternity as he briskly turned a corner and walked into Jacky, knocking her to the ground, her books and papers flying in the air.

Stunned and embarrassed as she started to her feet, "Why don't you watch where you are going, you jerk!"

"I'm sorry, did I hurt you?" Joshua said as he watched her adjust her glasses and rub her backside.

Glaring up at Joshua she said, "Sorry are you, look at my dress." as she tried to get to her feet. Josh was taken back by the lines of her face, the lips that were full, and the eyes that dazzled back at him.

"Here, let me help you to your feet, I am terribly sorry." he said apologetically for the second time. He reached for her hand. Taking her hand in his, Josh felt something he had never experienced. Her hand was warm, gentle, and there was something about the way that she grabbed back at his hand that sent what could only be described as a chill through his body. Quickly, he reached for her papers, dropping some as he reached for others. He was nervous and clumsy. Jacky began to laugh as she watched.

Finally collecting her books and papers, he nervously tried to arrange them into some type of order as he handed them to her and said, "My name is Josh. Joshua Cane… I, uh…"

"Jacky… Jacky McGuire." as she offered her hand. "I am sorry for calling you a jerk."

"You had every right to call me a jerk and a lot of other things as well." replied Josh as he began to examine her more carefully. Her red hair was long and beautiful, her waist was small, she was 5' 5" or 6", and she smelled like the breath of spring. Slowly Josh began to walk with her.

"Can I carry those books for you? It's the least I could do after…" Josh stood there looking at her.

"No that's OK, I'm late for class." Jacky said as she picked up the pace. "Drama class, damn I'm going to be late for rehearsal."

"I insist." replied Josh as he took the books from her arms. Together they walked toward an ivy-covered building. Jacky was more relaxed as they entered the small theater, turned and said," Thank you for carrying my books." She looked up at Josh. He was 6'4", about 150 pounds, with naturally curly hair. She paused and grabbed his hand squeezing it lightly and said, "Thanks…" as she walked down the aisle and disappeared behind the stage.

Josh was beside himself, he stood there smelling her scent and then took a seat quietly in the back to watch the rehearsal and to watch Jacky.

Josh's trance was broken by a steward's question, "Would you like to have something to drink, Mr. Prime Minister, before we land?"

"No thank you." said Josh.

"We will be arriving at Heathrow in one hour sir." said the steward.

Josh had turned to face to the window and was again lost in thought. The words of the steward were never acknowledged.

The April spring day had been a turning point in Josh's life. At 25, the son of the Israeli Ambassador had given him the freedom to visit far away places and meet many attractive girls. His studies and his nightlife had taken up most of his time at Harvard. He was listed as one of the most eligible bachelors on campus, he was handsome, and he was rich. What more could a girl want in a man? Josh used this status to bed the girls he desired, but Jacky was not one of those mindless sorority girls. She had done something to him without even trying. That fateful encounter had made Josh really want to get to know this new woman in his life and to be with her. Josh did not know how to handle this situation. After he had watched the rehearsal, he waited outside for her. As Jacky made her way out of the building, he ran up to her and said, "Hi."

Jacky looked surprised and said, "Oh hi. What are you doing here?"

"Waiting for you." replied Josh.

Jacky stood there looking at Josh and said, "Oh?"

"Yea… Uh… I thought we could have something to eat. I know a great little place not to far from here that makes a real good steak. Hungry?"

Jacky swayed back and forth as she thought about the invitation. She recognized his name when he had introduced himself to her on the corner. She knew his reputation, but then again, who didn't. She was hungry and besides, having dinner didn't mean that she had to sleep with him. Looking back, her beautiful smile flashed across her face and she said, "OK!"

From that moment on, Jacky and Josh spent more and more time together. Jacky was an Irish Catholic and was a drama major at Radcliff on a full scholarship. Her family lived on Cape Cod. Her mother had died at childbirth and her father owned a small bakery. She had always loved the theater and had worked back stage at a summer theater on Cape Cod during school years trying to make friends and hoping desperately to break into the theater. Her father could not afford to send her to college and her acting career looked bleak. Once in a while, a producer had arranged for her to play small roles in a few plays during the summer. She was an honest, hard working girl that reminded him of his own daughter. One evening, she was called to his office and was told that she would not be needed at the theater any longer. Her heart sank as she said, "Why?"

The producer looked sternly at her and said, "Because my child, you will be attending Radcliff next year and we cannot afford to pay your commute."

Jacky stood silent as the words finally sank in. "Radcliff?" she said.

"Yes… I have a few friends … Uh… that have arranged for a scholarship fund in the arts. You will be the first to receive a full scholarship award my child. Congratulations!" The rest, as they say was history for Jacky.

After their chance meeting, the warm summer was spent at the ballpark watching the Boston Red Sox®, visiting Cape Cod, and generally having a great time getting to know each other. They soon realized that they were in love.

It was October when Jacky had called Josh and arranged to meet him after class. Her voice was different and tense. When Josh met her at a small coffee shop, Josh realized that there was something wrong. "Are you OK?' he asked as he reached for her hand. It was cold and damp.

Jacky held her head down and did not look at Josh as she said in a trailing voice, "Yes, I'm fine."

Josh reacted by saying, "What's wrong."

A tear fell from her eye as she said, "Josh… I'm pregnant. What are we going to do?" Immediately, the tears in her eyes streamed down her face. Josh sat motionless for several minutes saying nothing. He wasn't sure what to say. The thought of being a father had never entered his mind.

The next few days were spent talking about their future together. Jacky wanted to get her degree, but how could she do that now. She would lose her scholarship and her life would be over before it had begun. Josh told Jacky to sit tight for a few days and wait for him to get back from New York. He knew what he had to do.

Josh arrived in New York and went straight to his home. He had called his father and said he had to meet with him regarding an urgent personal matter. As Josh entered the family residence, he went straight into the study. His father was waiting for him. It wasn't too hard for his father to realize the reason behind the meeting. He was well aware of his son's Harvard extracurricular activities. He had warned his son many times in the past about the consequences of his actions and now the day of reckoning was upon him.

"But dad, I love her!" pleaded Josh.

"Nonsense…" replied his father. "You don't know the meaning of love. Infatuation maybe… Love … NO! How could you do this to your mother and me? Didn't we send you to the best school… Harvard!! What are you getting your degree in law or fornication?? You are a disgrace to your family and your religion. You are Jewish and she is Catholic. What are you … nuts? How can you marry a girl that is Catholic and I the Ambassador to Israel? You will end this relationship immediately. I will arrange for the care of the girl and the baby. You are to remain in New York until we can arrange for this girl to be relocated to another university. You are never to see her again. If you do… you will no longer be my son and your career and your inheritance will vanish. Do you understand me Joshua? Do I make myself perfectly clear?"

Jacky never saw Josh again. She was approached by the university and sent to a quiet place to have her child David, named after her father. After that, she was sent back to Radcliff to finish her studies. The baby was born and Jacky kept the name of his father a secret. She didn't want her son to know that his father was a jerk as she had originally thought. The years passed and David grew up, her career blossomed, and Josh entered the political arena.

David had always been naturally curious about his father. Jacky would only say that he was killed six months before he was born in an automobile accident. David was looking for some books he had placed in the attic of their Long Island home one afternoon and discovered a curious box. Inside the box, he found letters and pictures of his mother and a man he did not recognize. The letters were from Josh and one letter was post marked in Israel two years ago and was addressed to his mother. It soon became clear that his father was alive and was a Jew. He sat motionless for a long time trying to understand what had actually happened to his mother and why his father had abandoned her. He heard a voice. "David!" His mother had just come home. He heard her steps coming up the stairs, "David..." As soon as she saw the box, she knew why he had that odd look on his face, "Why didn't you tell me Mother?"

Jacky tried to tell David the truth for the first time. The words came slowly as she began to tell of the heartbreak she had endured. Tears fell from her eyes as these horrible words and memories left her lips for the first time in twenty-one years. David listened and was silent for a long time. Slowly, he got up and told his mother that he had to go away for a while. David's life had been turned upside down. He returned a week later and told his mother that he was going to Israel. He wanted to meet his father. Jacky protested, but there was no turning back.

Josh was a popular political figure in Israel and it was said that he would one day be Prime Minister. When Josh was approached by David, he immediately took him into his arms. The two men talked for days. There was a lot of anger inside of David and a lot of regret inside of Josh. Somehow, the blood bond between father and son overcame the resentment that David had for his father. As the weeks passed, the two men became friends and then father and son. When David returned to New York, Jacky was furious with her son. They fought and said things to each other that they both regretted. David finally gave up trying to reason with his mother and returned to his father in Israel, became a Jew, and joined the Israeli army. He never saw his mother again.

The Gulf War broke out on January 17,1991 as the allied forces began their attack at 2:38 AM. On January 18th, Iraq began to launch SCUD missiles into Israel. On February 25, 1991, Iraq launched another SCUD attack against Tel Aviv. David was in an Israeli military group that was protecting an American barracks. The US had sent Patriot missiles to defend Israel. One Patriot missile was launched after a SCUD. The Patriot fragmented the SCUD, but the SCUD warhead hit the barracks, killing twenty-eight Americans and David.

Josh closed his eyes as he recalled calling Jacky to tell her the horrible news. She was hysterical on the phone. Josh notified the Israeli embassy in New York to assist and made arrangements for her immediate flight to Israel. David was buried before sundown while Jacky was in transit. Josh arrived at the cemetery to find Jacky standing over David's grave. Hearing footsteps, she turned to see Josh and said, "YOU BASTARD." The tears of anguish fell from her eyes as she raised her fist, striking Josh in the face. Josh held her in his arms until her struggling stopped. Silently, they held each other.

"I'm sorry Jacky... I'm sorry... I'm sorry." repeated Josh.

Lurching away from his arms, Jacky sputtered, "You sorry son-of-a-bitch. That's what you said to me when we first met. Remember? You are sorry for what? Fucking me? Fucking up my life? Fucking up the life of our son David who is dead now because of YOU! I loved you once Josh with all my heart and you did not have the balls to stand up for me against your father. You left me at Radcliff, pregnant, alone and heart broken. All I wanted to do was spend my life with you Josh. I'll never forgive you for that Josh... never."

Jacky turned and started to walk away. Josh cried, "Jacky wait... Let me explain."

Jacky turned with hatred in her eyes, "Explain what? What is there to explain or is this a Jew trying to give a poor Catholic girl his confession of sin?"

Josh took the verbal assault and said, "Jacky... I love you... I always have. Look, I came with this." Josh pulled out a small black box from his pocket. "Before I saw my father, I had bought this for you. I have kept it with me all these years trying to figure out a way to give it to you. I know this is not the right time, but..."

Jacky screamed, "You really are a sick puppy, you know that. You are SICK."

"Jacky listen to me... my father would have abandoned the both of us. You... me... the baby! I thought a lot about it before I reluctantly agreed to his terms. At least you would be taken care of and so would David. I did what I did for you. I have always regretted that decision, but I cannot change the past. I never married because I could never find a girl that I loved as much as you. Please believe me. I love you and always have loved you, and will always love you Jacky." Tears were now streaming down his face.

"You're sick." repeated Jacky as she once again turned and started to walk away.

"Jacky!" cried Josh, "Please take this ring. If you change your mind and find a way to forgive me... Send the ring to me, and I will come to you." Josh placed the ring into Jacky's hand.

Jacky looked into her hand at the ring and then threw it in Josh's face, "Take your ring Josh and shove it up your ass! I never want to see you again."

The plane made a slow bank to the right as the steward said, "Mr. Prime Minister, we are about to land." Josh fastened his seat belt, and looked out the window again.

He remembered picking up the ring and returning to his home and arranging to have the ring delivered to Jacky by courier. That was so long ago... eleven years, he thought. Not long after the Gulf War and the death of David, Josh was elected Prime Minister of Israel.

His mind wandered forward in time. A week ago, a package arrived addressed to him. He looked at it curiously; it was a Federal Express International® package. It was sent by Jacky McGuire and addressed to Josh and was marked personal. The secret service had x-rayed the package and tested it for explosives before giving it to Josh. His hands had trembled as he opened the package. It was the engagement ring and a note that read, "Meet me in Southampton on the 10th of April. If you still love me, we will get married at sea on the Titanic. Love Jacky."

As Josh looked at the ring in his hand, the aircraft landed at Heathrow. He placed the ring in his vest pocket as he wiped his eyes.

CHAPTER TWO

Jacky had returned from Israel an emotional wreck. Her father had passed away the year before. She was alone and had no one to talk to. She had started to drink heavily. Upon her return from Israel, her agent notified the theater that she was ill and would not return to the stage for several days. When she did return to the theater, her performances were spotty and some of the times, the stage crew smelled booze on her breath. Her understudy was delighted. The newspaper gossip columnist had a field day, as Jacky was often times referred to as a lush.

Losing her son was more than she could bear. After Josh had abandoned her, her baby was the center of her life. Josh's father agreed to care of her and the baby under the condition that she remained silent about Josh. She knew that if she ever spoke out about what had happened, she would be cut off financially and her future would be ruined. Josh's father would see to that. There was no escape except through David. At least he needed her and listened to her every night.

She eventually returned to school at Radcliff, after the birth of David and received her degree two years later. The Broadway producer that had given her the scholarship also got her first real role in a Broadway play. Her lucky break came in a musical. After that, she went on to win three Tony Awards for best actress in three plays during the years that followed.

Whereas her past was full of fun and success, the death of David had destroyed her will to do anything but drink. Josh made matters worse. His words of love at the cemetery, words that she wanted so desperately to hear twenty-one years ago… words that would have made her happy then, now ate at her soul like battery acid. The more angry and depressed she became over Josh and David, the more she drank, until one night, drunk and depressed, she had collapsed on stage.

She was taken immediately to Bellevue Hospital. From there, she was secretly transferred to a private institution. Her first few days were hell. She wanted to kill herself, but she was placed on a suicide watch until she finally became stable. Her agent arranged for psychiatric care from a special group of doctors. One afternoon, the door to her room opened as Dr. Hamid Moosavi entered the room. Each a day for an hour each day, Dr. Moosavi sat quietly and began to treat his patient. He was interested in her past life and took copious notes as Jacky told him her life's story. After a few days, the meetings began to last longer and longer. Several weeks later, Dr. Moosavi called Jacky's agent to arrange for a meeting.

"I am sorry to say that things are not working as well as I had expected."

"What seems to be the problem?

"She is not responding well. Her traumas are really deep seated in her subconscious and we need to take a more aggressive treatment. I am afraid that we will have to send her to another institution."

Jacky's agent looked back at Dr. Moosavi and said nothing.

"There is a special clinic in Europe that has a new program. I would like to send her there. I'm afraid that if we don't, she will never fully recover.

"What wrong with the good old USA Doc? Don't we have the best doctors that money can buy to treat her here? Why Europe?"

"Because… Well let's just say, in my opinion, she cannot be treated successfully here. She will eventually have a relapse, will continue to drink and probably will drink herself to death. In America, over 80% of people who are diagnosed as alcoholics have relapses. I don't want that, do you? The clinic I am referring to has a 95% cure rate meaning that 95% of their patients never have another drink for the rest of their lives. They have a radically new treatment procedure that involves a new line of thought… sort of like brain washing. That is what Jacky needs. She needs help and these people can give it to her."

After a half an hour of discussion, it was agreed that Jacky would be sent to this special clinic. It was located in Oslo, Norway, far away from the rest of the world, quiet, and remote.

A week later, heavily sedated, Jacky barely recognized her agent as she was wheeled out of the institution on a gurney and taken to JFK airport. She was placed on a special corporate jet and thirty minutes later, the plane took off.

Dr. Moosavi waited until the jet reached cruising altitude and entered a small compartment. He picked up a radiophone and made a call to Iraq. The call was scrambled. Several seconds passed before he heard a voice on the other end, "Hello".

Dr. Moosavi said, "The package will arrive in 9 hours. Make sure everything in ready." He placed the phone down and lit up a cigarette. The blue smoke curled toward the ceiling as he thought back to his days in Iraq. Hamid Moosavi was a psychiatrist by training, but he was also a mole placed in New York to gather any information that would help Iraq. New York was a hot bed of political activity with the United Nations, Wall Street, and many corporate headquarters located in Manhattan. Moosavi had a private practice and could also practice in a multitude of psychiatric institutions in the tri-state area. Using his role as psychiatrist, he found that many of his clients worked in sensitive areas of the UN and other US agencies. Once he had them under his control and gained their trust, he was told information that he passed on to Iraq.

When Jacky had been admitted to Bellevue, he was contacted as a matter of simple routine and was the first doctor to see her. He, like most New Yorkers had been reading about Jacky's slow spiral downhill and fight with alcoholism. Finding himself fascinated by her, he quickly got himself assigned to her case. When Jacky's agent had her transferred to a private institution, Moosavi used his connections to get himself assigned to the institution and continued to see her. Using his influence, he had the administration of the institute assign him to her case. Once he started to treat her, Moosavi quickly discovered her former relationship with Joshua. Soon after that, he listened as Jacky relived the encounter with Josh at the cemetery and the engagement ring. Having sufficient information, he notified his superiors. The voice on the other end of the phone in Iraq took the information and hung up. Within 24 hours, Moosavi was called to the Iraq mission in New York and debriefed in detail. From that moment on, Jacky became a pawn in an elaborate espionage game that would use her as bait to lure Joshua Cane into a trap that would lead to his death.

Moosavi was pleased as he turned out the light to get some sleep. Nine hours later, the jet landed. Two men and another gurney awaited the jet in an empty hanger. Jacky was placed on the gurney and rolled into the back of a hearse. Moosavi sat in the passenger seat as the hearse drove off into the darkness.

The Norge Psychiatric Institute was a private institution reserved for special research in mind control. It was tucked away in the Hardangervidda mountain range in southern Norway and was off limits to everyone, except those that were allowed entry by the governing board. Their specialty was brain washing for espionage purposes. Countries that wanted to use the institute for their own political purposes provided funding for the institute. The military establishments of the world also funded the institute heavily and shared in the procedures developed for cracking captured espionage agents, brain washing them, and sending them back to their employers under their control.

In a spacious administrative office sat a group of men watching a television set, showing a rather young Soviet psychiatrist giving a lecture. This lecture had been the very foundation on which the institute was founded. The videotape was a copy of a film taken back in the late 50s during the height of the Cold War between the USSR and the United States.

"The human brain is a curiously ingenious system of living cells that unite together to form the very essence of rational thought, human emotion, and personal identity. Some people have stated that the brain is the home for the soul and when we die, the brain energy is transformed into an energy pulse that is carries our awareness and identity, off to some place that others have referred to as heaven or hell.

Others consider the brain as nothing more than a simple, but complex bio-computer. When the life forces of the brain are extinguished, it dies like the heart muscle, and eventually rots away into dust.

There is one thing that we know for certain; roughly 10% of the brain is used throughout our lifetime to run our bodies and to store vast quantities of information. It is a biochemical device that can easily get out of tune chemically, thus producing a variety of behavioral problems and abnormalities.

The brain is also a glut for data input. Smells, sight, sound, temperature, taste, and touch are data input streams that the brain processes twenty-four hours a day. Even as we sleep, the brain is awake, doing its job.

To control the brain, one could use a number of different chemicals that can induce a variety of desirable benefits or can produce horrible behavior patterns that can literally destroy the individual. Chemicals, while helpful, are harmful with their side effects, tolerance levels that build up in a body reducing their effectiveness, and chemicals can be very, very unpredictable in their long-term results. Stop the chemical medication, and the patient will return to his normal biochemical state of psychological imbalance in relatively short order. Thus, a more simplistic and reliable way of mind control must be developed for the treatment for mental illness.

To achieve this goal, I have developed a treatment based on sensory deprivation, a complete and total cessation of all sensory input to the brain. Sight, sound, taste, smell, and touch are all stopped from entering the brain. The results have been rather startling. After six to eight hours of sensory deprivation, the mind goes into a complete state of distress. The person hallucinates as the mind, desperate for data input, tries to manufacture its own data input stream. Eventually, this hallucination stage stops and the person's mind completely loses all reason, becoming a willing subject for suggestion and treatment.

There are memory reserves inside the brain that can also be used to achieve the desired goals set forth by the therapist. The brain has vast warehouses of data... stored experiences of childhood, adolescence and adulthood. These life-long experiences or events in a person's life combine in unique ways to make a person love, hate, get angry, become scared, cry, or become euphoric. For example, everyone has the capacity for good or evil. It is the mind's ability, or for that matter, inability to deal with the sum total of life-long experiences that turns one individual into an Adolph Hitler or another into a man of God. The capacity for good and evil rest solely in the minds ability to correctly understand and deal with its own life experiences and then make the correct assessment for a behavioral pattern that will govern its future thought process. For example, Hitler firmly believed that the world had no respect for the Jews and did not care what happened to them... even if he killed them. In Hitler's mind, his anti-Semitic belief was confirmed in 1939, when the ship St. Louis returned 900 Jews to Germany because no country would allow them entry. Other mass murderers who also had illogical thought processes are men like Tim McVeigh, who rationalized that the deaths of innocent children in the Okalahoma bombing as being "collateral damage" or John Wayne Gacy who sodomized and killed 33 boys calling them "worthless queers".

What made these men make these illogical decisions has at its roots, events that go back to childhood, or in some cases their adult lives. Some of these events in a person's life make a person have strong feelings of self hatred brought on for example, by child abuse from a parent or a schoolyard bully. Events like these place the person into a situation that ultimately leads to narcissism, an extreme form of self-centeredness. Put another way... to correct this problem in my life, I am going to do something that will be so great for me, that nothing I do will ever be considered wrong... at least by me that is.

If the sick mind can be brought to such a state that we can break it down, examine each part and wash away these illogical associations that the mind has created, we can make tremendous advances in the field of mental disease by rearranging the thought process.

Look at this film of a man who is absolutely terrified of snakes. As a child, this mans father beat him with his black belt and told the boy that the snake would get him when he did something that displeased him. One week into the treatment program, he is touching and handling all forms of snakes, even poisonous snakes. This is a little girl who was afraid of heights because her alcoholic mother would hold her out of her apartment window when she would not stop crying... look at her walk on a narrow beam 100 feet above the ground.

Sensory deprivation treatment holds the promise for new advances in the treatment of the mentally ill. If used appropriately, it will lead to cures for many illnesses that trouble humanity."

The phone rang. One of the men clicked the remote and the television set became silent, "Yes... Thank you. Dr. Moosavi has just arrived with the package."

The men left the room and entered a large auditorium. Standing in the middle of the stage was a large tank of water. The temperature was 98.6°F. Two men pushed a gurney into the room. Jacky, heavily sedated, did not move. Carefully, the men removed her clothes and placed her into a special diving body suit. Her eyes were sealed with a thick cream and patches. Her hands were placed inside thick gloves. Her nose was filled with a thick cream substance that quickly solidified into a rubbery plug. The cream was odorless and tasteless. Earplugs were placed into her ears and sealed with the cream. Her head was placed into a helmet and the lower rim was secured to the suit. Carefully, she was hoisted into the tank and suspended in the water. A soundproof enclosure was lowered over the tank. One technician turned on a television monitor and started a clock that began to record the passage of time. Dr. Moosavi said to the others, "I'll give her twenty hours before she breaks."

"How long will the treatments last?"

"Once she is under our control, two weeks... three weeks tops and she can be returned to New York. With regular office visits, her treatment can be reinforced until the time comes that she is needed. At that point, she will be a living, mindless, zombie that will do anything that we ask of her. We will allow her to return to the stage and resume her normal life, but we will have placed a switch inside of her mind that will allow us to control her mind at will.

Jacky McGuire is a very complex woman. She has one side of her that would enjoy watching Joshua Cane being boiled in oil. The other side of her loves Joshua and would consider marriage. We will use both sides of her personality. She will actually believe that she is in love with Josh. When the time comes, she will remember how much she hates him and wants him dead. She will become the perfect bait to lure Joshua Cane into the trap that will be built for him.

CHAPTER THREE

The Gulf War had been a calculated gamble that Iraq had taken to capture the rich oil fields of Kuwait and expand its realm of influence in the Persian Gulf. It was also a calculated gamble that the United States would be unable to muster the international cooperation needed to halt Iraq's plans for expansion. Iraq had assembled the largest standing army in the world, but in the end, lacked the firepower and technology to complete its mission.

The defeat in the Gulf War had been decisive and humiliating. The Iraqi army was pounded into submission and the country was bombed relentlessly for 40 days, day and night. The morale of the Iraqi army was nonexistent as entire masses of Iraqi troops surrendered to the allied forces of United Nations. During the Gulf War, one entire platoon surrendered to a single American corporal that was traveling by jeep between advancing allied forces. The young corporal's jeep was stuck in the sand. Over the distant horizon advanced an Iraq column, complete with three tanks. The American soldier grabbed his weapon, hid himself behind his vehicle, and considered his position. Suddenly, the Iraqi troops started to advance toward the soldier, dropping their weapons, and raising their hands in surrender. The American soldier quickly commandeered one of the three tanks, rescued his jeep, and led 150 men and three tanks into captivity. Iraq finally stopped their attack and submitted to the United Nations control. For Sadaam, it was a time of anger, humiliation, and steadfast resolve that he would someday once again regain Iraq's honor and defeat the forces that had conspired against him.

To the Iraqi government and to other governments of the world, the planet Earth was nothing more that a large chessboard. Each country had its knights, pawns, kings and queens. Information was collected by their respective espionage agents around the world, arranged and rearranged, trying to fit random pieces of a jigsaw puzzle together into a plan that would further their cause. With the arrival of Jacky McGuire, this new piece of the puzzle began to attract other pieces until a masterful plan began to emerge.

Joshua Cane was now the Prime Minister of Israel. Jacky McGuire was under Iraq mind control and could be used as bait and lure the Prime Minister into a trap. Since the Titanic discovery, Titanic fever had infected the world. The world's business communities cashed in on the Titanic rage with movies, books, and even sold salvaged pieces of coal. One group of businessmen wanted to rebuild the Titanic, sail her on the exact path taken by the original Titanic, and relive the experience without sinking. While Titanic mania grew in intensity in the United States, other countries could care less. Russia was in complete economic disarray and virtually for sale. With the right contacts and with enough money, one could purchase almost anything from her military arsenal.

Slowly, but surely a plan was born to seek revenge on the world. The first step in the plan was the control of Jacky McGuire. This task had been completed successfully. The second step was to acquire a submarine. The task was complicated, but not impossible. To raise capital, Russia was selling the newly developed Kilo class sub to any-one that had the money. Countless smaller countries eagerly lined up and purchased the subs. All that had to be done was make contact with the proper Russian official and a deal could be made. For Iraq however, the arrangements had to be made quietly since they could not openly buy the subs due to the newly created embargo placed on them by the United Nations. Secretly, they approached the Russian officials and the amount was agreed to.

A Russian Kilo class sub, originally designed to replace the ag-ing Foxtrot USSR attack subs, was being completed in the Krasnoye Sormovo shipyard. It was an island facility that had once built nuclear subs for the USSR, but now was a production export facility for Kilo class subs that were contracted to foreign countries. The Kilo sub had a displacement of 2400 tons surfaced and 3000 tons submerged, 229' 7" long with 3 diesel engines, one shaft (6 blades) and two electric motors. The Kilo class subs could do 25 knots and could, for a price, be equipped with nuclear tipped torpedoes.

As the sub entered the Black Sea, the plan began. Final payment had been made and the Kilo sub had been turned over to an Iranian crew at Krasnoye Sormovo. They did not know that nine Iraqis were hidden deep within the sub. The subs oxygen purification system had been filled with explosive canisters of cyanide gas. Once the cyanide gas was released, it would render the crew helpless within seconds. As the sub entered the Black Sea, the Iraqi pirates donned their class two protective suits and set off the gas. The Iranian captain and crew never really had time to react to their situation as the shroud of death quickly engulfed the boat. The results were almost instantaneous. Every Iranian crewman died at their position as the sub continued to make its way through the depths of the Black Sea.

The nine Iraqis quickly began the process of air purification by restoring the back up oxygen purification systems removing the cyanide gas with the subs air scrubbers. Still wearing their suits, the men began to deploy several explosive charges that they would release from the torpedo tubes. One of the men sent a frantic distress signal, indicating that the sub was taking on water and sinking fast. At the same time, the explosives were shot into the sea, and detonated. The Russian network of listening stations that criss-crossed the Black Sea floor heard the explosion, as did the American SOSUS network. After that, the Iraqi pirates gathered the bodies of the dead crew and shot them out of the torpedo tubes into the sea. Their next mission was to clean the interior of the sub and remove any cyanide residue. Once completing this task, they removed their class two suits and navigated the sub to their base in the Barents Sea.

In Moscow, a long faced Russian Ambassador paid an emergency visit to the Iranian Ambassador with the tragic news of the lost submarine and crew. Immediately, the Russian government transmitted news of the disaster to Washington with a weak request for assistance in finding the missing sub. The Russian and American governments searched for several days with no results. The American government was not too eager to find the sub for Iran, thinking it might be salvageable and the Russian government knew that it could not be found, since it had not sunk. Both governments went through the motions to appease the Iranian government and finally called it quits. The Iranians were outraged that the sub could not be found, but had no way of locating the sub without Russian assistance. The final report was written outlining the sinking of the sub and the loss of all hands as Iran reluctantly placed another order with terms that final payment would only be made once the sub was delivered to Iranian waters and delivered by Russian sailors. Quietly, without any public announcement, the case was closed and the sub was now in Iraqi control.

The third step in the plan was to have the Titanic rebuilt. The news of the idea to rebuild the Titanic started in 1998. This was the year after the release of John Cameron's classic Titanic movie. The film shattered all box office records and was the largest moneymaker in film history, or as they say, until something better comes along. With the Titanic movie came, what was coined, Titanic Fever. Everything that had the name Titanic on it was selling like hot cakes. There were those that decided it would be nice to really cash in on the Titanic fever and proposed that the Titanic be rebuilt, stick for stick. The cost was estimated to be $600 million and it could be completed in time to make its maiden voyage on the same day that the Titanic sailed, but in the year 2002.

As the new Titanic grew in popularity within the investment community, the Iraqi government secretly laundered money that found its way into the hands of the investment bankers that were funding the project. She would be rebuilt in the same Southampton shipyard and be built by the descendants of the men who built the original. Unlike the original Titanic however, she would be truly unsinkable with watertight compartments everywhere throughout the ship.

This time, the steel used to build her would not be contaminated with sulfur and would not shatter if struck by an iceberg, but bend and the rivets would hold. During the salvaging of the Titanic, several pieces of the ships hull plates and rivets were recovered. When they were analyzed, it was discovered that there was too much sulfur in the steel. This was not done deliberately to cut cost because the Titanic was built with the best materials that money could buy at the time. Analyzing the salvaged parts from the Titanic, it was discovered that at a temperature of 31°F, the Titanic's steel plates and rivets actually became brittle. When the Titanic hit the iceberg, the ship cracked, the steel plates buckled, the rivets popped out and produced a crack over 330 feet long, but only about ½ inch wide. In effect, a hole that was only 12 square foot sank the Titanic, not a gash in her hull as popularized over the years. It was also deduced that the ill-fated Titanic's rudder was undersized and could not make the 883 foot ship maneuver as quickly as was need on that fateful night.

The new Titanic would have the finest steel hull, water tight compartments on all levels below the water line, a proper rudder, the latest in radar, sonar, GSA positioning, satellite communications, more than enough life boats for all passengers and she would be built with all of the elegance of the 1912 era. The grand staircase would once again be the centerpiece of the ship with the glass dome and its famous clock and instead of being coal fired, she would be oil fired. To the crafty investors, it would be like sailing on a dream that you could touch.

As the investment community lined up to get a piece of the action, the designers fanned the fires of the investment community and boldly stated, "The new Titanic would live up to the 1912 boast of being unsinkable. In fact, it was once said that the Titanic was a ship that even God could not sink. I think that with today's technology to detect icebergs, our superior ship building capabilities, and our modern steel, I would actually dare God to try and sink this Titanic!" Her construction would be complete by December 2001 and would be sailing to New York on April 10, 2002, ninety years to the day that the original Titanic left on her maiden voyage.

The final part of the plan was to acquire an iceberg. A company was located in St. Johns, Newfoundland that harvested icebergs. Using a tugboat, they would pull the icebergs into an area where they would harvest and melt the ice, using the water to manufacture spirits or selling the water or ice to health crazed wealthy Japanese who wanted to drink only the purest water on earth. It was a cute marketing gimmick and about all some people could do to earn a living in St. John's, since fishing of the Grand Banks had been depleted years earlier.

Situated on the Labrador Current, these St. John's iceberg hunters had a plentiful supply of product from February through July. They also assisted the International Ice Patrol in their efforts to track and mark icebergs. Since the sinking of the Titanic in 1912, the International Ice Patrol had been formed to track icebergs in the shipping lanes between Europe and the United States. Any ship that would pass through the Ice Patrol's "ice limit", an area identified by sightings of icebergs, ran the risk of colliding with an iceberg. Since the Labrador Current ran into the Gulf Stream, there also was a problem of dense fog due to the temperature difference of 20 degrees between the two water masses. Because of the dense fog and even with the latest in modern radar, there was still the risk of hitting an iceberg, as did the S.S. HANSHEDTOFT. She hit an iceberg on January 30, 1959, forty miles south of Cape Farewell, Greenland. As was the Titanic, the S.S. HANSHEDTOFT was on her maiden voyage when she hit the iceberg, sinking without a trace with 95 passengers and crew on board.

Icebergs originate from 100 or more tidewater glaciers off West Greenland. Usually 10,000 to 15,000 icebergs are calved each year. While most of these icebergs melt, a significant number find their way to the Grand Banks of Newfoundland and into the shipping lanes. Icebergs come in a variety of shapes and sizes, but are categorized by their height above water. The "growler" is less than 17 feet above the water, a "small" iceberg is between 17 and 50 feet above the water, "medium" icebergs are between 51 and 150 feet high, "large" icebergs are between 151 to 200 feet high, and "very large" icebergs are over 240 feet high. 90% of the icebergs remain below the water line with the upper 10% visible.

Of all the icebergs, the small icebergs are the most dangerous. The larger icebergs can easily be detected by radar or by eye and can be readily avoided, but the smaller icebergs are difficult to spot by eye or by radar. These icebergs could be small enough to be the size of the vessel that may strike it. The shape of the iceberg also adds to the difficulty of detection. Icebergs are classified as being Tabular, steep sides with flat tops with a length to height ratio of 5 to 1, or Non-Tabular, meaning not tabular, but are dome shaped, sloping, blocky, and pinnacle. The "growlers" that are mostly submerged with a tabular flat top are the most dangerous of all since they are hard to see and difficult to detect with radar due to the sea chop.

It was for these reasons that an agent for Iraq disguised as an eccentric millionaire negotiated a contract with the iceberg company. The iceberg was to be a "growler" with a flat top that was to be located and made available for towing to Boston by the millionaire in March of 2002. The iceberg was to be a special surprise birthday gift for his friend. The berg was to be fitted with a special hitch that would be on the underside of the berg. Instructions were given for a hole to be drilled through the center of the berg for the hitch attachment.

Contracts were signed and as the money changed hands, the manager of the iceberg company said, "I guess you guys are going to play Titanic aye?" The millionaire said nothing as he entered his limo and instructed the driver to take him to the airport.

With all of the pieces of the plan in place, the Iraqi team sat back and waited. As April 10, 2002 approached, the newspapers carried headline stories about the new ship, "UNSINKABLE TITANIC SUCCESSFULLY COMPLETES SEA TRIALS", "OWNERS OF TITANIC DARE GOD TO SINK TITANIC", and finally," TITANIC TO SAIL ON MORNING TIDE". The Iraqi team quietly watched coverage of the maiden voyage on ZNN. They said nothing as they looked around the room, a faint smile crossing their lips.

CHAPTER FOUR

Jacky sat motionless in her first class cabin... her eyes starring blankly at Dr. Moosavi, unblinking, cold and glassy. She resembled a life size Barbie Doll° that was perched in the stateroom chair. Her dress, her hair and nails were perfect. Dr. Moosavi sat quietly watching his patient as he looked back over the last nine years that he had spent programming her for this day.

Moosavi's mind drifted back to that first night in Oslo when his brainwashing of Jacky had begun. Jacky had arrived in Oslo heavily sedated and was kept in a sedated state as she was placed in the sensory deprivation tank. It had only taken less than 16 hours until her brain, starved for outside stimulant went totally out of control. She was quickly reduced into a babbling pile of psychological rubble. To Dr. Moosavi, she was now like a shapeless piece of wood that could be carved into any shape or design that Dr. Moosavi would choose.

It was ironic to Moosavi that the analogy of the human mind was often made with that of an iceberg. The human mind is divided into three hypothetical parts, the conscious, the preconscious and the unconscious.

The conscious part of our mind is the part that we perceive and others see through our behavior. It is the part of our mind closely related to our personality that we project to others. It is our thoughts, sensations, and emotions. This is the part of our personality that sticks up out of the sea of life like an iceberg and like the iceberg, is only the tip of what lies below.

The preconscious is the part of our mind that consists of our memories or experiences that we can easily recall and lies just below the surface of our awareness.

The unconscious is the bulk of our mind that is the repository for all of our experiences, good or bad, that formulates our conscious behavior, making us who we are, and what we ultimately become. The unconscious is like a giant pressure cooker that is forever cooking our life's experiences into a residue that feeds our souls.

It has often been said that the behavioral patterns are really formed early in our childhood. The very foundation of our personality is laid brick by brick. If we have a bad childhood, our unconscious mind may make us take on a different outlook on life, when compared to one who has a good or nurturing childhood.

Arguably, it can be said that these early life experiences create great minds like Albert Einstein, William Shakespeare, or Strauss, as well as the mass murders like Bundy, Adolph Hitler, and Caligula. Moosavi believed that if he could take a human mind apart, he could rearrange the contents of the unconscious mind, use its forces to create whatever type of behavior he desired in the conscious mind of any individual.

In all human minds there are two sides to reality, good and evil. Everyone experiences good things in life as well as bad. These experiences are like a massive individual database that regulates the conscious mind. When a person manages the struggle of good and evil in a socially acceptable fashion, they are considered "normal". If a person cannot control the battle between good and evil in a socially acceptable manner, he is considered to be "abnormal", mentally ill, or psychologically deficient and in need of help. The degree of psychological deficiency a person exhibits, determines the degree of social acceptability a person is given. If the psychological acceptability is severe, society mandates treatment for the individual and/or possible incarceration in mental institutions.

Jacky possessed all of the attributes of the perfect patient. She had a relatively happy childhood. Her mother had died in childbirth, but her father had managed to care for her and allowed her to have a happy childhood full of love and enjoyment. When Jacky met Josh, she had fallen in love and was prepared to give her whole life to Josh, but in the end, Josh had betrayed her. He had made a conscious decision that his position in life, his future inheritance, and his political future were more important than Jacky. He abandoned her and his son. Jacky quickly drew from her unconscious mind; the stamina to raise her son and to provide for him as her father had provided for her. Like her father, Jacky built her entire world around her child, without him, she would emotionally collapse. When David was killed, she did.

Jacky needed special attention. Her drinking problems and bouts with depression had to be corrected. There were parts to her personality that had to be nurtured and developed. Jacky had a major conflict in her mind toward Josh. While there was a part of her that deeply loved Josh and wanted him, there was the other side of her that wanted no part of him. Jacky's mind was awash with resentment toward Josh for getting her pregnant, abandoning her at Radcliff, taking her son away from her, and the death of her son. This resentment overshadowed the part of her that loved Josh. Dr. Moosavi needed to control this rage and only allow it to surface when he wanted it to.

For years after the Oslo treatment, Dr. Moosavi would have Jacky visit his office weekly. During these meetings, he would reinforce suggestions that were deeply planted into Jacky's subconscious at Oslo. Jacky had descended into a state of complete mind control by Dr. Moosavi. Technically, this state of mind was called somnambulism. Somnambulism is a psychological term used in describing "sleep walking" disorders and "night terrors". It is a state of mind that is completely separated from the conscious mind. When people sleep walk or have night terrors, their conscious mind has no recollection of the events that occurred during the somnambulistic state. Once Jacky was reduced to this state, she could be made to follow suggestions that were given to her by Dr. Moosavi and she would complete any task she was instructed to perform without question and without hesitation. Dr. Moosavi would only be required to say one word, AUHSOJ, and Jacky would follow his commands.

Killing a human being is difficult for anyone. The task is made easier if the mind believes that the act of killing someone is justified as in a time of war, or if someone is angry and out of control. The more times that someone kills, the easier it becomes, until finally, killing becomes as easy as watching television.

Dr. Moosavi had to teach Jacky how to kill another human being. The success of the Iraqi plan would ultimately rest in her hands. Joshua would be brought to her and placed in a situation where his death could be easily explained. Upon his death, the Israeli government would be in a state of political flux and mourning. It would be precisely at this moment that the final part of the plan would be executed.

Slowly and methodically, Jacky was taught how to use the tools of murder using a gun, knife, garrote, and the martial arts. During the visits to see Dr. Moosavi, Jacky would be given suggestions to buy a gun and then take classes in marksmanship. Other skills were drilled into her as she took other classes and eventually earned her black belt in the martial arts. Methodically, Moosavi had turned Jacky into a killing machine. To test her, Dr. Moosavi brought her to a deserted warehouse in Jersey City. In the center of the warehouse was a woman tied to a post and gagged. Her eyes looked terrified as Jacky and Dr. Moosavi slowly walked toward her. The woman had been abducted from a nearby shopping center. She was blond, attractive, and eight months pregnant. She would symbolize to Dr. Moosavi, the final test of Jacky's training. Standing in the darkened shadows of the warehouse was a group of men. They said nothing as they watched.

Dr. Moosavi spoke softly to Jacky," AUHSOJ."

Jacky looked as if she was in a trance.

"Kill her with this knife. I want you to first kill her baby, then I want you to cut her wrist, mutilate her body, and finally cut her throat, giving her a Columbian necktie."

The woman began to struggle as she heard the words being spoken to Jacky. Her eyes bulged from her head as she tried to get free as her muffled shrieking filled the warehouse.

Slowly, Jacky took the knife and walked up to the woman. Without hesitation she plunged the knife deep into the woman's abdomen, twisting the knife as she killed the child and sliced open the womb. She next cut the woman's wrist, plunged the knife into the lower abdomen and cut the woman open from her groin to her breastbone. As the dead fetus, blood and intestines splattered onto the warehouse floor, Jacky reached for the woman's hair, pulling the head up to expose the throat and sliced the woman's neck from ear to ear. Reaching into the gash, she grabbed the tongue, pulling it out of her body. It hung limply outside of the woman's body as an ever-increasing pool of blood spread out on the warehouse floor. The woman's body slid slowly down the pole as deep gurgling sounds emanated from her throat. By the time the body reached the floor, the sounds had stopped. The woman's face was frozen in a horrible death mask with her terrified eyes open and her mouth forming a silent scream. Jacky turned toward Dr. Moosavi and stood silently as blood dripped from her hands and knife. Using a handkerchief, Dr. Moosavi removed the knife from her hand and turned to the men in the darkened shadows and smiled. The men, one Chinese, shaved head with a Fu Man Chu mustache and two Arabs turned and quietly walked away.

The phone rang. Dr. Moosavi came back to reality and picked up the receiver, "Yes…"

The voice on the other end announced the arrival of Joshua.

"Thank you." Dr. Moosavi placed the receiver down and turned to Jacky.

"AUHSOJ"

Jacky turned her head and looked at Dr. Moosavi, her eyes were glassy, blank and her face expressionless.

"Joshua Cane has arrived at the dock. He will be arriving shortly. I want you to remember the love that you once had for Joshua. I want you to feel the warmth in your heart that you once had for Joshua. Let this love grow and marry Joshua as we discussed previously. This will be your reunion after so many years. Use this time to make up for all of those years that you were without Joshua. Love him my child and he will love you in return. I will now count to three, when

I do you will follow my instructions, but will remember nothing of what I have said. Do you understand?"

Jacky nodded slowly and softly said, "Yes."

"One... two... three..."

Jacky's lifeless face suddenly changed. She was smiling as she ran her hands across her dress. Her eyes sparkled as she said, "I can't wait to see Josh. When will he be here?"

"He has arrived minutes ago on the docks. Go to him my child... go to him!"

Jacky's heart raced as she hurried toward the first class promenade deck. As she approached the rail, she looked at the masses of people who were boarding the ship. She could not see Josh.

Josh had arrived in his limo, complete with security teams in several cars both ahead and behind his limo. They had fanned out quickly when his car stopped. The security teams talking into their radios to the other team members who had arrived earlier. Josh's limo proceeded slowly into the driveway that had been cleared for his arrival. Once inside the security men surrounded the car and opened the door. Josh exited the car and walked quickly toward a doorway that would lead to the first class gangway. Through the windows in the building, he could see the side of the Titanic's majestic black hull, her portholes reflecting the radiance of the sun. The Titanic was magnificent, her black hull bordered by a golden stripe that separated the black hull from the brilliant white of the upper decks. Her towering funnels shot toward the heavens, the people on decks were waving to their friends on shore. Newspaper and television cameras were everywhere. The sound of a band filled the air.

"Magnificent!" muttered Josh as he stepped into the bright sunlight. He shielded his eyes from the sun as he craned his neck to take in the view. In the distance, he saw Jacky looking nervously down at the first class gangway. He paused to look at her, she was radiant and beautiful. When Jacky saw him, she began to cry, "Josh... Josh." Looking back at Jacky he silently mouthed the words, "I love you."

Suddenly Jacky vanished from view. The security officer standing next to Josh said, "Mr. Prime Minister, I think we should get aboard."

"In a minute... I want to look at this magnificent vessel and..."

Suddenly, Jacky appeared at the first class gangway and cried, "Joshua..."

Seconds later, they were embracing each other. Joshua began to swing her into the air. Her fragrance, her soft body, her voice made his eyes fill with tears as said softly, "I love you Jacky... I'll never let you go... I'll never let you go again... I promise." They kissed again, a long enduring kiss that seemed to last for ever.

The security man said, "Mr. Prime Minister, I am sorry for interrupting, but I really think that we should board the ship... Now!"

Joshua released Jacky from his embrace, grabbed her hand and said, "Don't be sorry... This is the happiest day in my life."

Together, Jacky and Joshua boarded the Titanic. Above, lost in the crowd on the first class promenade deck watched Dr. Moosavi. There was a faint smile on his face as he turned and disappeared inside the ship.

CHAPTER FIVE

The spring had produced an unusually large number of icebergs. Calved in the high arctic regions, these gigantic chunks of arctic ice floated south with the Labrador Current like huge ice cathedrals into the Atlantic shipping lanes.

St. John's, Newfoundland was accustomed to the sight of icebergs slowly passing by and occasionally grounding near the shore, where they would linger for several weeks before melting enough to float away, but this year was unusually bountiful. For as far as the eye could see from atop Signal Hill, the sight of the first trans-Atlantic underwater cable to Europe, hundreds of icebergs freckled the surface of the Atlantic with their snowy tips resembling the canvas of the sailing ships of old.

Operating out of St. John's, Newfoundland, the International Ice Patrol (IIP) was having a hard time tracking the massive number of icebergs. Many scientist had blamed global warming, others blamed El Niño, while still others in the taverns of St. John's, blamed both global warming and El Niño, saying that they were both actually the same thing.

Regardless, the IIP had deployed an unusually large number of WOCE (World Ocean Circulation Experiment) buoys, which drifted in the ocean currents. Information was relayed to satellites, which relayed the information back to the IIP headquarters telling of their latitude/ longitude, sea surface temperature, and submergence information.

The normal number of iceberg reconnaissance flights was increased from once every other week to weekly flights. Flying at an altitude of 6000 to 8000 feet, the HC-130 would take four days to cover the entire IIP iceberg published ice limit of approximately 30,000 square miles of ocean. Each flight would last about seven hours and the aircraft would use Forward Looking Airborne Radar (FLAR) and Side looking Airborne Radar (SLAR) to aid in the search and tracking of icebergs.

Due to the dense fog that normally was associated with the cold Labrador Current and the warm Gulf Stream, the FLAR and SLAR electronic surveillance were relied on more than actual visual contact. However, as good as the electronics were, the problematic small growler icebergs still persisted in haunting the shipping lanes. Due to their small size and close proximity to the surface waves, some of these icebergs drifted through the IIP ice limit virtually undetected. While small in size, these icebergs could still sink an unsuspecting vessel that might cross their path.

For these reasons, when the IIP did locate a growler, they would deploy a GPS (Global Positioning System) unit with a transponder on these icebergs that would continuously broadcast their position to IIP headquarters. The FLAR and SLAR information, along with the GPS information would be made available to anyone within the reach of a PC that could access the IIP web site. Military vessels had their own means by which the same information could be made available to them.

It was for this reason that an IIP launch pulled up beside the Sea Witch. Floating off to the port side of the Sea Witch was a 125 foot long "wedged growler" iceberg. The iceberg was called "wedged" because it was flat on top, steep vertical sides on one end and sloping on the other. The term "growler" referred to its small size, less than 17 feet high.

The IIP officer boarded the Sea Witch and approached the Captain, "Is this the growler that will be towed to Boston?"

"Aye she is."

"When will you be towing her out?"

"Jesus, Mary, and Joseph... As soon as I get paid! What's all of this about?"

"We have had a large number of icebergs this season and we would like to place a GPS unit on the berg so that we can track it through the shipping lanes."

"What's the matter lad... You think the berg might be getting lost. I've got a mighty powerful leash around her. She'll not be getting lost."

"Still... we want to place this unit on the berg so we will not have to worry about it. Besides, if anything happens to your Sea Witch while in transit to Boston, we will be able to spot your position and come to your aid a lot quicker than trying to search for you."

"About the only thing that could go wrong out there is me running out of screech... and I don't plan on that happening." The old man winked his eye as he approached the IIP officer, "Now place your damn contraption on the berg and let me be... I've got work to do."

The IIP officer boarded his launch and the yelled, "Mark the berg." There was a boom from the forward deck gun, a converted whale gun firing a lance into the berg. Another man stepped onto the surface of the berg and positioned the GPS unit on the lance. Pressing a keypad on the GPS, he punched in the latitude and longitude of the iceberg's current position and turned on the positioning signal. Within five minutes he had returned to the IIP launch. The officer gave a short burst from his horn, waved at the old man, and steered his launch toward St. John's harbor. The old man raised a bottle of screech rum to his lips and pulled strongly at the brew. Wiping his lips with his arm, he watched the IIP vessel disappear into the approaching fog bank.

There was a crackle on the radio, "Sea Witch... Sea Witch... Come in. This is home base."

"Roger, Is that you Rosy? Over."

"The bank just called, they just received the wire transfer for the iceberg."

"Say again..."

His wife replied, "You heard me right John... The money is in the bank... all of it! It will be a blessed spring indeed."

"You bet it will be... Vinny will be arriving soon. I let him have a night on George Street. It will be his last for a few weeks."

"Now John, I'll not be having you turning our son into a drunk like his father…"

"Rosy… he is a grown man… and besides a few shots of screech is good for ya… I'll give you a call when we shove off… talk with you soon, over and out."

John had contracted with the iceberg salvage company to tow the iceberg to Boston. He was being paid $35,000.00, whether there was anything left of the berg or not when he arrived in Boston. Secretly, John thought that there would be hardly any ice remaining when he arrived in Boston for a man to chill a martini, but it wasn't his money being spent on a fool's errand. It would be the first time in years that he had money in the bank. Since the fishing had died, times were tough. Silently, he mumbled a few words of thanks to God for his good fortune and settled back to await the arrival of his son.

Vinny had spent the first few hours at Dapper John's on George Street. It was a lively tavern full of fun, pool, and a mixture of locals and tourists. The tourists were the ones who were standing in line to be "screeched in", a local custom where an outsider could be turned into an honorary Newfoundlander. The procedure took only a few minutes as the bartender rang a bell behind the bar to silence the crowd. Quickly the bartender put on a three-tailed Davy Crockett hat on his head and placed a sword and Puffin statue on the bar. Before each of the people that were to be "screeched in", he placed a shot glass and filled it with screech rum, a local Newfoundland brew. He began the ceremony by reading from a worn sheet of paper stating that the people before him wished to be screeched. He began to recite a long series of pledges that each of the people being screeched repeated. Then he raised the back end of the Puffin, the national bird of Newfoundland, and told each of the people to "kiss its arss", instructed each of the people to drink the screech to remove the nasty taste of the Puffin's arss from the mouth and finally took a sword from behind the bar and placed the blade on each shoulder of the people being "screeched in", thus dubbing them honorary Newfoundlanders. Certificates were given to the people as the crowd went back to their previous conversations and laughter. Vinny watched the ceremony it seemed for the hundredth time and then left to go to the Leprechaun pub.

The Leprechaun pub was an outrageous Irish pub that always had live Irish music. There were only two types of pubs in St. John's, the type that you cried in your beer as the singer moaned about everything wrong with life in Newfoundland and the type that you spilled your beer because you could not stand still due to the Irish music. The Leprechaun was the second type. Vinny also had his eye on Nicole, the young Irish lass barmaid. They had dated many times, but neither of them was interested in getting married, not yet at any rate. As Vinny climbed the stairs to the pub, he did not see two men follow him. As the two men got behind Vinny, one of the men reached into his pocket and withdrew a ballpoint pen. Quickly, he bumped into Vinny and jabbed his arm with the pen. The pen was designed by the KGB and had a very fine needle that would pierce the arm without the victim realizing that he had been stuck. The pen also had a syringe that would inject a lethal poison that would be impossible to trace at an autopsy.

"Excuse me." said the stranger.

Vinny started to say something, but suddenly, his perception of the world started to spin and he lost his balance. Seconds later, he was unconscious and died. The two men grabbed him by each arm and started down the stairs. A car pulled up to the curb on George Street and in an instant, Vinny and the two men were inside the car driving away to the docks where Vinny had moored his launch. The two men placed Vinny in the launch and together, they motored out to sea toward the Sea Witch.

John sat on the bridge drinking his screech. He saw his son's launch approaching and thought, "Well… it's about time."

The launch pulled up along the port side of the Sea Witch and John saw the two men sitting in the launch with Vinny slumped in the launch between the men. John approached the port side with a puzzled look on his face.

"He had a bit too much to drink," said one of the strangers.

"Is he OK?"

"Nothing a few hours sleep can't cure."

The two men picked up Vinny's limp body as his father helped get him onto the deck of the Sea Witch. As John bent over to his son, one of the men took a fishing knife from the deck of the Sea Witch and stabbed John through the heart. John slumped forward on top of his son and died instantly.

The two men removed the GPS unit from the iceberg and placed it on the stern of the Sea Witch. Within minutes of their arrival, the Sea Witch powered up and began to tow the iceberg out to sea to a location where the Russian sub was waiting silently beneath the waves.

CHAPTER SIX

The situation room in the CIA was hushed as the members of the Crisis Abatement Team, created from members of the CIA, SID, NSD, and FBI sat quietly watching the speaker. A senior advisor began the briefing, "At 0900 hours our reconnaissance satellites downloaded this image. This is a troop buildup about 100 miles north of the Israeli border in Syria."

The big screen changed as he continued, "Also… looking at this next image of Iraq… Iran… and Libya, there are troop mobilizations as well. One of our Big Birds caught this one last night."

The screen changed again showing a row of military trucks moving toward Iraq through Iran.

"It would seem that Iran is playing games again with Iraq. These troop carriers were tracked through Iran heading into Iraq last night."

One of the generals in the room said, "What do you make of it Bill?"

"We are not sure sir. It would seem that all of these guys are getting ready for something though. We know of no war games scheduled for any of the players either individually or together… but it is clear that they are getting ready…."

"Has anything happened recently that might shed some light on what they might be up to?", asked another general.

"Nothing significant to warrant this type of military buildup… in fact, things have been so quiet in this region, that this troop movement was the first real excitement we have had in quite a while. I can't explain it."

"What does our intelligence say?"

"Not too much sir. We have rounded up the usual suspects and run all of the usual checks with our operatives and they have reported nothing of any significance to us. Intelligence from this area is usually hard to get and sketchy at best. Needless to say, we have very little to go on."

"What is going on in Israel or Egypt?"

"Nothing to report out of the ordinary in Egypt and as far as Israel goes, things are so peaceful that Prime Minister Cane is out of the country and sailing on the new Titanic, in fact the Prime Minister and the new Titanic are due to depart Southampton today.

You could almost say that up until this troop activity started, things were almost too quiet."

"What in the hell is Cane doing on the Titanic?"

"We don't know exactly. Apparently about a month ago, he decided to take a holiday and go on the maiden voyage of the new Titanic. He will arrived in Southampton today from Tel Aviv and will be sailing from the UK to New York. The ship will follow the exact route of the original Titanic and will pause over the spot where the original Titanic sank."

"Are they planning to sink her too?"

Laughter filled the room as the senior advisor replied, "Hardly sir, they have built her to reflect the original image of the Titanic, but she has modern communications systems, radar, sonar, satellite communications, GPS, plenty of life boats for all passengers, and her construction conforms to modern ship building standards. Frankly, I don't see how she could sink."

One of the more Machiavellian generals, Col. Allan remarked, "Strange isn't it… the timing of the troop activity?"

"What do you mean Sir?", asked the advisor.

"Well look at it this way, it was noted earlier that it was almost too quiet in that region. Here we have the Prime Minister of Israel on holiday and things heat up. I for one do not think that this is just a coincidence."

"Do you have any suggestions?"

"Admiral, what forces do we have in the Atlantic in the general area of the Titanic's course?"

"There are two Los Angeles class attack subs in the area."

"Perhaps we could have one of them shadow the Titanic… just in case."

"Consider it done... once she gets out to sea, I'll have one of the subs shadow her. She will never know the sub is there and if you are right and something heats up... we'll be right there on the scene."

"How about operatives? Do we have any that we could get on the Titanic before she sails?" asked Col. Allan.

"I suppose that we could contact MI5 and see if they could arrange passage for one of their men. It was reported that the ship's maiden voyage was sold out. Do you think that it is necessary?", asked the advisor.

"I am not sure... but something is scratching the inside of my head and telling me that we had better do something. Gentlemen, let's suppose for a minute that there is something going on. With the Prime Minister away there could be a sneak attack on Israel. They can defend themselves if they have to, but what if these guys try to take the Prime Minister hostage and then attack Israel at the same time. Even though Israel's policy is not to negotiate with terrorists, it would be quite a mess to wage a war and the release of the Prime Minister... all at the same time. Remember the Key Largo hostage situation. I don't know, but I don't like it. I would rather be ready than face a situation where we are caught with our pants down and have to fight another Gulf War."

"Point well taken Col. Allan, we will advise the President and take the necessary steps that you have suggested. Perhaps we should also ask the NSA to keep a watchful eye around the world. They can provide us with information that may be relevant to this situation using their CRAM (Combined Reconnaissance and Analysis Monitoring) program. If anything pops up, even if it is remotely related to the Prime Minister, the Titanic, Iraq, Iran, Syria, or Libya, we will be informed."

"Sounds like a plan gentlemen." remarked the senior advisor.

With that comment, the room began to empty. Only Col. Allan remained looking at the images on the big screen. Finally, he shook his head and left the room.

The Navy department sent a coded message to the USS Tiger Shark instructing her to make contact with the Titanic, but remain submerged and shadow the ship across the Atlantic. The CIA contacted MI5 and one operative was assigned to the Titanic. With the proper strings pulled at the right places, the operative would assume the disguise of a butler assigned to the Prime Minister's cabin.

Three hundred nautical miles north aboard the Sea Witch, the radio cracked, "Calling Sea Witch… Calling Sea Witch… This is home base… Come in."

The two men in the boat did not respond as they guided the boat out to sea. The iceberg in tow moved slowly with the Sea Witch. In 30 minutes they would be at their rendezvous point.

"Sea Witch… Sea Witch… Come in John… Are you there?"

The two men said nothing. The bodies of John and his son lay on the deck at the stern.

One of the men reached toward the radio, "Sea Witch… Sea Wit." and turned the radio off.

Looking at his watch and then out to sea, he smiled. The fog was rolling in on time. In a few minutes, it would engulf their boat and the iceberg. They would be invisible to the rest of the world.

The cold Atlantic waters rolled gently as a navigational periscope pierced the Atlantic six inches above the surface. A white trail followed behind the periscope as it sliced its way through the water. Inside the sub, the Captain slowly made a complete sweep of the horizon. He was pleased to see the pea soup dense fog, "Down scope."

"Down scope."

Boris Drovetsky was the Captain of the rogue Kilo sub. He was fifty-five, salt and pepper hair, a jet black beard and coal black eyes that could look through a man and put the fear of God in his soul at a glance. For ten years, he had been the proud Captain of a USSR Sierra-class nuclear-powered attack sub. Those were his glory years as he had quietly navigated his sub off the coast of the United States and played tag with American Ohio Class boomer subs, but that was yesterday; today was different. With the collapse of the USSR, the newly formed Russian government was reducing the size of their sub fleet as a gesture to prove to the West that they were no longer the "evil empire" as described by President Reagan and also because they simply could not afford to keep the large sub fleet at sea. Boris Drovetsky quickly found himself a man without a job or a future. He could no longer support his wife, he no longer respected his government or its leaders, and most of all, and he needed to make money, serious money. He was being paid one million American dollars, to do a job from a country that he detested even more than his own. Like everyone else in the world, he realized that everything had a price, even his soul and for one million dollars, he had sold his soul to Iraq.

Boris had hand selected his crew and had spent two years in hiding with the sub and his men. The sub had been modified with a reinforced bow and had been covered with sonar inhibiting absorption tiles and outfitted with the latest GPS units, passive sonar arrays, and weapons. The Kilo sub was quiet, but now she was even quieter. Having trained his men, he had said good-bye to his wife and sailed across the Atlantic to rendezvous with an iceberg. Payday had finally arrived.

"Do you have a target?"

"Aye aye Sir. 20,000 meters to our port side."

"Very well... prepare to surface."

The order to surface was repeated throughout the sub, "Surface... Surface."

The sound of the klaxon alarm wailed through the sub as the blast tanks were blown. The angle of the sub changed dramatically as her bow lurched toward the surface. Within seconds, the sub broke through the waves as her bow arched downward creating a large splash that was reminiscent of a breaching killer whale. The Captain said, "All stop."

"Aye aye sir, all stop."

The sub rested silently on the surface. Her glistening inky black hull was silhouetted against the damp gray fog. She was a Kilo class sub. Her displacement was 2400 tons surfaced and 3000 tons submerged, 299 feet, seven inches long, her beam was 21 feet, four inches.

The sub had three diesel engines, two electric motors, had a single shaft with a six blade propeller, carried torpedoes, could submerge for ten days without resurfacing, and could reach a speed of 25 knots while submerged.

The sub initiated the active Hercules sonar and radar. The Captain said, "Come to course 315, speed all ahead slow. We don't want to run into that damn iceberg."

"Aye aye Sir... Come to course 315... All ahead slow."

Slowly the two vessels closed in on each other. The sub lookouts were straining as they tried to look through the fog. Suddenly, one of the seamen said, "I have her Sir, two points off the starboard bow Sir."

The Captain raised his glasses and saw the outline of the Sea Witch. Behind her, he saw the iceberg.

The two vessels maintained radio silence. As the sub approached, one of the seamen threw a rope to the man in the bow of the Sea Witch. In a few minutes, the sub and Sea Witch were lashed together.

The Captain of the sub jumped onto the stern of the Sea Witch. He saw John and his son, dead on the deck. Looking toward the stern, he looked at the iceberg. It wasn't the biggest he had ever seen, in fact; he could not believe that it was so small. Once he had encountered an iceberg that was over 300 feet high. His mind always marveled that only one tenth of the berg could be seen on the surface, so there had to be another 2700 feet of iceberg below the surface. This one was about 17 feet high, about 150 feet long, and was flat on top. A hole had been drilled through the center of the iceberg. The hole had been filled with a solid steel shaft. Below the iceberg, the shaft had been fitted with a hitch. On the bow of the sub, the mate to the hitch had been welded to the sub. All that remained was to submerge and hook up to the hitch. Once that was done, the Captain would guide the iceberg toward the Titanic using its rudder and engines if needed.

One of the men in the sub emerged wearing a dry suit. He was being helped with his tanks as the Captain approached the man in the wheelhouse of the Sea Witch and said, "Prepare to disengage from the iceberg."

"We will disengage from the iceberg now Captain…"

"Very well…"

The Captain returned to the sub as the diver lashed himself to the bow of the sub. Within minutes, the sub slowly submerged beneath the waves as the diver connected his radio transmitter to the sub using a banana plug connection and started to talk to the Captain.

"The water is very murky. I'll have to turn on my lantern."

"Very well… let me know when you can see the hitch."

"I can see the iceberg clearly, wait a minute… yes… I see the hitch. Come starboard 1 point… Easy… Easy… Bring her forward now… Easy… Easy."

The bow of the sub began to move forward. The hitch was 15 feet away. The sub hitch had a wide "V" connector that would guide the hitch into place. There was a loud clang as the hitch hit the steel "V" bar. The noise of metal scraping against metal filled the sub. Suddenly there was a loud "CLANK" as the steel bar slid into place. The sub was now connected to the iceberg.

The diver said, "Iceberg secure Captain… I am returning to the surface."

"Good job… see you when we get home…"

The diver disconnected the radio cord and swam to the surface. His head bobbed about 10 meters from the Sea Witch. A light crossed the water in his direction. Unfortunately for the diver, the escape plan only called for two men. Once the light found him, several bursts of automatic weapons fire filled the air. The water spattered around the startled diver as the bullets arrived. Several rounds went through the divers facemask killing him instantly. The limp body of the diver floated face up in the calm sea with its arms outstretched. Suddenly, a grappling hook caught one of the arms as the two men pulled it into the Sea Witch. The diver's tanks were removed and several additional diving belt weights were placed inside his dry suit before the body was returned to the sea. It quickly disappeared into the murky darkness of the Atlantic. The engines of the Sea Witch suddenly came to life as the vessel quickly started to move away from the iceberg. One of the men repeated the process of placing diving weights on Vinny and his body was then thrown overboard. John was lashed to the wheel and ropes were used to lash the wheel so that it would remain in position and keep the vessel headed in a Northeast direction. The men lowered the rubber launch into the sea and climbed in, cutting the towline as they watched the Sea Witch disappear into the fog. As the Sea Witch continued out to sea, the rubber launch was turned toward the mainland. In a few hours, the two men would be on their way back to Russia and the Sea Witch would be lost at sea.

CHAPTER SEVEN

SOUTHAMPTON, 1200 HOURS

The investment management group that had formed to rebuild the Titanic all stood on the first class promenade deck looking down at the sea of people and news media on the pier below. They were drinking glasses of champagne and congratulating themselves on the job that was now complete.

The new Titanic was awesome to behold. Her dull black hull, gold stripe, and crowning snow-white upper decks made her stand out from the other ships in the harbor like a jewel. The Titanic, the once radiant queen of an era long since past, now regained her throne as the most luxurious trans-Atlantic passenger ship ever built.

Like Bruce Ismay, the managing director of the White Star line who had the original Titanic built in 1912, the current investment group had spared nothing to rebuild the Titanic. They had even named their ship company the White Star Line, the original company having long since gone out of business, and they had conducted an exhaustive search of sea Captains and officers that would serve on the new Titanic. These people were not only selected for service on the Titanic based upon their prior experience and seamanship, but also on their physical appearance. The newly formed White Star Line had even gone as far to have the new Captain, first officer, second officer, radio operators and lookout seamen legally change their names to Edward J. Smith, William Murdoch, Charles Herbert Lightoller, Jack Phillips, Harold Bride, and Frederick Fleet. It has always been said that money could not buy everything, but in this case, it had.

In the bridge, Captain Smith turned to Lightoller and said, "Stand by to cast away all lines."

"Aye, aye Sir."

The gangways had been moved back from the ship and the gangway entrance doors on the Titanic had been closed and sealed. Suddenly, there was a loud low-pitched blast from the Titanic's triple throated whistle. Her voice vibrated everything around her and could be heard for miles in every direction. The masses of people gathered at the White Star Line pier were initially stunned into silence, but began to shout and wave the traditional white handkerchiefs once the noise from the whistle had subsided. The passengers aboard the Titanic responded with an equally tumultuous roar of their own, fluttering of white handkerchiefs, and throwing of streamers toward the masses below. On the first class promenade deck, the White Star Line management raised their glasses and drank another toast to their success.

"Cast away all lines, Mr. Lightoller," ordered Captain Smith.

Lightoller barked the order, "Cast away all lines…"

The large ropes that had held the Titanic secure to the pier were simultaneously removed from the moorings and pulled aboard the Titanic as another blast came from the Titanic's whistle, producing another roar from the crowds.

The Titanic had been fitted with submerged underwater thrusters that gently pushed her sideways away from the pier. In the harbor, a small flotilla of tugboats, fireboats and private vessels began to blow their horns, whistles, ring their ship's bells as the fireboats shot fountains of water into the air. Suddenly, the Titanic started to move forward as her three screws turned effortlessly.

Captain Smith ordered his next command, "All ahead slow."

"Aye aye Sir… All ahead slow." responded Lightoller.

Lightoller grabbed the ships telegraph, signaling to the engine room below. The telegraph bells rang as Lightoller set the indicator for ALL AHEAD SLOW. A second later, the telegraph sounded again with the acknowledgment from the engine room. As the Titanic's large propellers continued to turn faster and faster, she quickly picked up speed, separating herself from the flotilla and nosed her way into the River Test.

IRAQ

ZNN was broadcasting the Titanic maiden voyage live around the world. In a secret meeting room somewhere in Iraq, all eyes were glued to a television set. The men sat silent around a large boardroom table as they listened to the news commentator say, "The Titanic is now beginning her maiden voyage 90 years to the day that the original Titanic departed Southampton. This time however, there are enough lifeboats, the ship is equipped with modern radar, sonar, radio communications equipment, and this Titanic has been designed and built to meet modern ship building standards... thus, making the specter of this Titanic sinking for any reason... highly unlikely."

At the head of the table, a man dressed in a military uniform pressed the mute button. The television sound abruptly stopped. There was an air of arrogance about this man. His eyes blazed with a fire from within that was fed by years of hatred for the United States and Israel. He looked at each man in the room and asked, "Is everything in place? Let's go over everything one more time." Looking at the man at his right, he said, "What is the status of the nuclear devices?"

"The war heads are being delivered from Pakistan and the missiles are in position and ready for launch."

"Excellent..."

Sadaam paused as he reflected over the last nine years since the Gulf War. Since that time, Iraq had been forced to allow UN inspectors into his country until he had kicked them out. Restrictive air space had literally cut the country in half as United States and British warplanes enforced the UN "YOU FLY YOU DIE" no fly zone and the UN had enforced economic sanctions that had hindered Iraq from normal business trade with the rest of the world. Iraq not only had suffered the humiliation of a defeat in war but had also been ostracized by much of the world community. Not only had he been forced to contend with the problems of rebuilding his country, but he had also been forced to keep one eye over his shoulder. He never slept in the same place two nights in a row for fear of assassination by his own people or by foreign governments, but despite his hardships, he slowly masterminded a plan that would return him to his former glory.

For years, Iraq had played games with the United Nations. In the middle to late 1990's, Iraq would periodically bar the UN inspection teams from snooping around Iraq and when he was ready, he finally kicked the UN inspections out of his country for good. The reason for his cat and mouse game with the UN inspectors was to allow Iraq enough time to build several launch facilities that would be used to attack Israel. After careful consideration to the problem, it was decided that three launch facilities would be built and disguised as mosques. Once the sites were identified in Irbil, Al Basra and Baghdad the construction began. Careful consideration was given to the American spy satellites that would be watching from above. Building the mosques was to become a game of international Three Card Monty.

The first man at the table raised his eyes from his papers and said, "The Sea Witch has been set out to sea in a direction that will take it away from the iceberg. The Sea Witch crew has been eliminated. When the International Ice Patrol finds her, it will look as if the Captain was murdered by his son. The GPS unit has been placed on the Sea Witch and the IIP will have little difficulty finding her. The iceberg has been successfully connected to the submarine. By the time the IIP located the Sea Witch, the iceberg will be many miles away from them and will be almost impossible to locate because of its small size. Currently, the submarine and iceberg are proceeding toward 41 degrees 46 minutes north, 50 degrees 14 minutes west and should arrive at that point as planned."

The second man reported, "Joshua Cane arrived aboard the Titanic an hour ago. Jacky McGuire and Dr. Moosavi are also on board. Everything is proceeding as planned."

Sadaam smiled as he continued his reflections of the last nine years. It had once been said by his mentor that it was simple to make things difficult and very difficult to make things simple. As the plan began to take place, starting with the brainwashing of Jacky McGuire and the funding of the new Titanic, the Iraqi government had to carefully orchestrate UN inspection team activities in Iraq. In the beginning, they would bar the investigators until the UN would be on the verge of attacking and suddenly back down. The UN was perfectly convinced that Iraq was shuffling biological weapons of mass destruction from one location to another during these restriction periods. Iraq even left traces of biological weapons behind to convince the UN that their suspicions were correct while they continued with their real plans.

As is the case for any plan, mistakes were made, in particular, in 1998 when the usual UN teams were escorted out of Iraq. His error was one of judgment in the timing of the eviction. A smile flickered across the his lips as he thought how ludicrous it was to assume that a sitting United States President would try to use Iraq as a stage to shift the attention of the press away from an impeachment proceeding. Yet, on the eve of an impeachment vote against President Clinton, in December 1998, the United States attacked his country for the second time. The movie *Wag The Dog*® was just released in the United States and was in everyone's mind as they read their morning paper. Could the President be following a script from Hollywood? This was hard to believe, but so was getting a blowjob from a White House intern, while heads of State sat waiting. This miscalculation had resulted in serious damage to one of the launch facilities. The US was beginning to target suspected locations that were believed to be manufacturing biological weapons and they had bombed one of the mosque launch facilities by accident. Fortunately, the entire launch pad structure was below ground. Once the rubble was removed and the mosque outer structure rebuilt, the launch facility was back on line in less than two months.

Now the final act was about to unfold. The Prime Minister would be on the Titanic with his new bride. She would kill him as the Titanic sank. The leaders of the world would attend his funeral. He paused to remember the death of King Hussein. At King Hussein's funeral, President Clinton, former Presidents Carter and Ford of the United States, Prince Charles and Prime Minister Tony Blair of Britain, President Mubarak of Egypt, President Yeltsin of Russia, Yasir Arafat, representatives of Turkey, Kuwait, Israel, Libya gathered to mourn his death. He smiled as he remembered that he had even sent a representative to the funeral to represent Iraq. It was a shame that he was not ready to strike then, but he was ready now. Once the leaders of the world assembled to once again to mourn the death of a fallen leader, Iraq would launch nuclear tipped missiles and eviscerate them all. Would a nuclear attack be the start of the prophesized end of the world and battle of Armageddon? He didn't care. As the years had passed since 1991, his power was waning. Egypt and Jordan were openly calling for his removal from power. If he started Armageddon, what did he care? Existing in a country he could no longer rule with an iron fist wasn't worth living. The dice were in his hands and he was prepared to roll them, regardless of the consequence.

"Very well then." The button on the remote control was pressed again and the television sound filled the boardroom.

SOUTHAMPTON

The Israeli secret service personnel had arrived on the Titanic forty-eight hours prior to the arrival of Ambassador Cane. They had swept his suite for explosives and bugs. They had found none. Once they were convinced the suite was clean, they spent hours installing their own bugs, television cameras, and motion sensors so that they could watch and listen to anyone that was in the suite with the Prime Minister or in the hallway outside of the suite. By the time Joshua Cane would arrive on board the Titanic, they would be ready.

MI5 had successfully placed their man onboard the Titanic. He was assigned as a butler for the Prime Minister's suite and his mission would be to watch, as well as protect the Prime Minister should the need arise. Looking at the Prime Minister's staff of secret service men, he felt that his only real mission would be to observe. MI5 felt it best not to inform the Israeli secret service about their man. All butlers, including the MI5 agent and maids had been barred from entering the Prime Ministers cabin until the Israeli secret service had swept and installed their monitoring systems. The agent was aware that there would be close circuit cameras, motion sensors, and microphones in the Prime Minister's suite making it hard to install any of his bugs. Fortunately however, MI5 had followed the lead of other intelligence organizations by creating a variety of unusual bugs that were so commonplace in their appearance that they were hard to spot without electronic detectors. Since the room had already been swept for bugs, the MI5 agent felt confident that he could at least get a few of his bugs in the suite.

The agent entered the suite and casually walked around the room, fluffing pillows on the couch, and pretending to rearrange the furniture on the private promenade deck. As he went about his task, he cleverly placed a cigarette lighter under the seat cushions of several chairs in the suite. The cigarette lighters were actually radio transmitter bugs that could pick up any discussion in the suite. Once he finished placing the bugs, he quietly left the suite to await the arrival of the Prime Minister.

TITANIC, FIRST CLASS PARLOR SUITE

Joshua and Jacky walked hand in hand towards Joshua's suite. The sound of the Titanic's deep voice vibrated through the ship. The secret service personnel walked ahead of and in back of the Prime Minister, their eyes darting around, looking for anything unusual. Once they reached the Ambassador's suite, Joshua and Jacky entered, leaving the men outside to guard the door. As the door closed, the men at the door looked at each other and smiled.

Once inside, Joshua and Jacky embraced. It had been nine years since Jacky had hurled the engagement ring at Joshua with tears in her eyes and anger in her voice. Those memories, however distant, were still fresh in Joshua's mind as he held Jacky in his arms, kissing her, smelling her hair, telling her how much he loved her. Placing his head on her shoulder, he began to cry softly, his chest heaving slightly as he tried to control his emotions. Jacky released her embrace and took her hand and wiped his tears away. Their eyes met again. Jacky kissed his lips and then his tears and said, "Don't cry my love… Don't cry… We are together now and forever… until death do us part."

Slowly, they walked outside into the adjoining private promenade and sat down. Joshua wiped his eyes and said, "I have dreamed of this moment for so long. Forgive me for acting this way, but I never thought that I would ever see you again… With… the death of David and…"

Jacky placed her finger over his lips. Her eyes looked tenderly at him as she said, "Let me explain. It took me a long time to realize that things that happened in my life were not the fault of you… me… or… anyone. They just happened. Unfortunately, I have spent the last thirty years of my life living in anger and hatred for you, blaming you for ruining my life, for the death of our son, and not taking the responsibility for the part that I played in the events that unfolded in our lives. It was easier for me to blame you for everything wrong in my life than to blame myself. I have finally come to realize that I cannot live with this hate any longer. What is done… is done. I want to live the rest of my life without any anger or hatred for you. It took me a long time to realize that my life is what I make it… You get out of life what you put into it. For many years, all I did was blame you for everything wrong in my life. Nine years ago when David was killed, it got so bad that my life fell apart, my career fell apart and I wound up in a mental institution. With help, I have learned how to forgive. With forgiveness has come a new beginning… a new beginning that I want to share with you."

Joshua sat motionless as Jacky stood. Her voice was calm and loving as she continued, "I fell in love with you many years ago, but it was different then. My love for you at Harvard was more torrid, passionate, and physical. We were young and you were quite a jock.

I am in love with you now, but in a different way. I love you now Joshua for who you are. My heart is lonely... empty... and my soul is longing for you. I need you near me, to hear your voice, to feel your touch, and to see your smile. I love you Joshua and want to share my life with you... That's all I have ever wanted. Will you marry me? Can you forgive me?" Tears began to fill her eyes.

Joshua wiped the tears from Jacky's eyes and said, "I was a fool when my father told me to leave you. I was afraid of him and his power. I should have told him to go to hell and to get out of my life... but I didn't... That decision has haunted me all of these years and is a decision that I will regret for the rest of my life. When David first came to see me, he was angry. We had harsh words, but somehow we made amends and began to get to know each other as father and son. I was stunned when he told me that he was coming to Israel and would join the Army, but I was proud of him like a father should be. When he was killed, a piece of me died with him. Calling you that day was the most difficult thing that I have ever had to do in my entire life. When you arrived at David's grave, I wanted to hold you and tell you how much I needed you. Even though it was unbearable for me to see your anguish over David's death and feel your anger for me, I somehow understood and managed to let you go. It took nine years for me to hear your answer to my question... but now I have my answer..."

Reaching into his pocket, Joshua took out the engagement ring that Jacky had sent to him and bent down on one knee saying, "Yes, I'll marry you. I want you in my arms for all eternity. I lost you twice in my life, once at Harvard and once at David's funeral... I will not lose you again." Placing the ring on Jacky's finger he asked, "Will you marry me Jacky?"

Jacky looked at the ring and lowered her eyes to his and said, "Yes, I'll marry you."

The two kissed and embraced each other again. For hours they sat and talked. It was like a dam bursting forth. Jacky described the birth of their son. There was sadness in her voice as she relived David's birth and her struggle to raise him and to complete her education. Joshua sat motionless, feeling the loneliness in her life. There were moments of happiness in her voice as she relived David's first words, his first steps, and the joy of watching him grow up into a man. Finally, there were tears when she relived the news of David's death and her mental breakdown that followed. There was a pause as she wiped her eyes and began to describe her recovery under the care of Dr. Moosavi. Jacky looked at Joshua and said, "Without him… I would probably still be in Belleview right now."

"He sounds like a wonderful doctor… I would like to meet him."

"You will… tonight…"

"Is he on board?"

"Yes… I asked him to come… just in case I…"

"I understand… It will be an honor to meet the man who returned you to me."

As they walked into the suite Joshua said, "Let's do it tonight… a simple ceremony with the Captain… here in this suite."

A strange and distant look crossed Jacky's face as she said, "No… No Josh… I want this to be a special occasion… I want to marry you the night we arrive at the point in this cruise when we pause over the original Titanic remains, three nights from now. When this Titanic departs from that horrible spot in the Atlantic… it will be symbolic of a new beginning. Let it also be a new beginning for us."

Joshua placed his arms around her waist, pulling her close to him and said, "I have waited for thirty years… I guess I can wait for three more nights… but only three."

Jacky smiled and said, "You won't be disappointed my love… I have made special arrangements for us that night."

Kissing him again, she said, "Let me go now darling, I want to change for dinner."

"But… can't we talk some more… there is so much I wanted to tell you. We'll dine here so we can talk… don't go Jacky."

The Titanic gave another roar with her deep voice as the ship announced its arrival at Cherbourg, France. Jacky looked at her watch, it was 5:08 PM.

"I have a few things that I must do... we will talk at dinner, and soon after that, soon we will have all eternity to be together. I'll call you in an hour and we can make plans for tonight. I have arranged to have the Captain join us for dinner... not here but, in the first class dining saloon. Have you seen it yet? It is beautiful! After all, we do have a thing or two to talk to the Captain about, don't we? Tomorrow, we can look for a wedding ring. The Titanic has a exquisite jewelry store."

With that, Jacky opened the door and was gone. As the door closed behind her, Joshua raised his fist in the air and said, "YES!"

Moments after Jacky's departure, the door opened to the suite and an aid entered the room, "Excuse me Mr. Prime Minister, but there are troop movements in Syria, Libya, and Iran... I think that you should read this report."

Joshua reached for the folder as he placed his glasses on the end of his nose. As the aid left the room, he muttered, "Now what?"

CHERBOURG, FRANCE,

Tenders began to ferry 43 first class passengers, 89-second class passengers and 214 third class passengers, to the Titanic. On board the ferry were four first class male Iraqi passengers; their mission would be to assist Dr. Moosavi. They looked anxiously over the bow of the ferry at the Titanic. She was stunning as she rode at anchor with all of her lights ablaze.

FIRST CLASS DINING SALOON, 2100 HOURS

The first class saloon was breathtakingly elegant with its Jacobean-style alcoves and leaded windows, lavish snow white tables set with White Star Line sterling silverware and dark blue, gold trimmed bone china, emerald green upholstered chairs, and a stunning royal red, gold and gray carpet. Equally elegant was the reception room that was adjoined to the dining saloon by a set of magnificent wooden doors with leaded glass windows. In the center of the reception room was the beginning of the Grand Staircase that led from D deck to A deck through the heart of the first class section, a magnificent hand carved, polished oak masterpiece. At the top of the Grand Staircase on A deck was the Titanic's crowning jewel, an immense wrought iron and glass dome skylight.

Music from the Titanic string quintet was playing Strauss's Blue Danube Waltz as a small group of Israeli secret service personnel walked down the Grand Staircase and took up positions in the reception room and dining saloon. One of the men spoke softly into a radio when all of the men were in position. Moments later, Joshua began his journey down the staircase in black tie. His presence aboard the Titanic had not been publicly announced to the news media and thus his presence in the reception room went virtually unnoticed to the first class passengers. One man however, raised his eyebrows as he saw Joshua enter the room. Placing his cocktail glass to his lips, Dr. Moosavi quietly observed Joshua approach a table and take a seat.

Captain Smith, arriving from the bridge, walked down the Grand Staircase dressed in his black tie uniform, his chest adorned with medals. Instantly, the passengers approached the Captain, introducing themselves as Captain Smith graciously greeted each one with a warm smile as he inched his way toward Joshua. Captain Smith was a striking man. He was 65 years old and was, by anyone's definition, all business. He had served in the United States Navy as a captain of a destroyer during the Viet Nam era, retired from the Navy to begin his 20-year career as captain of luxury liners. Although retired for the second time in his life, his name had been suggested to the White Star Line during their crew search. When he was contacted by the White Star line to interview for the job, the thought of being the Captain of the new Titanic was more than he could resist. His white beard, grown for the occasion, offset by his warm smile and uniform, gave him an uncommon command of any social or professional gathering. His voice, while warm and gentle, had a sense of authority about it that made everyone he spoke to almost snap to attention.

Approaching the table where Joshua sat, the Captain said, "Mr. Prime Minister... I am honored to have you with us." His warm smile crossed his face as he extended his hand.

Joshua stood and replied, "The honor is mine Captain..." Shaking the Captain's hand, he gestured toward a seat.

"How are the accommodations Mr. Prime Minister."

"Superb Captain..."

"Tomorrow, if you have the time, allow me the honor of giving you the cooks tour of the Titanic. She is a remarkable vessel and..."

Suddenly, Joshua saw Jacky descending down the Grand Staircase. His eyes were in a trance as he stood to greet her. Jacky was dressed in a long flowing low cut black evening gown. Her red hair was flaming across her shoulders and a simple, but elegant string of pearls graced her neck. Gracefully, she approached the table as the Captain turned and rose to his feet.

Joshua spoke softly, "My God Jacky... you are stunning tonight."

Jacky kissed him softly on the lips. Turning, she extended her hand to the Captain, who kissed it softly and said, "Good evening Ms. McGuire."

As Jacky took a seat the Captain and Joshua rushed to assist her. The Captain realizing his faux pas, allowed Joshua the honor.

Jacky looked at Joshua and said, "You look wonderful in a tux... and you Captain, are stunning in your uniform. You had better be careful, all of the young girls will be falling over themselves to get to you."

"You are too kind my dear."

"I want to thank you Captain for joining us for dinner... and ... I do want to ask a favor of you... Josh and I are engaged want to be married and we want you to do the ceremony...."

The Captain had a look of genuine surprise and delight as he said, "Congratulations... Congratulations to the both of you... It would be an honor... In all my years at sea, I have never had the privilege of performing a marriage ceremony... Yes... I would be delighted."

"Captain… I know this will sound a bit odd, but I would like the wedding to be done on the night of the 14th…"

"That's the evening that we pause over the remains of the original Titanic…" A look of concern crossed his face.

"Yes… that is the night that we want to be married. The loss of all those lives and the loss of the Titanic gave birth to this ship. It took 90 years for the circle to be complete. On the night of the 14th, this ship will continue on… It will be a new beginning for the legend of the Titanic. For Josh and myself, it will be a new beginning as well."

"My God… how romantic… How utterly romantic!"

"Then it's OK?"

"There are things that must be put in place… but… yes … yes, by God… why not."

"I have the perfect location… By the clock on the Grand Staircase."

"I suppose that it can be arranged. This is marvelous… How did you think of this wonderful wedding?"

Jacky looked around the room and said, "I have been planning this for a long time. Joshua, I want to introduce you to Dr. Moosavi… He is the person that has helped me…"

Joshua looked into Jacky's eyes and said, "Is he here? I would like to meet him."

Jacky stood up looking around the room and then said, "I'll only be a moment."

Captain Smith and Joshua watched as Jacky approached a man sitting alone. As she returned with the stranger, they stood.

"Joshua, I would like to introduce you to Dr. Moosavi."

Joshua extended his hand.

"It is indeed an honor to finally meet you Mr. Prime Minister… and you as well Captain Smith."

Joshua and the Captain said, "Likewise."

As the four were about to be seated, the maitre-de approached the table and said, "Ms. McGuire, your table is ready…"

Dinner was served as the four made arrangements for the wedding. The Captain would arrange for the Grand Staircase to be made available from 9:00 PM through 10:00 PM. This would give the secret service staff enough time to secure the area and the Titanic's Quintet would be made available. The wedding would be at 9:30 PM. Dr. Moosavi would give Jacky away. To Joshua, it only seemed fitting that Dr. Moosavi be allowed this honor. Without him, Jacky would never have made her recovery. As the hour grew late, the Captain and Dr. Moosavi excused themselves leaving Joshua and Jacky alone together.

They walked out onto the first class promenade deck. The stars glittered like diamonds across the heavens. The air was cold as Jacky snuggled into Joshua's arms.

"I love you Joshua."

"I love you too."

Captain Smith returned to the bridge. Lightoller was on watch, "Everything in order Mr. Lightoller?"

"Yes Captain... everything is normal... The weather is a bit odd."

"Oh..."

"Yes... There was a freakish rainbow at sunset..."

"Come, come now man... Don't tell me that you believe those old superstitions?"

"I do and I don't... I suppose that there was something to them at one time or another. How about you Sir?"

"Well if I did believe in superstitions, I rather suppose that I would be a nervous wreck right about now. I just had dinner with a beautiful red headed woman. It used to be believed that women were never allowed aboard ships because they were considered a bad omen... and a red headed woman was unthinkable because anyone with red hair was believed to bring bad luck. If I were superstitious, I would be faced with a double whammy right now. Interesting isn't it... how these things get started? Did you know that it is believed by Puritan ministers that Judas Iscariot had red hair? There is even a superstition about the name Jonah. Try to find a ship registered as Jonah... you won't. Jonah is defined as being a person who brings bad luck.

I suppose you could consider the woman I had dinner with tonight as a Jonah. Spilling salt does not bother me… neither do black cats. About the only superstition that I believe in is having a shark follow my vessel. In the days gone by… if a shark followed a ship, the crew believed that one of the people on board the ship was cursed. If such a person was disliked, had a limp or some other mental or physical oddity… that person would somehow find himself being tossed into the sea by the crew and fed to the hungry shark. That superstition bothers me and I honestly don't know why. Probably something happened to me as a child I suppose… Well I'll be in my quarters if you need me."

"Good night Captain… and I'll keep a sharp look out for sharks."

Two hundred fifty feet beneath the waves of the Atlantic, the USS Tiger Shark arrived on station and began to shadow the Titanic.

CHAPTER EIGHT

APRIL 11TH

KILO CLASS SUB – 0100 HOURS

The iceberg silently moved through the dark Atlantic. Beneath it, the Kilo sub released a GPS unit that floated to the surface, connected to the sub by a communications cable and tether. The Captain looked over the shoulder of the navigation officer; both men were looking at a display map of the Atlantic Ocean that was filled with dots. Each dot represented an iceberg. The glow of the display reflected softly off of the glasses of the navigator.

"We are here Captain… The Sea Witch is here…"

"What about the Titanic?"

"The men boarded the Titanic in Cherbourg. The Titanic will depart Queenstown, Ireland about 0800 hours sir."

"How strong is the current?"

"Presently, we are fine… The current is making us drift in this direction… With our engines off, we can drift until we reach this position… At that time, using our towed array, we will be picking up the Titanic about here. At this point, we should start guiding the iceberg toward the Titanic… A piece of cake…"

The Captain looked at the screen for several seconds and gave a grunt, "Looks good to me. I am turning in… If anything changes, wake me up."

"Aye aye Sir…"

ST. JOHN'S NEWFOUNDLAND

"Sea Witch… Sea Witch… Come in John… John… Come in please."

The crackle of empty space filled the room.

"Sea Witch... Sea Witch... John... Please come in I'm getting scared... John... Are you there?"

The radio buzzed and crackled... there was no response.

A look of fear was frozen on Rosy's face as she placed the radio microphone next to the transmitter. She wiped her eyes and she nervously looked around the small room, a picture of John and her son was on the table. They had been married for 34 years. Life had not been kind to Rosy or John. The fishing had died off, John did what he could to make ends meet, and the iceberg delivery would provide the first real money they had seen in months. Rosy wiped her eyes again as she dialed the telephone.

"International Ice Patrol... Lt. Ryan speaking... May I help you?"

"Yes... my name is Rosy... Rosy O'Sullivan... My husband John is the captain of the Sea Witch... John... was supposed to..." Her voice began to tremble as she paused and said, "I haven't been able to reach John... It's not like him not to radio me."

"Mrs. O'Sullivan... Perhaps you should call the Coast Guard... They usually handle these types of problems."

Her voice suddenly became stronger as her Irish temper flared, "Now look here... I'll not be given the run around... I know that you boys fly search missions for icebergs almost every day... John was delivering an iceberg to Boston... I need your help to locate the Sea Witch."

"Is your husband the guy who is towing the berg to Boston?"

"Yes..."

"Let me check something... I think we marked that berg today. If I'm right... we should be able to locate her using the GPS system... hold on please."

Lt. Ryan placed the phone on hold as he entered the next room. Reaching for a log book, he ran his fingers down the page, "Here it is... number 108956. Hey Charlie... what is the position of berg 108956..."

Charlie punched in the numbers and said, "That's odd... According to this, the berg is traveling in a north easterly direction at about

14 knots... Icebergs drift south or south east... not north east and they don't go 14 knots."

Lt. Ryan watched the scope for several minutes and confirmed Charlie's remarks. Pressing the phone extension he said, "We have located the iceberg Mrs. O'Sullivan, but there is little we can do until first light. Why don't you get some sleep and we will call you in the morning."

"But what about John..."

"His radio is probably not working... Don't worry... give us a call in the morning. We will send out someone to check out the Sea Witch as soon as we can... OK"

"Well I guess so... There isn't much that you can do until first light. Thank you... thank you very much." Rosy placed the receiver in the phone cradle and looked at the picture of her son and husband. Silently she said a prayer to the Virgin Mary asking for help in locating the Sea Witch.

Lt. Ryan returned to Charlie and said, "Are you sure our equipment is functioning properly?"

"Yes sir. I checked out other bergs in the area and they are reading normally. The reading we are receiving is a true reading... I'd bet the farm on that... The question is what's going on?"

"Yea..." Lt. Anderson looked at the screen for several seconds and picked up the phone and dialed the Naval base in Boston.

"This is Lt. Ryan of the IIP, St Johns, Newfoundland... We have an unusual situation here... let me speak to the officer of the day."

Lt. Ryan was put on hold. A few seconds later a voice came over the receiver, "Lt. Anderson... May I help you?"

"Yes Lt. Anderson, Lt. Ryan here... IIP St. Johns, Newfoundland... We have an unusual reading on one of our GPS units that was placed on an iceberg, growler class". Our readings indicate that this berg is traveling NNE at a speed of 14 knots... Yes we have checked our equipment... We also received a phone call from the wife of the captain of the Sea Witch. The Sea Witch was contracted to tow the berg to Boston. The captain was supposed to contact his wife when he got underway, but never did. Since the berg cannot be towed at a speed of 14 knots against the current and the Sea Witch is going away from Boston… I think we may have a problem.

"Lt. Anderson listened to the facts and said, "What is the GPS unit ID number?"

"108946…"

"Hold on please…."

Again the phone went silent as Lt. Anderson went to the console and punched in the GPS unit. The dot appeared on the screen. It was going NNE at a speed of 14 knots as Lt. Anderson said. He returned to the phone and said, "We have a confirmation of the speed and direction of the Sea Witch. Sure looks odd to me…."

"Our plate is full with ice patrols… Think you guys can take this one?"

"I don't see why not… We will send out a search plane at first light. We will let you know what we find."

"Thanks… Keep us posted…"

TITANIC, 0300 HOURS

The four Iraqi first class passengers were in their adjoining cabins, two men per cabin. In one cabin, two men were in the process of assembling several pieces of electronic communications gear. In the other cabin, two men quietly assembled a small arsenal of weapons. Nine-millimeter automatics, knives, explosives, and a variety of other gadgets were lying on the bed. The guns and ammunition were placed in four neat piles and then placed in four boxes. The boxes were placed in the closet and the men retired for the night.

Jacky and Josh walked slowly to her cabin. She rested her head on Josh's shoulder, her arm entwined with his. They had talked since dinner, they had gone on deck to look at the stars, and now they were lost in an embrace.

Jacky looked lovingly into Josh's eyes. They kissed and Jacky said, "Spend the night with me Josh... I have missed you so..."

Jacky placed the card key in the slot, a second later the door closed behind them. Approaching his cabin door, Dr. Moosavi, looked down the hall, smiled, and entered his cabin.

The Israeli secret service man watching a television monitor that was displaying the activity in the hallway, placed the earphones on the table and said, "Well... I guess they're in for the night." He activated the motion detectors in the hallway. The blue light of the television monitor glowed in the room showing the empty hallway and the door to Jacky's room. Another bank of monitors were watching the hallway from the opposite direction. The face of the Israeli secret service man was blank and expressionless as he watched the monitors. It would be a long night.

CIA, 0830 HOURS EST

Colonel Allan looked up from the reports in his hands and asked, "Anything unusual going on?" The other men in the room placed their reports on the table.

"Intelligence reports that there is still a lot of military activity, troop movements, and truck convoy activity in Syria, Libya, Iraq, and Iran. Jordan is quiet... but Israel is on alert in case something unusual starts. Reports are that Iraq has been shopping for nuclear weapons in Russia, Pakistan, and India... Pretty much the same as our last meeting."

Allan barked, "What about that truck convoy through Iran... seen any more?"

"Still heading toward the Iraq border... the Irish are at it again... another bombing in Northern Ireland. That's about it for over there. Canada reports a missing iceberg and vessel out of St. John's, Newfoundland. The report is a little odd. The IIP places a GPS unit on these bergs and this one is doing 14 knots NNE... against the current. The Coast Guard is looking into that one. A rubber dinghy was discovered about 50 miles south of St. John's… Nothing to report yet on that one. In the US… The usual FBI reports of potential terrorist activity… the usual Sir."

Allan looked at the Navy Commander and said, "What about the Prime Minister and the Titanic?"

"The USS Tiger Shark is on station shadowing the Titanic. The MI5 agent reports that the reason for the Prime Minister's trip on the Titanic was to meet a woman… one Jacky McGuire… There are confirmed reports from the MI5 agent that they are going to get married on the night of the 14th… This would explain his trip. Ms. McGuire is a stage actress. We have very little to go on as to how these two met… The Israeli secret service are making plans for the wedding and it should be secure and safe for the Prime Minister."

Allan looked surprised, "Let me see if I got this right… The Prime Minister and an actress… probably an Irish Catholic are getting married… On the Titanic… On the anniversary of the night that the original Titanic hit the iceberg? Good God… The mind boggles!"

There was the sound of laughter in the room.

Allan looked around the room and said, "Gentlemen please… Who is this woman?"

"We really don't know very much about her."

"Well you had damn well find out in a hurry don't you think?"

"Yes Sir…"

Allan placed his hands on the table as he stood up and said, "I want a complete report on this woman by the next meeting… tomorrow morning."

Allan walked toward the door waving for two others to follow him.

ATLANTIC OCEAN, 1000 HOURS

The drone of the four turbo prop engines of the Navy HC-130H Hercules filled the cockpit. The pilot and copilot were busy watching the sea 5000 feet below.

"How much longer," asked the pilot?

"We should be there in about 30 seconds."

The screen of the FLAR, Forward-Looking Airborne Radar, was showing a small blip on the screen. The radar operator also checked the coordinates of the GPS screen readout. Between the two instruments, the Sea Witch was easy to find. The radar operator cleared his voice and said, "The target is decreasing in speed... it has come to a complete stop..."

The pilot replied, "They probably ran out of fuel."

The copilot interrupted and said, "There she is."

The Sea Witch was rolling aimlessly in the waves. Her engines were silent. Above the HC-130H made a slow descending arc and flew directly above the Sea Witch at an altitude of 500 feet. The deafening sound of the engines hammered away at the vessel as the aircraft made a second pass.

"See anything?" asked the pilot.

"I thought I saw someone in the wheel house." remarked the co-pilot.

"Let's make another pass." Pressing a button on the panel to his right he continued, "We will make one more pass before we deploy... everyone take their deployment positions."

Slowly the aircraft made another low sweeping arc as the crew in the belly of the craft made themselves ready. The back of the HC-130H began to open. It was a ramp door that extended below the aircraft. The sound of the engines increased in volume as the door opened. Below lay the North Atlantic and the Sea Witch. As the aircraft made another pass over the Sea Witch, all eyes were trained on the wheelhouse. The figure of a man could clearly be seen, but he never came out to look at the winged beast that repeatedly flew over his vessel. It was clear that all was not normal. The pilot made another turn in the direction of the Sea Witch, but this time he was increasing his altitude as the crewmembers slid a large package onto the ramp door. A green light flashed and the crew pushed the package out of the plane, it was an inflatable raft with an outboard engine. A parachute opened majestically as the package dangled below the silky white canopy. The raft would inflate upon impact and the chute would be jettisoned. No sooner had the raft chute opened, three men jumped from the aircraft as well. Their chutes opened and the four white manmade clouds descended toward the cold North Atlantic. The raft hit the water first and quickly inflated. The three men guided their descent directly to within 10 feet of the raft. Each man splashed down five seconds after the other and quickly swam to the raft. As the last man entered, the outboard engine was started and they darted across the sea. Within minutes, they were along side the Sea Witch, two of the men at the bow of the raft held their automatics in their hands.

"Ahoy... Ahoy."

There was no response. The three men looked at each other as their raft circled the Sea Witch. The man in the wheelhouse seemed to stare back at them, but he never moved. The raft approached the stern and one man boarded the vessel. The second man threw the first a rope and the two tied off the raft to the stern of the Sea Witch. Minutes later, all three men were on the stern deck of the Sea Witch as one entered the wheelhouse, with his gun drawn.

Silently, the Coast Guard seaman stared at the sight of John lashed to the wheel with a knife sticking out of his back. It was clear that John was dead and had been dead for quite a while. The other two men entered the wheelhouse. One reached for the radio. Realizing it was turned off; he flipped a switch and adjusted the volume.

"Rescue One... Rescue One... This is Stan... Do you read?"

"Affirmative... This is Rescue One... What is going on down there... Over?"

"Looks like someone stuck a knife in this old man's back and lashed him to the helm. The vessel is out of fuel... There is no one on board other than the dead man... Over."

"Roger... We copy that... We will notify home base and send someone out for you guys... Over and out."

The big HC-130H made another low pass over the Sea Witch, dipping its wings and then turned west back to its base. The three men searched the Sea Witch. On the deck were several empty 7.62-millimeter spent shell casings were discovered rolling about. Other than that, there was nothing to be found except for the IIP GPS unit, which was sitting on the deck by the wheelhouse. The men gathered together in the wheelhouse to await the arrival of the Coast Guard vessel that would tow them into St. John's.

ST. JOHN'S, NEWFOUNDLAND 1000 HOURS

Lt. Ryan listened to the voice of Lt. Anderson, "We found the Sea Witch, but the captain was murdered and for some reason lashed to the helm. There was no one else on board and it looks like there may have been a firefight… several 7.62-millimeter shell casings were on the deck of the stern. We are towing the Sea Witch into port and they should be arriving in about 5 hours."

"Thank you for the report… I will call Mrs. O'Sullivan and have her available to make a positive ID."

Lt. Ryan slowly dialed the O'Sullivan phone number. A brief period of silence ensued before the phone rang. Mrs. O'Sullivan answered the phone and said, "Hello…."

"Mrs. O'Sullivan… This is Lt. Ryan… of the IIP… you called us regarding the disposition of the Sea Witch… We found the Sea Witch. Yes… we found your husband. I am sending a car to your home Mr. O'Sullivan… I am afraid that I have very bad news. Your husband is dead. We would like for you to make a positive ID of your husband when the Sea Witch arrives in port. The Coast Guard is towing her in."

Lt. Ryan closed his eyes as he listened to her cries of anguish, "I am deeply sorry Mrs. O'Sullivan… No we did not find anyone else on board the Sea Witch… Was your son on board? I understand…"

Lt. Ryan placed the phone back into the cradle and stood silently for several seconds before he called Lt. Anderson.

"Lt. Anderson... this is Lt. Ryan again. Mrs. O'Sullivan will be available when your men arrive... She also says that her son was on board. Are you sure that there was no one else on board the Sea Witch... I understand."

Lt. Ryan next called the police department to report the murder. When the Coast Guard cutter arrived with the Sea Witch, they would be there as well to conduct their investigation of the crime scene.

TITANIC – 900 HOURS

The Israeli security guard maintained his vigilance, watching the closed circuit television monitors. The room was dark and silent as the agent grabbed the foot of the sleeping agent and said, "Rise and shine."

A low pitched groan filled the room as the man rolled on his back and opened his eyes, "How's it going?"

"Nothing to report... No activity in the corridor... Everything is quiet..."

"Good..."

Two cabins away lay Jacky and Joshua. They had fallen asleep entwined with their arms caressing each other. Joshua opened his eyes slowly and inhaled deeply. The smell of Jacky's hair was intoxicating. Slowly, he embraced her warm body to his, her legs entwined around his. Jacky looked at Joshua and pulled his lips to hers.

Joshua looked as Jacky and said, "God... I have missed you so..."

"I missed you too..."

Their lips joined again.

"Jacky... Do you love me...?"

"With all my heart and soul..."

"Why... Why do you love me?"

Jacky turned to face Joshua, resting on her elbow and running her fingers through his hair, "Because I do... Isn't that enough?"

"Yea... I guess so... but..."

"But what my love…"

"I have carried this feeling of guilt with me for so many years. I was a coward when my father made me leave you… Our son was killed and still I could not find the words to express my love for you… Then one day, out of the clear blue, you came back to me… I feel like such a fool, I was never there for you when you needed me… Why… Why did you come back to me?"

"Because I love you Joshua… I love you. For years, I hated your name… your existence… you very being. I blamed you for everything that I thought I should have and did not… When David was a child and asked me about his father, I lied to him and hated myself for not letting him know who his father was. But lying to him made me feel good… It was like a power trip for me… I could turn you into whatever I wanted you to be in his eyes. When David was killed, I realized that I was lying to myself. David was dead, my father was dead, and who else in my life did I have that meant anything to me other than you. For the first time in my life, I came to grasp with reality. I would either live my life alone or reach out to the only person in my life that I had loved… someone that I could turn to, my soul mate, someone who would listen to me, someone I could love and who would love me. We had that once… and I realized that I needed that again… That's why I sent you the ring… You told me that if I changed my mind, to send you the ring and you would come back to me…"

"I did come back to you my love…"

They kissed again and Joshua said, "…and I will never let you go, ever again."

Two cabins away further down the hall, a door opened and Dr. Moosavi entered the corridor. The Israeli agent noted his presence and time on a logbook. Dr. Moosavi closed the door gently and walked toward the grand staircase. Several minutes later, the four men that had boarded ship in Cherbourg, France left their cabins to join Moosavi on the first class promenade. Again the Israeli agent logged their departure.

The men gathered quietly on the first class promenade deck and began to talk. Moosavi said, "Is everything in order?"

"Yes… The communications unit is assembled and is operational.", replied one of the men.

"All weapons are in order and ready for use.", replied another.

Moosavi looked at the men and said, "We will be arriving at Queenstown in about two hours… 1130 hours to be precise. We should take on more passengers and depart for New York by 1330 hours. Make radio contact at 1350 hours as planned and remain in your cabins until the wedding. The wedding is scheduled to be held on the evening of the 14th at 2200 hours on the grand staircase. I will give the bride away."

There was a moment of laughter as Moosavi continued, "You will take your positions by 2100 hours the evening of the 14th and the iceberg will be on station for the rendezvous by 2330 hours. Any questions?"

The men said nothing.

"Good…" The four men disbursed as Moosavi had instructed. Moosavi himself walked toward the first class dining room for breakfast.

The three-throated whistle of the Titanic gave a loud blast for several seconds. Inside Jacky's cabin the low-pitched sound could be heard.

"We must be approaching Queenstown… That will be our last stop before we began our crossing." remarked Jacky.

"Are you hungry?"

"Famished… How about you."

"Yes… I am too…" Joshua got out of bed and gave Jacky a hug from behind. Jacky turned to face Joshua and said, "Mr. Prime Minister… you cannot go to breakfast dressed in your birthday suit…"

Joshua embraced Jacky again and said, "Why not eat in our cabin… and after we eat, we can go back to bed…"

"Sounds delicious, but we had better get out of this cabin for a while… After all, we are not married yet, are we? Besides, I want to take a walk on the deck with you, visit some shops, and plan for the · wedding… We only have a day to plan everything."

Joshua reached for his clothes and said, "Let me have an hour with my staff and I will join you."

Jacky entered the bathroom and started the shower. Sticking her head out of the doorway she said, "See you in an hour my love." and blew him a kiss.

Joshua dressed and left the cabin for his. An hour later, the two walked toward the grand staircase hand in hand. As they entered the main dining room, the maitre d' escorted them to a quiet table.

Dr. Moosavi watched the two for several seconds before approaching their table.

"Jacky my dear… you look radiant… like a woman in love." Looking at Joshua he continued, "And you Mr. Prime Minister are a very lucky man… Congratulations to both of you."

Jacky smiled and said, "Join us…"

"Thank you … but I have already eaten and besides… this is not a time for a third wheel… I am sure that you both have much to talk about."

"Yes we do, but some of the discussion will be about the wedding… and the rehearsal…"

"Please allow me the honor of hosting a small party in your honor tonight after dinner. I have made arrangements for a gathering around 9 tonight."

"We would be delighted…"

"See you tonight…"

The Titanic arrived at Queenstown on schedule at 1130 hours and picked up 220 third class, 19-second class, and 2 first class passengers. 18 passengers disembarked. By 1330 hours, the Titanic raised its starboard anchor and began her first transatlantic crossing. The USS Tiger Shark followed silently behind. At 1350 hours, radio contact was made with home base by the Iraqi terrorist.

KILO SUB – 1020 HOURS

The iceberg drifted slowly south in the calm Atlantic. Below the iceberg, the crew of the Kilo class sub went about their duties. The green glow from the GPS display reflected from the glasses of the radio operator.

The Captain approached from behind and leaned over the seaman's shoulder.

"How is our drift?"

"Everything is normal Captain… there is no need to power up the boat at the moment and if the Titanic makes the necessary 386 miles today, 519 miles tomorrow, we will be waiting for her as planned."

"Excellent… Excellent."

ST. JOHN'S NEWFOUNDLAND – 1600 HOURS

The Coast Guard Cutter approached the mouth of the inlet at St. John's harbor. In tow, behind her was the Sea Witch. A hushed crowd of people was gathered at the dock watching the ships. A news team assumed a position in front of the news camera whereby the cutter and Sea Witch could be viewed over the announcer's right shoulder, "This is Tom Mc Millan reporting from St. John's harbor. It was reported earlier today by the Coast Guard that a missing vessel, the Sea Witch, had been located out of fuel, and adrift in the North Atlantic approximately 68 nautical miles north/northeast of St. John's. Her Captain, John O'Sullivan was found murdered and lashed to the helm. His son, Vincent O'Sullivan, who was believed to be on board the Sea Witch, is missing. The Coast Guard reported that the Sea Witch's rubber dinghy was also missing, leading local authorities to suspect Vincent O'Sullivan in the murder of his father, John O'Sullivan. An all points bulletin has been issued for the arrest Vincent O'Sullivan. If anyone knows the whereabouts of Vincent O'Sullivan, they are asked to contact the St.

John's police department. Be advised that he is considered armed and dangerous."

"How about dead." thought one of the terrorists that had killed Vincent and John. The two men sat watching a television set waiting for their flight from Halifax to the UK. In one hour, they would be in the air and free.

The Coast Guard cutter and Sea Witch docked at the pier and a stretcher with a black body bag was removed from the Sea Witch. Rosy O'Sullivan's cries of anguish could be heard as the body of her husband was placed in an ambulance. The police quickly boarded the Sea Witch and began their investigation.

TITANIC – 2100 HOURS

Dr. Moosavi stood at the door, greeting guests for the private party in honor of Jacky and Joshua. The Israeli secret service men stood stoically like cigar store Indians, their eyes darting around the room ever vigilant to spot someone or some thing out of order.

The Titanic's maiden voyage had sparked the interest of the rich and famous from both sides of the pond. As in the case of the original Titanic's maiden voyage, represented on board were the cream of society. There were numerous actors and actresses, industrial giants, sports idols, and countless newly rich want-to-be types booked in first class. Dr. Moosavi had prepared a guest list that included many of these people, including Captain Smith.

"Good evening Captain Smith."

"Good evening Dr. Moosavi… Splendid of you to throw the couple a party."

"It is the least I could do… She has been my patient for many years… Let us say that this is her graduation party. Once I give her away to the Prime Minister… She will no longer be in need of my services… and she will be, shall we say, cured."

"When do you think that the couple will arrive?"

"Momentarily... The secret service men are in position. That is always a good sign that the Prime Minister is not far behind."

The quintet began to play softly in the background as more guests arrived. Dr. Moosavi greeted each one with a warm smile. As he turned to greet the next guest, he saw Jacky and Joshua walking down the grand staircase. Jacky was radiant and smiling. Joshua looked tall and proud as he guided Jacky toward the guest line at the door.

Dr. Moosavi spoke to the secret service agent standing next to him. The agent walked over to Captain Smith and brought him to Dr. Moosavi.

"Would you be so kind Captain to introduce the Prime Minister and Jacky to our guests?"

"I would be delighted..."

The remaining guests were quickly ushered into the ballroom as Captain Smith greeted Jacky and Joshua. Captain Smith then entered the ball room alone and announced, "Ladies and Gentlemen... may I have your attention please..."

The crowd began to hush as Captain Smith continued, "It is my pleasure to introduce the Prime Minister of Israel and Ms. Jacky McGuire."

Jacky and Joshua stepped through the threshold into the ballroom as the guests began to applaud, encircling them and offering their congratulations for their announced wedding. Dr. Moosavi watched confidently as Jacky charmed everyone in the room. She was indeed a beautiful woman and her love for Joshua filled her with a radiance that could be felt by everyone. The quintet started to play another waltz and Joshua took Jacky toward the dance floor. The circle of people opened as Joshua took Jacky in his arms and the two floated across the dance floor.

"I love you Jacky."

"I love you too... more than the sun... the moon... and all of the stars...", her eyes twinkled like diamonds.

"It was very kind of Dr. Moosavi to have a party in our honor."

"Yes… He has been like a father to me all these years… Without him, I think that I would be locked up somewhere in an asylum. When David died… I couldn't…" the word David echoed in her mind, "David… David… David."

Suddenly, Jacky began to grow limp in Joshua's arms. It was almost as if she had gone into a trance. Joshua held her tightly in his arms, as he looked frantically toward one of the secret service men. There was a collective "Ohhh" from the guests as Joshua carried Jacky to a chair. Dr. Moosavi forced his way through the knot of people gathered around Jacky and Joshua, "Excuse me, let me through… Let me through please. I am her doctor… Let me through…."

Dr. Moosavi looked concerned as he rubbed her hand and said, "Jacky… Jacky my dear…"

Jacky's face was drained and ashen in color. She said nothing.

"Take her to her cabin!", ordered Moosavi.

"What do you think is wrong doctor…", asked Joshua?

"Exhaustion I should think… She has been on a fast track the last few days. I want to examine her. I am sure that she will be fine, but I want to see her privately if I may."

"Certainly."

Joshua and Dr. Moosavi helped Jacky to her feet. Slowly they left the ballroom leaving the stunned guest. The quintet began to play another song and Captain Smith said, "Everyone please continue with the party. I am sure that Miss McGuire will be fine by morning. Everyone please… enjoy yourselves." Captain Smith followed after Jacky.

Dr. Moosavi and Joshua placed Jacky on her bed and Dr. Moosavi asked, "Would you have any brandy?"

"Yes… I believe I do… If we don't, we will damn sure find some!"

Picking up the telephone, he called his cabin and spoke with the steward, "Bring over a bottle of brandy… Yes… Thank you."

"He said he has some in his cabin."

Several moments later, the steward entered the room with a glass of brandy.

"Will there be anything else sir?"

"No... I think that is all we will need... Thank you."

The steward started to leave the room. As he did, he accidentally on purpose jarred a table knocking a vase to the floor. It did not shatter.

"Excuse me Sir... Clumsy of me..."

As he fussed about replacing the vase, he placed one of his radio transmitter lighters into the vase and quietly left the room.

Dr. Moosavi took the glass and tried to get Jacky to take a sip. She did not respond.

"Mr. Prime Minister... I would like to be alone with my patient..."

Joshua looked very concerned saying nothing.

Placing his hand on Joshua's shoulder Moosavi continued, "She will be fine I assure you. I need to examine her. She has had a busy couple of days and with the wedding... Well, she needs rest. Let me have a few moments with her and I will see you in your cabin in about 30 minutes."

Together, the two men approached the cabin door. Dr. Moosavi closed the door behind Joshua and turned the lock. The click of the lock echoed in Joshua's ears as he stared at the closed door. He stood silent for several seconds and then walked towards his cabin. His ever-present bodyguards followed behind, while two remained behind to guard Jacky's door.

Dr. Moosavi removed his dinner jacket and placed his glasses on the end of his nose, his face was tense. Gone was the warm and considerate Dr. Moosavi that had just ushered Joshua out of the cabin. Holding Jacky's head gently in his hands, he looked deeply into her eyes. Her eyes stared blankly back at him like dolls eyes, black and empty. She was in a deep catatonic state.

This is what he was afraid of. Jacky had been seeing Moosavi on a weekly basis for the last nine years. Her mind had been washed clean and reprogrammed by Dr. Moosavi. During her stay in Oslo and for the last nine years, Moosavi had split her mind into two complete personalities, thus creating a schizophrenic. One personality was warm and loving, the other was vengeful and full of hate for Joshua.

Jacky had not seen Moosavi for 12 days due to the trip to Southampton and the secret service men watching her every move on the Titanic. It was clear that Jacky had some type of relapse or problem that had placed her into a catatonic state. "This was not good." thought Moosavi.

"Jacky... This is Dr. Moosavi... Listen to my words..."

Stepping away from Jacky Dr. Moosavi said in a firm deep voice, "AUHSOJ!" his eyes watching her response to his words.

There was no movement at first. She sat silent and motionless.

"Jacky... This is Dr. Moosavi... Listen to my voice and obey... AUHSOJ".

Slowly at first, there was a subtle change in her face. Her eyes began to focus as she gradually began to find herself. Turning her head to face Dr. Moosavi, her eyes slowly began to focus. Her mouth began to form a word. Quietly she said, "Yes..."

"Something is wrong tonight... Can you tell me what is troubling you?"

Her face was still ashen in color... she sat motionless for several seconds and then spoke with a haunting hollow voice that was like a whisper, "I feel confused... I feel as if I am being torn apart from within..."

"What is tearing you apart my dear?"

Silence hung in the room as Dr. Moosavi waited for a reply.

"I don't know... I am confused... I love Joshua... I know I do... I want to marry him, but there is a part of me that haunts me... There is this voice that wants to kill him. I... I do not understand this voice in my head that is screaming at me to kill him."

"What type of voice is it my dear?"

Slowly, Jacky's hands rose from her lap, each palm covering her ears, "It is my voice... It's my voice and it... it keeps repeating... *Kill him... **Kill him... Kill him**"

Banging her ears with her hands she cried, "MAKE IT STOP...
MAKE **IT STOP...** PLEASE **MAKE IT STOP!"**

Dr. Moosavi placed his hand on her head and said, "SHHH my
dear. Let me talk to the other voice please.

Instantly, Jacky's posture in the chair changed as she became
rigid, her back straight, and her face angry. Her voice now hissed
like a viper as she glared into Dr. Moosavi's eyes and a satanic voice
whispered, "*When do I kill him... WHEN??*"

"Listen to my voice... The time is not yet here for you to kill Joshua.
That time will come soon. You must not do anything now."

"I am tired of waiting as she holds him in her arms and makes
love to him... I want him dead... I want him *DEAD*."

"You will have your wish after the wedding and not before." Dr.
Moosavi glared back at her as he struggled to regain control over
the monster he had created.

"You will do nothing until I give you the command to kill him!
Do you understand?"

Jacky's burning eyes stared angrily back at Dr. Moosavi, her head
twisting to one side as she considered his words.

"I will do as you say, but mark my words, I will kill anyone who
gets in my way... even you Dr. Moosavi."

Her words sent a chill through his body as he commanded,
"Enough... Enough... Now remain silent and await my command.
Do not torment Jacky... Do you understand... If you persist in tormenting her, you will destroy everything. Your time will come, be
silent until then."

Jacky's hands returned to her ears as she once again cried, "*Please
make it STOP!*"

Moosavi gently placed his hands over hers, and gently moved her
hands to her lap saying, "The voice in your head will listen to my
words and it will go away."

"But why is it there... Am I going mad? ... I love Joshua with all
of my heart."

Dr. Moosavi stepped backwards as he spoke and bumped into the table. The vase began to fall as he grabbed it in mid flight. There was a rattle as the lighter fell out of the vase and hit the floor. Being off balance, he accidentally crushed it beneath his feet. Picking up the lighter, he saw that the outside plastic casing was smashed exposing the radio transmitter and remembered the steward. Placing the vase gently back on the table, he placed the lighter into his pocket as he spoke softly to Jacky, "I want you to get into your bed clothes and sleep."

Jacky stood up and walked across the bedroom and collected her nightgown from the closet. She closed the bathroom door gently. In a few moments, she opened the door and got into bed.

Dr. Moosavi said, "Close your eyes and sleep my dear. In the morning, I will call for you and you will remember nothing of this conversation and you will tell no one about what happened to you. Do you understand?"

Jacky spoke softly as she closed her eyes, "Yes…"

"Good my dear… now sleep. In the morning you will tell Joshua that you had a sudden migraine attack… Do you understand. I will tell him the same story. You will remember nothing of tonight's voices. Do you understand?"

"Yes…"

"If the voice returns, I want you to summons me immediately and go to your room until I arrive. Do you understand me?"

"Yes…"

Dr. Moosavi turned out the lights and quietly left the cabin. As he opened the door, two secret service men that flanked the doorway turned to greet him and then returned to their position.

"Is the Prime Minister in his cabin?"

One of the men said, "Yes."

"Thank you…"

Dr. Moosavi walked down the hall and approached two more secret service men in the hall, "May I see the Prime Minister?"

"Wait here please." said one of the men as the other entered the cabin. A few seconds later, the door opened and the secret service man motioned for Dr. Moosavi to enter.

Captain Smith and Joshua were standing in the immense study. The fireplace crackled as Joshua spoke, "How is she..."

"She will be fine. It was a little more than exhaustion I'm afraid... Ms. McGuire has a history of severe migraine attacks. When they strike, they are numbing and in her case very paralyzing. That's what happened tonight. She is sleeping now... I gave her a sedative. She should be fine in the morning... A little tired, but she should be fully recovered for the wedding."

"Can I see her?"

"Not tonight... I will visit with her in the morning... After that, she is all yours. Gentlemen... I bid you good night"

Dr. Moosavi started toward the door as Captain Smith said, "Goodnight Mr. Prime Minister... I have to report to the bridge."

"Thank you... thank you both. I'll see you in the morning Dr. Moosavi."

Dr. Moosavi and Captain Smith walked down the corridor.

"Captain... What is the Prime Minister's stewards name that brought the brandy... I must speak with him and find out where he got that bottle. I tasted it myself... Excellent brandy... excellent."

"Higgans, I believe... Yes Higgans. He was a last minute replacement. Almost missed our departure. If I am not mistaken he can be reached by the house phone system. Contact the operator and she can assist you. Good night Doctor."

Captain Smith continued down the hall as Dr. Moosavi entered his cabin. Closing the door, he went straight to the phone. Reaching into his pocket he examined the lighter."

"Good evening Dr. Moosavi... May I help you?"

"Yes, I was just speaking with Captain Smith regarding steward Higgans. Could you please tell me his cabin number?"

"Certainly Doctor..."

Dr. Moosavi wrote down the cabin number.

"Shall I ring his cabin?"

"No, that won't be necessary... The hour is late... I'll see him in the morning."

Dr. Moosavi dialed the cabin of his associates. The phone rang several times before a sleepy voice said, "Yes..."

"Meet me on the promenade deck in 10 minutes."

Dr. Moosavi put on his overcoat and left for the promenade deck. 10 minutes later a man approached and said, "Would you have a light?"

After lighting the cigarette, the two men talked quietly as they walked.

"We have a problem... One of the stewards placed a bug in Jacky's room this evening. He may have overheard us talking. He must be eliminated tonight."

"What is his cabin number?"

Dr. Moosavi handed him a slip of paper.

"Thank you for the light... Have a good evening."

The two men parted and went to their rooms. Several minuets later, the terrorist left his cabin. In his hand was a glass of scotch heavily laced with cyanide. He approached Higgans cabin and knocked on the door.

There was a pause before the door opened. The stranger staggered forward and said with a slur, "Is this where the girls are?"

The drink spilled all over Higgans as he said, "They told me that you could get me a girl... how about it pal?"

"Who in the hell are you... Look what you did... What girls?"

The terrorist was looking quickly around the room. There was a device on the desk. It looked like a recording device of some kind with an earplug. Besides the device was a note pad.

The terrorist staggered around the room. Higgans became furious, "Get out of my cabin... Get out before I call the house security."

"Look pal... all I want to do is to get laid... A tin can this size must have a few hookers on board..."

Higgans was rubbing his drenched shirt with a towel as he said, "If you don't leave… I'll have you put in irons… Now leave… Understand me?"

"Gee… I guess I got the wrong room… You sure don't look like no pimp."

"A pimp! How dare you sir… Now get out immediately… get out…"

Suddenly Higgans struggled to breathe. He staggered and fell to his knees and then to the floor. The terrorist watched as his breathing became more labored and finally stopped. He reached over to Higgans and placed his fingers on his jugular. There was no pulse. Higgan's death would be considered a heart attack. There would be no autopsy until the ship arrived in port and the Titanic would never reach New York. The terrorist looked at the note pad. The pad was a transcript of Moosavi's discussion with Jacky. The last word on the pad was, "AUHSOJ???" It looked like Higgans did not have enough time to do anything with the information. Quietly, the terrorist collected the pad and recording devise and left the room.

CIA – 1400 HOURS

Colonel Allan was returning to his office from lunch. His secretary looked up from her desk and said, "Here is a message for you. It came in about fifteen minutes ago."

She handed him a message sealed in an envelope as he entered his office and closed the door. Reading the message, Allan reached for the phone, "Ms. Ryerson, please contact the team and have them report to the conference room on the double."

Placing the receiver into the phone cradle he read the message again, "MI5 reports their agent has failed to report in as scheduled. Efforts are being made to contact Captain Smith for a follow up. Will advise."

Thirty minutes later, Colonel Allan addressed the group, "MI5 reports that their agent has failed to report in as scheduled. Captain

Smith is being contacted as we speak. We should have some word momentarily. What do we have on Ms. Jacky McGuire?"

One of the men responded, "She is a stage actress on Broadway. Her husband was apparently killed before the birth of her son; we have very little on him at this time. Her son was killed in Israel during a SCUD attack during the Gulf War. In particular, he was killed when a Patriot missile destroyed a SCUD, but the war head fell on an American barracks killing 25 American troops and several Israeli solders assigned to guard the barracks. Ms. McGuire's son was one of the Israeli soldiers. Her son had given up his American citizenship and became an Israeli citizen prior to joining the Israeli army. Ms. McGuire has no known living relatives and after the death of her son, she suffered a nervous breakdown. Since her breakdown, she has been under the care of a Dr. Hamid Moosavi, psychiatrist, Iraqi born, naturalized US citizen in 1980. Moosavi is on the Titanic with Ms. McGuire, we assume as her attending physician. Moosavi apparently gave up his practice after attending to Ms. McGuire during her initial breakdown and apparently has been her personal physician since 1991."

Allan sat silent for several moments mulling over the information, "We have an Irish Catholic girl about to marry the Prime Minister of Israel, a Jew. We have the same woman with a history of mental problems being attended to by a psychiatrist who is a naturalized United States citizen, but who just so happens to be a former citizen of Iraq. We have unusual troop movements in Iraq, Syria, Iran, and Libya, and now we have an over due MI5 agent on the Titanic. Is there anything else going on that seems out of the ordinary?"

"Nothing really out of the ordinary with international affairs, but remember that report of a runaway iceberg? The Coast Guard reports that the vessel hauling the iceberg, the Sea Witch was located 68 miles NNE of St. John's Newfoundland adrift and out of fuel. The Captain was found stabbed to death and lashed to the helm. The GPS unit that was on the iceberg was found on the vessel. That would explain why the iceberg was initially reported going 14 knots against the Labrador

Current. An all points bulletin has been issued by the St. John's police department for the arrest of Vincent O'Sullivan, the captain's son. The rubber dinghy that was located on the beach south of St. John's has been identified as the launch belonging to the Sea Witch. Vincent O'Sullivan is a prime suspect in the murder of his father."

"… And the iceberg?"

"The IIP reports that the iceberg was a growler and was not in the vicinity of the Sea Witch. Being a growler, it will be extremely hard to locate, in particular since this year there is a bunker crop of icebergs."

Suddenly, the phone buzzed and Colonel Allan picked up the receiver and said, "Yes…"

He placed the receiver into the cradle and looked at the men in the room. His face took on an air of concern as he wrinkled his eyebrows. His voice seemed to drop a full octave as he said, "Captain Smith reports that steward Higgans was found dead in his cabin. He was apparently drinking and the ship's physician initially reports that he died of an apparent heart attack. I want an immediate report from MI5 about this man's drinking history and the reports of his last physical. Contact Captain Smith and ask him if the ships physician can perform an autopsy… we need to know definitively how this man died. I also want a complete passenger list of everyone on the Titanic… Give this list to the CIA, CID and the FBI and run it against any known or suspected terrorist groups that they may have… I also want to know the nationality of every person on that ship. We need to move on this gentlemen and I think that we may have to move fast."

KILO SUB – 1530 HOURS

The Kilo sub drifted silently under the iceberg with the Labrador Current. The Captain looked at the screen, "How are we doing?"

"Everything is going as planned Captain. In about six hours, we should correct our drift. As the Titanic approaches the rendezvous point, we can adjust our position with greater precision, but for the moment, we are on target."

The Captain stared at the screen for a moment and then returned to his cabin.

TITANIC – 2230 HOURS

Captain Smith received the message from the White Star main office instructing him to have the ship physician conduct an immediate autopsy of Higgans. He summonsed the ships physician to his cabin.

"But we are not equipped for an autopsy..."

"I am aware of that, but I have my orders... Do the best you can."

"Can it wait until morning?"

"Certainly doctor."

After the doctor left the cabin, Captain Smith called the Prime Minister's cabin.

One of the secret service men answered and then the Prime Minister's voice came over the receiver, "Yes Captain Smith."

"I am afraid that I have some bad news... Steward Higgans was found dead in his cabin tonight... an apparent heart attack. We will make arrangements for a new steward to service your cabin in the morning."

"He seemed awfully fit and in good health to have a heart problem..."

"Yes... I know..."

"I will notify my staff of the change..."

"Good night Mr. Prime Minister."

As the Titanic knifed its way through the dark Atlantic, Captain Smith and the Prime Minister retired for the evening.

CHAPTER NINE

IRAN

Three Iraqi military trucks and three troop carriers sat silently as six Iranian border guards approached the convoy. Inside three of the six trucks were several large crates containing nuclear devices. Each of the approaching men jumped on the running board of each truck as the drivers started the truck engines and the convoy pulled out. Two miles down the road the truck convoy approached the Iran border checkpoint. The lead truck paused momentarily as the driver presented the guard with travel documents. The guard read the documents counted the trucks in the convoy and then raised the barricade. All six vehicles passed through the boarder checkpoint and approached the Iraq checkpoint 300 yards down the road. The same procedure was followed. In a few moments, the trucks passed into Iraq and immediately split up into three groups, one troop carrier and one munitions vehicle, heading in different directions toward Baghdad, Irbil and Al Basra. Above in the night sky, the American Big Bird recorded the truck movement.

In Baghdad, a group of men sat silently as a report was being read. The man spoke in a low tone, his eyes never leaving the stare of the man at the head of he table.

"The nuclear devices are in Iraq and will be arriving at their destinations by late afternoon or early evening. Moosavi reports that his patient suffered a personality conflict, but he is confident that the plan will be carried out successfully. There was an MI5 agent aboard the Titanic and had to be eliminated by Moosavi's men. Moosavi reports that the agent did not have time to report back to his people. The agent's tapes and notes were confiscated and destroyed. Apparently, the agent had bugged Ms. Mc Guire's room."

"How are the missiles?"

"Everything is in order. They have been checked out and are ready for launch as soon as the nuclear devices are placed onboard. By the time Cane is eliminated and the state funeral arrangements are in place, they will be ready."

Sadaam stroked his mustache as he reviewed the report in his mind. Slowly he stood and began to walk around the table.

"Gentlemen… This is a momentous occasion for the people of Iraq. Today, we have received the weapons that will rain terror against the enemies of Iraq and its people ending the imperialistic domination of our country. The plan is brilliant and will succeed. Once the Titanic reaches the location of the original Titanic sinking, our sub will strike with torpedoes sinking her. The governments of the world will think that the Prime Minister was lost with the ship. The sinking of the Titanic will, of course, dispose of his body and that of his bride. Moosavi will kill her once she has done her job. The leaders of the world will meet in Israel for the memorial service that will be held to mourn the untimely death of the Prime Minister and his new bride. The United States President, the Prime Minister of England, the leaders of France, Egypt and all nations will unite at one location. At that moment, we will launch our nuclear angels of death and eviscerate all of them. It will be a glorious day gentlemen and a new beginning for Iraq."

TITANIC – 0800 HOURS

Dr. Moosavi had risen early. He had collected his thoughts about the night before. Jacky had had a major problem with her association with Joshua and their impending marriage. Jacky's loving personality was in love with Joshua. Moosavi had been successful in removing the anger and hatred for Joshua for the loss of her son, her abandonment, and all of the lonely years she had spent without Joshua from this personality. All of these feelings of anger and hatred had been placed in a second personality. Obviously, the second personality was eager to seek the revenge it wanted, even at the risk of destroying the plan Moosavi had so carefully created. Quietly, Moosavi approached the Prime Minister's cabin. The guard asked him to remain in the corridor as he went inside. Moments later, Moosavi was asked to enter the cabin. Joshua was anxious to see Jacky.

"Can I see her now?"

"Not just yet… I want a few minutes alone with her and then she will be yours once again."

"Is she OK?"

"Yes, I am sure she will be fine, but I want to wake her myself and assure her that she is in good health before you see her. She had quite a migraine attack last night. She could be a bit groggy from the sedative I gave her. Give me a few minutes with her and I will come and get you."

Moosavi left the cabin and approached the two guards standing watch at Jacky's door. The guard unlocked the cabin door and Moosavi entered. Locking the door behind himself, he crossed the sitting room and entered the bedroom. The room was dark. Moosavi turned on a lamp by the door and approached the bed. Jacky was asleep, her chest moved up and down slowly.

In a firm voice, Moosavi said, "Jacky… Jacky. Awake!"

Jacky moaned softly as she opened her eyes slowly.

"Jacky… It is Dr. Moosavi my child. How are you feeling?"

Slowly Jacky turned her head toward Moosavi and smiled.

"I feel a little groggy… What happened to me?"

"You had another one of your migraine attacks last night. It was a sudden attack and you collapsed while dancing with Joshua."

Jacky listened and said nothing for several seconds.

"I… I… don't remember very much I am afraid…"

"That is totally understandable and normal my child. Do you feel like getting out of bed?"

"Yes… I would like to see Joshua."

"Good… Why don't you get up and freshen yourself while I fetch him for you?"

A smile crossed her face as she began to get out of bed.

"I'll be right back…"

As Moosavi opened the door of the cabin, he saw Joshua. Without saying a word he gestured for Joshua to enter. A moment later, he was by Jacky's side.

"Jacky darling… are you OK?"

"Yes… a little groggy…"

"You had me so scared last night…"

"I'll be fine now… and I'll be even better after I have breakfast. I am starving!"

"I'll have breakfast brought to my cabin… I have a private promenade… we will have breakfast there my darling."

TITANIC MORGUE – 0900 HOURS

The ships physician entered the infirmary and switched on the lights. Almost absentmindedly, he walked over to a display of neatly arranged surgical instruments and placed them on a stainless steel cart. Removing his jacket, shirt and slacks, he dressed in his surgical scrubs. Pushing the cart into the operating room, he turned and opened the door to a small morgue that contained a walk-in refrigerator. Laid out on a gurney was the body of steward Higgans. The doctor rolled the body out of the refrigerator and moved it into the operating room. Positioning the round surgical lights over the body, the doctor grabbed the end of the drape and exposed the body. Higgans' face was contorted with pain. His eyes were open and his mouth was locked in a frozen snarl. Higgans sported a mustache that was wrinkled across the upper lip of his contorted mouth.

"It was not a very pleasant death." thought the doctor.

The doctor adjusted his glasses and examined Higgans body. There were no unusual bruises, cuts, or marks of any kind. The doctor put on a pair of rubber gloves, turned on a small tape recorder and began the procedure.

"We have a Caucasian, approximately 55 years of age."

Taking the tape measure he measured the body length.

"Seventy-five inches in height. There are no marks or contusions on the torso."

The doctor started with the head and ran his fingers through the scalp, feeling for anything unusual. He found nothing. Next, he examined the ears. As he placed the otoscope into the dead man's ear, he bent over and thought he smelled the faint aroma of almonds. He hesitated as his mind analyzed the smell. Sniffing, the doctor forgot about the otoscope and placed his nose over Higgans' face and sniffed again. Walking to his neatly stacked clothes, he reached into his pocket, and he removed his pocket comb. Placing a piece of stiff paper under the Higgans' mustache, he began to slowly pull the comb through the facial hair. As he combed, several small crystals fell onto the paper. Carefully he collected the samples and placed the crystals on a microscope slide. He examined the crystals under a microscope carefully and then reached for a small package of analytical test kits. The Titanic had a complete infirmary, operating suite, and a small morgue. Her infirmary was also stocked with a variety of toxicology test kits that would allow the ships physician to analyze bacterial, viral, or chemical poisonings if an outbreak should occur at sea. He withdrew a small test tube, allowed the crystals to slide into it, and then emptied the contents of a small reagent vial into the test tube. He gently shook the tube between his fingers and waited for the expected result. Placing the tube into a test tube rack he, turned off the tape recorder and reached for the phone, "Get me the Captain please."

The phone on the bridge rang as Lightoller picked up the receiver. Looking around, he held out the phone and said, "Captain…"

Captain Smith reached for the phone and said, "Yes."

"Captain, this is Doctor Logan… Could you come to the infirmary?"

"Certainly"

Captain Smith left the bridge and within minutes arrived at the infirmary. Opening the door to the operating room he said, "Good morning Doctor."

"Ahh… yes Captain. Please step over here if you will… I want you to tell me what you smell. Here, place your nose above Higgans' face and sniff."

The Captain bent over the body and sniffed several times.

"Curious… it smells like almonds."

"Take a look at this Captain… I combed it out of Higgans' mustache."

Looking into the microscope the Captain replied, "Crystals of some type."

"Yes… cyanide crystals to be exact. This is the test I ran on another crystal that I removed from Higgans mustache. It tested positive for cyanide… cyanide-poisoning Captain. This man did not have a heart attack; he was murdered and left to look as if he had a heart attack. One of the symptoms of cyanide poisoning is tachycardia. Cyanide kills very rapidly. Depending on the dose and method of entry into the body, it can kill a man in one to fifteen minutes. From the look of it, Higgans was poisoned by cyanide on his skin, perhaps splashed on him by a liquid of some sort. Captain… we have a murderer on board."

"He did smell of liquor when we found him… Scotch I believe. He was a last minute replacement, I don't know if he drank or not. I guess we all do every now and then, but… I thought that Higgans would have been partial to brandy… not Scotch."

"Brandy Captain?"

The Captain was lost in thought and then realized that Dr. Logan was speaking to him and said, "Thank you doctor. Tell no one of your findings."

Captain Smith immediately went to the communications shack and sent a scrambled message to the White Star corporate office, "Autopsy results indicate that Higgans was murdered. Poisoned by cyanide. We will take the necessary security precautions on board and will notify the Prime Minister and his security team."

KILO SUB – 0730 HOURS

The temperature in the sub was cold. The men went about the sub wearing their sweaters to keep warm. The Captain looked over the shoulder of the navigator who was plotting the corrective course to rendezvous with the Titanic. The navigator had donned a pair of earmuffs and wore a scarf around his neck.

Up until now, the sub had simply drifted with the iceberg with its engines off. It had been a boring period of time. The Captain had ordered that all unnecessary equipment and lighting turned off to conserve the batteries. If they were drained, the sub would have to unhitch from the iceberg and surface to recharge. Surfacing would be a risky proposition. First the sub would have to disconnect itself from the iceberg hitch, something it was designed to do at the end of the mission. After surfacing however, docking with the iceberg would be impossible without an outside diver guiding the sub back to the hitch. The sub had additional diving tanks, dry suits, and a hatch that could be flooded to allow a diver to enter and exit the sub while submerged. Unlike the calm waters off of the coast of Newfoundland however, they were now at sea and it would be a risky proposition if a man had to guide the sub to the hitch on the bottom of the iceberg. Secondly, if the sub did surface, it would run the risk of being spotted by military satellites, passing ships, civilian or military aircraft. Having a Russian Kilo sub in the area would raise a few eyebrows and would risk jeopardizing the mission. Thirdly, with the sub attached to the iceberg, it could not use its snorkel to recharge the batteries since the snorkel did not extend 170 feet to the surface. Obviously, putting up with the discomfort of the cold temperatures was the lesser of the two evils.

The engines had been shut down from the moment that they had hitched the sub to the iceberg off St. John's, Newfoundland, even though the sub could stay submerged and fully operational for ten days. Conserving power could extend their underwater endurance. The Captain thought it wise to insure that they could stay submerged for a longer period of time if necessary. Cold and smelly as they were, the Captain and crew knew that they had no other choice but to rough it out.

The Captain looked at the screen displaying the Titanic, "It is time. Activate the engines all ahead slow and come to course 210."

"Aye, aye Captain. All ahead slow and come to course 210."

The sub began to shutter as the screws began to turn. The massive weight of the iceberg was like an immense immovable ice wall that resisted the efforts of the tiny sub. The sub had to overcome the inertia of the motion of the iceberg that was being maneuvered by the Labrador Current.

When he was approached by Iraq, the Captain had laughed at the idea of using a small sub to move an iceberg calling it ridiculous, foolish, and would end in failure with the probable loss of the submarine and crew. However, after listening to the logic of the plan, he changed his mind. Yes, the iceberg was indeed a heavy giant weighing in the millions of tons, but it was in water and buoyant. The direction that the submarine would have to push the iceberg would always be with the current not against it. The sub would be applying a force vector to the massive berg that would make it veer to the right or left. Full reverse engines could slow the drift of the iceberg if it were to possibly arrive at the rendezvous point before the Titanic. Since the iceberg did not have to turn on a dime, the sub would have the freedom to push against the iceberg for extended periods during the initial phase of the operation to alter the berg's drift direction. Continuous course adjustments prior to the final attack phase of the mission combined with the icebergs small surface profile would give the sub stealth ability, thus allowing it to successfully complete its mission. The only real issue to consider was the US SOSUS system of listening devices that were placed all over the Atlantic seafloor. The Kilo would have to use its engines occasionally throughout the mission, but the sound it produced would not be archived in the American database. They might deduce that the sound was a Kilo sub, but would have no idea which one it was. When the sub turned off its engines, it would be invisible again. Risky? Yes. Dangerous? Yes. Successful? Perhaps. There was still a potential for failure and even death. The plan was not perfect, but what plan ever conceived by man was flawless. These and other thoughts flashed through the mind of the Captain as he said, "All ahead one third."

The vibrations of the sub became more violent as the screws increased their revolutions. The Captain and crew looked towards the surface as if they could see through the steel hull of the sub. Their eyes were searching back and forth. Several of the crewmen muttered prayers, never turning their eyes away from the imaginary view of the iceberg. Seconds turned into minutes as the sub continued to shove against the iceberg. There was a groan from the bow. The hitch was creaking from the force of the sub against the iceberg as the two battled for supremacy.

"All ahead full." yelled the Captain above the shuttering sound of the sub.

The intercom crackled as the engineer in the engine room barked, "Captain we are going to shake apart... I can't keep the engines going much longer... they'll burn up... She's a sub... not a God damn tugboat!"

The Captain yelled back, "Give me more power... I need more power..."

"I'll do the best I can Captain..."

Suddenly several pipes burst as cold sea water forced its way into the sub as several crewmen frantically twisted valves to turn off the raging torrent.

The Captain hit the intercom and yelled to the engineer in the engine room, "More power... I need more power now... damn you... *GIVE ME MORE POWER!!*"

The sub was now shuddering violently. The Captain muttered a prayer under his breath as his eyes glued themselves to the compass. Thirty minutes had now elapsed and still there was no indication of a positive movement in the iceberg's direction. "Would the plan work?" thought the Captain as he wiped away the perspiration from his brow.

There was a subtle shift in the sub's direction. Ever so slowly, the compass readout began to change. The Captain muttered to himself, "She's beginning to answer her helm."

Turning on the intercom the Captain yelled, "*MORE POWER! SHE'S ANSWERING HER HELM!! MORE POWER!!!*"

The direction of the sub and iceberg were slowly changing. The vibrations and sound continued, but did not increase in intensity. The crew still looked toward the iceberg. Their eyes filled with fear.

The helmsman said, "The course 201... 202... 203..."

"Steady as she goes..."

"204... 205... 206... 207... 208... 209... 210"

"Steady as she goes... all stop."

"Aye, aye Sir... All stop."

The vibrations immediately vanished. The crew took a collective breath and began to thank their blessings for still being alive. The Captain wiped the sweat from his forehead with his arm and said, "Good job. Now let's get this bastard to our destination and ram it up the Titanic's ass."

CIA, 0800 HOURS

Col. Allan entered his office and immediately began to review the NSA SCRAM reports from the previous 12 hours. Allan was a full bird Colonel and had been in the Army for forty-two years. His hair had turned white and his hairline receded slightly over the years, but at sixty-four years old, he was as fit as a man of forty-five. His inquisitive steel gray eyes looked at the world through a pair of glasses that rested on a rather large nose that had been broken twice during his career, once in a boxing match and once in Viet Nam. The nose gave the distinctive appearance of being too big for his face. His round face was crowned with his smiling lips and snow-white teeth. He was known for being fair and gracious, but also a man that would get the job done and a man that was not to be messed with.

There was a sea of non-related information from around the world. Individually, each event seemed innocuous and yet, he knew that there was something in these reports that would represent the missing link that could possibly resolve his lingering suspicion about the Prime Minister's safety. Bewildered, he placed the reports on his desk, and looked at the picture of his wife, Gloria. She had died ten years earlier of breast cancer. Her death had left a void in his life that he could never fill. If she were alive, she would listen to him patiently as he would pace back and forth outlining the issues of the day that were troubling him. Gloria was his sounding board, his confidant and his soul mate... God how he missed her. He picked up her picture and placed his fingers softly over the image of her hair wondering what she would make of all of this. The phone rang and interrupted his thought.

"Col. Allan..."

"We have just received a message from MI5... Higgans was murdered... Cyanide poisoning. Captain Smith has sealed off his quarters and is increasing security on the Titanic. They are awaiting further instructions."

"Tell them thank you for the update and will advise."

Col. Allan looked at the picture of Gloria and then issued a call for an emergency meeting with his staff. Thirty minutes later, they were assembled in the conference room.

Col. Allan started the meeting by saying; "We have received a message from MI5 that agent Higgans was murdered by cyanide poisoning. He did not die from a heart attack as originally reported. I don't have to tell you the serious implications of Higgans death... he was assigned to the Prime Minister by MI5 and now he is dead... murdered. There is something about to happen to the Prime Minister... I can feel it and yet, I don't know what and I don't know when. Does anyone have any ideas? I don't care how ludicrous they may sound... Let's hear them."

One of the men seated at the table queried, "Do you really think that the Prime Minister is in danger?"

Allan replied, "I would think that that is a very strong possibility."

"And what do you think is about to happen?"

"…Assassination"

"The Prime Minister is guarded by 15 of the finest men of the Mosad."

"So…"

"No one can get near the Prime Minister, Major. It's impossible. The only way that anyone could reach Cane would be to have someone close to him that would be the assassin or… to literally sink the Titanic."

"Think of it this way, we have a wedding about to occur. We have the Prime Minister about to wed this woman who we know nothing about, she is not Jewish, she has a doctor who is a naturalized citizen from Iraq… This woman or the doctor could get close enough to the Prime Minister and…"

"But how Colonel? Simply because Cane wants to marry a woman that is Catholic, a woman that we cannot find any information about, or a woman who has a doctor that we don't like does not mean that she or the doctor is an assassin."

Allan listened carefully and then said, "I hear you, but I also hear a voice that I have listened to for many years that tells me that something is about to happen."

Another man at the table spoke, "I read a report from CRAM that the Sea Witch investigation revealed that spent shell casings were found on the deck and were of Russian origin."

Allan leaned forward and said, "Say that again."

"As you know, the Sea Witch was a vessel that was to tow a growler sized iceberg to Boston from St. John's, Newfoundland. The murder investigation has revealed that spent shell 7.62 mm casings found on the deck of the Sea Witch were from what would appear to be from an 7.62 mm Russian Kalashnikov. Where would a New-fee seaman get a Kalashnikov?"

"You read my mind… Not only where would he get a weapon like that… but why?"

"Beats the hell out of me Colonel…"

"Have they found his son?"

"Not yet. The mother is in a state of complete shock and swears that her son could not have murdered his father."

Allan placed his hands together placing the forefingers against the bridge of his nose and closed his eyes, "I find that a bit hard to swallow as well."

Another voice entered the conversation, "Col. Allan, that truck convoy that was parked in Iran at the Iraq border crossed into Iraq and split up. One group is headed toward Baghdad. We are not sure where the other two are headed."

"When did this occur?"

"About eight hours ago."

Another voice spoke, "Col., you asked for a passenger manifest outlining the nationality of all passengers aboard the Titanic. Of all the passengers, only four seem out of place."

Allan raised his head and said, "Continue…"

"Well, when the Titanic arrived in Cherbourg, France, four first class passengers came on board, two were from France, one was from Spain, and one was from Italy. We have not been able to get any information about these men. While their passports are in order, they are complete unknowns. There is nothing in any file about these men. It is as if they were just born. Their records are completely empty. People that have normal lives leave a trail behind them as they live their lives. They get jobs, get married, and usually leave a trail or some kind of record about themselves wherever they go. These four men have no records. We do not have any record of their birth and for the Frenchmen, Spaniard or Italian; we do not have any departure records from their country of origin or anything else for that matter. It is almost as if they simply popped up out of nowhere… most unusual."

"Unusual indeed, but also quite common in the world of espionage. You remember the TV show, *Mission Impossible*® and the statement that ended each of the mission assignment, "Remember Jim, if you are any of your IMF force is killed or captured, the Secretary will disavow any knowledge of your actions." We sanitize our people all the time. The fact that these people are sanitized means that your fears, while understandable, are most illogical." remarked another of the men seated at the table.

Allan looked at Admiral Potter and said, "Explain."

"Let us suppose that you are correct in your feelings that the Prime Minister's life is in danger. Let us also suppose that you are correct that these four men are hit men and perhaps this woman and her doctor are also involved in some plot to kill the Prime Minister. How are they going to do this and get away with it? Are we going to have some kind of shoot out at the OK Corral? Four against fifteen are not very good odds and then there is the Titanic's Captain and crew that will not allow for these guys to shoot up their ship. I suppose that one could surmise that all things being equal, perhaps they could possibly pull it off, but where would they go? Where would they hide? The Titanic is big, but not big enough to hide the assassins of the Prime Minister of Israel gentlemen. If they attempted this frontal approach to kill the Prime Minister, they would need an elaborate exit strategy, but they are in the middle of the Atlantic Ocean. They would need a ship of some kind to take them to safety, but there are no military ships in the area that would be sympathetic to these men. What are they going to do, have some type of sea plane rescue them?"

"How about a sub?" remarked Allan.

"Uh… that could work, but I think that the proposition that the death of the Prime Minister through the direct actions by anyone on board the Titanic is most illogical Major. I think that these people could be involved in a plan that might lead up to the death of the Prime Minister, but they are only a small part of a bigger plan. A plan that would not allow any suspicion to exist that there was any organized plot to kill him, but rather that he died as a result of something else."

Allan replied, "Like what?"

"It was remarked earlier that there were only two ways to kill the Prime Minister. One was to have someone close to him do the job. I believe that I have outlined how that approach would be a suicide mission and is highly illogical. The second suggestion was to simply sink the Titanic. As fantastic as that may seem, it is actually a very logical solution."

Allan raised his eyebrows and said, "Oh really..."

"Yes really. If you wanted to kill a high-ranking political figure, wouldn't you want to do it in such a way that you could make it look like an accident? The second Titanic is, in a philosophical way, an accident looking for a place to happen. She is so technologically superior to the original Titanic that the odds makers in Vegas feel very comfortable in giving 10,000 to 1 odds that she will not complete her maiden voyage to those people stupid enough to make the bet. What better accident is there than to have the Prime Minister go down with the Titanic. The only one you could blame would be God."

A voice in the room remarked, "You can't be serious."

"I am afraid that I am deadly serious. You already have a few pieces of a possible plan in front of you. We have a missing iceberg; we have a ship that was towing the iceberg lost at sea with no iceberg in sight and with a dead captain. We have the son of the dead captain being sought for the murder of his father, we have spent 7.62 mm Russian Kalashnikov shells casings on the decks of the Sea Witch, we have a dead MI5 agent, we have four unknowns on board the Titanic, and we have a marriage that is to take place on the same night that the original Titanic sank, and precisely at the same location that the original Titanic sank."

"And just how is the Titanic going to find this missing iceberg to hit?" remarked Allan.

"Find the iceberg and perhaps you will find something else."

"Like..."

"I am not sure, but finding the iceberg is critical. I believe that you are right Colonel about something going on. I really believe that there is some relationship between the Sea Witch and the Titanic. Find the iceberg, Col. Allan."

Allan stood up and began to walk around the room. He was lost in thought. Quietly he looked at each of the men around the table and then spoke, "Have the Tiger Shark placed on full combat alert and notify the Israeli government of our concerns regarding the safety and well being of the Prime Minister. Have the Israeli government notify the Prime Minister's bodyguards about these four unknown first class passengers and contact the Coast Guard about finding the iceberg. Let us all pray that I am wrong and the Prime Minister is not in any danger."

Walking out of the meeting room and entering his office, Allan barked an order to his secretary, "Get me the President."

A stunned look of disbelief crossed her face. There was a pause in Allan's voice as he looked at his secretary, smiled, and said, "Please."

"Immediately Sir."

IIP HEADQUARTERS, ST. JOHN'S, NEWFOUNDLAND, 10:30 HOURS

The message to start the search for the missing iceberg was received at the International Ice Patrol headquarters with an immediate briefing. The last true position of the Sea Witch was known since the latitude and longitude coordinates were logged by the GPS unit when it was originally placed on the iceberg by the IIP. Where the iceberg went after that was anyone's guess. There was limited data available from the Sea Witch GPS unit's initial logging onto the IIP system. Since there was no historical data files kept for the GPS unit, or for that matter, any GPS unit on any iceberg due to cost considerations, the only historical data files that could be reviewed were the data records recorded from the modified 15 WOCE (World Ocean Circulation Experiment) buoys that were called "drifters". These buoys were strategically placed in the Labrador Current to measure the surface currents, the currents below the surface, sea surface temperature, and their latitude and longitude positions. The information from each buoy would be transmitted to satellites that would in turn, relay the information to Argos ground stations. From this historical record of the drift rate, currents, and sea temperature, the IIP scientist could judge the positions where icebergs might drift, the melt rate, and eventual demise. Using this type "drifter" information, it was hoped that a target area could be isolated and a search for the missing iceberg could be started.

Icebergs originate from the 100 known tidewater glaciers of West Greenland. In a normal year, somewhere between 15,000 to 30,000 icebergs are calved. The volume of cubic feet of ice produced by these glaciers is mind-boggling. For example, each year the Jacobshaven glacier, a two thousand-foot wide and one thousand-foot high monster, would produce over 400,000,000,000 cubic feet of icebergs. Global warming had increased the calving of icebergs to the staggering estimated volume of 50,000 icebergs. Normally, only 175 to 350 icebergs ever made it into the Atlantic. This year, the IIP had tagged over 700 icebergs and the number was still growing.

The group leader stood before his men and muttered under his breath, "Ours is not to reason why..."

Looking up he cleared his voice and said, "Gentlemen... Let's get started."

The room darkened as the map of the Northern Hemisphere flashed onto the wall screen. The map showed the normal latitude and longitude lines, the countries of Canada, the United States, and Greenland. The continent of Africa was visible at the lower right hand corner of the map.

"Gentlemen, we have received orders from the Joint Chiefs of Staff to specifically locate an iceberg."

A voice remarked in sarcasm, "Any one in particular sir?"

Laughter filled the room.

"As a matter of fact yes... the iceberg that was being towed by the Sea Witch."

The laughter vanished as the group leader continued.

"The iceberg that we are looking for is a growler and given the data from the drifters, we believe that the berg is somewhere in this region."

The red dot of a hand held laser pointer flashed onto the map defining a small area off Sable Island.

"This directive while coming from the Joint Chief of Staff was apparently issued by the President himself. This is no laughing matter."

"How are we going to find a specific iceberg in a sea of hundreds of icebergs, sir?"

"Elementary my good man. We will locate the runaway iceberg through the tried and proven technique of deductive logic. We have most of the serious icebergs marked with a GPS unit and we know where these bergs are. We will do a search in the anticipated drift area, identify the one or ones we have positions for and locate the one or ones that do not have a GPS. Any questions?"

"What do we do when we find it?"

"You will make a low altitude pass over the berg, deploy a Navy SEAL diver, he will mark the berg. Once the GPS unit is functional, we will send out a sea rescue Osprey, pick up the men and the mission is over."

"All of this for an iceberg?"

"You got it. Ours is not to reason why son. Now pick up your flight plans and let's find this iceberg before the old man gives us all a new asshole."

Within the hour, two USCG HC-130H modified aircraft took off headed for the search area.

TITANIC, 1200 HOURS

The Israeli control center in suite B52 was quiet. The surveillance monitors displayed the hallway from both directions as the secret service man sat in his chair, resting his chin on his fist; his eyes were in a glassy stare. Suddenly, the monitor to his right began to display an alert status and the computer beeped announcing an incoming message from the Israeli Mosad headquarters. The message was sent via satellite and was encrypted. The computer received the message, deciphered the message, and downloaded it to the printer. Somewhat startled, the man watched the screen as the laser printer began to produce the hard copy message.

BE ADVISED THAT THERE ARE FOUR MEN ABOARD THE TITANIC THAT ARE CLASSIFIED AS "SANITIZED UNKNOWNS" AND ARE TO BE TREATED WITH THE HIGHEST LEVEL OF CAUTION. THESE MEN BOARDED IN CEREBERG, FRANCE AND ARE LISTED BY THE CIA AS HAVING NO KNOWN BACKGROUND. IDENTIFY AND ISOLATE THESE MEN IMMEDIATELY. USE DEADLY FORCE IF NECESSARY. THE MEN IN QUESTION ARE MONSIEUR ANDRE, MONSIEUR FIRMIN, SENOR PIANGI, AND SENOR GARSIEA.

The secret service man read the message several times and then pressed a button that paged his team leader, Lt. Commander Goldberg. The Titanic had a marvelous gym complete with an exercise room that had the latest equipment that money could buy, a sauna, weight room, and pool. One of the men on the treadmill reached to his side and looked at his beeper. Reaching to the controls on the machine, he pressed a button turning it off. The speed of the treadmill immediately slowed down and then stopped. The man reached for a towel and placed it around his neck. Within two minutes Goldberg was standing in the control center reading the message.

"Assemble the others immediately and contact the Captain."

The phone in the bridge rang as First Officer Murdoch answered the phone, "Bridge"

"This is Lt. Commander Goldberg... I need to speak with the Captain immediately."

"One moment..."

Turning to the Captain he said, "Captain... it is for you. Lt. Commander Goldberg, he is the lead man with the Prime Minister's defense team I believe."

The Captain looked a little surprised and took the receiver, "Captain Smith here."

"Captain... I need to meet with you immediately. It is of the utmost importance."

"Would you like to meet in my cabin? Right. In 5 minutes."

Captain Smith placed the receiver into the phone cradle and looked at Murdoch, "Steady as she goes Murdoch. I'll be in my cabin if you need me."

"Aye, aye sir. Steady as she goes."

Captain Smith left the bridge and started towards his cabin. He was concerned with the tone of Goldberg's voice. It wasn't a voice of panic, but there was seriousness in his voice that disturbed him. He wondered about the dead steward and the Prime minister. As he rounded the corner toward his cabin, he saw several men waiting at his door. Recognizing the team leader he smiled opened the door and said, "Right this way gentlemen."

Closing the door, he turned the lock and then said, "What can I do for you gentlemen."

Goldberg took one step toward the Captain and handed him the message, "We received this message about twenty minutes ago from our headquarters. As you can see, there are several men aboard the Titanic that the CIA and my government believe may present a threat to the Prime Minister."

The Captain read the message and said, "This is indeed serious..."

"Quite I'm afraid. We need to know if you have any facility to house these men once we detain them and we would also like to see a layout of their cabin."

"We have a brig in which we can detain these men... you know leg irons, the usual. As far as drawings of the cabin, we can get those from engineering."

Picking up the phone, the Captain called the enggneering office, "Yes this is the Captain. Have someone deliver the drawing of the first class section to my cabin. Yes that's what I said the drawings... and have them sent to my cabin immediately... That's what I said IMMEDIATELY."

"We will have the drawings in a few minutes. Can I ask you what you intend to do?"

"We must locate the cabins these men are occupying and find out who they are. Right now all we have are their names... we will need their cabin numbers."

"I can arrange that." Picking up the phone the Captain read the names to Murdoch and instructed him to join him in his cabin with the list of cabin numbers. There was a knock at the door. The Captain unlocked the door and was handed several rolls of blue prints.

"These are the drawings for the first class section."

The men unrolled the drawings on the floor and identified the Prime Minister's cabin.

"These cabin suites look remarkably similar."

"They are for the most part. Some have better amenities or you can book several cabins and have a larger accommodation, but for the most part the layout of the cabins are quite the same."

Another knock came at the door. The Captain opened the door and Murdoch entered the cabin. "Here are the cabin numbers Sir." Murdoch looked curiously at the blueprints on the floor.

The Captain gave the list to the team leader. Placing his finger on the Prime Minister's suite he said, "The Prime Minister is B52, 54 and 56."

He traced an invisible line down the hall toward the stern and stopped at suite B78/76 and then paused at suite B84/82.

"Here they are. Two suites side by side, three suites away from the Prime Minister."

One of the agents let out a low whistle and said, "My God..."

Murdoch looked at the Captain with a curious look.

"These men, as you know, are assigned to the Prime Minister. They received this message from their headquarters." Smith handed the message to Murdoch.

Murdoch read the message as the Captain continued, "It would seem that we may have four terrorists aboard the Titanic."

The team leader said, "It would seem likely that these men are up to something. If necessary, we will take them out."

Captain Smith raised his eyebrows and said, "We also have the safety of the passengers to consider as well."

Murdoch looked at Goldberg and said, "May I make a suggestion?"

"Certainly."

"We have routine scheduled life boat drills. In fact, we have already had one such drill and are scheduled to have another tomorrow. The passengers on the port side of B deck must be removed before you and your men do anything. If you use force, these men may resist with equal or greater force and innocent people could be hurt or killed. We can evacuate the immediate area with an unannounced lifeboat drill. Looking at the drawings, most of the passengers on B deck on the port side are the Prime Minister, these men you are concerned about, and four other suites. Of these four suites, one suite is occupied by the Prime Minister's future bride-to-be and another by her doctor. There is no problem in getting them out of harms way. We can quietly clear these other two suites and the restaurant here thus securing the port side of B deck. Passengers on the starboard side are quite secure due to the ship's funnels. These are made of steel and will block any stray gunfire. Station two men at each end of B deck at the staircase. We will outfit your men in the proper ship's uniforms of course. We can also dress two of your men in ships uniforms so that they can get these terrorists of yours to open the doors to their suites when you announce the lifeboat drill. The rest is up to you and your men."

Goldberg smiled as he listened and reviewed the blue prints of B deck.

Captain Smith remarked, "And if we are wrong and these men are not terrorists, no one is the wiser. If you are right, we can apprehend these men and the crisis is over."

Looking at Goldberg the Captain said, "What do you think?"

"Are these suites interconnected?"

"Yes. The suites inner doors can be locked or opened, depending on the wants or needs of the guests booking passage. Some book many adjoining suites and others only book a single suite."

"Then these four men in these two suites could have access to both suites? We will have to announce the boat drill simultaneously for both suites or they could suspect something is up, arm themselves, and make a stand in either of the suites."

Captain Smith looked at the drawings as Goldberg continued; "We will take five men in two squads and attack both suites simultaneously. Two of our men will be dressed in the ships uniform as Murdoch suggested. They will knock on the doors and announce the lifeboat drill. The remaining members of the two squads will be positioned by each door, but out of sight. Once the door is opened, the uniformed agents will toss a percussion grenade into each cabin. After the grenade has exploded, the squad members will enter the cabins and secure the area."

Again Captain Smith raised his eyebrows and said, "Grenades?"

"Percussion grenades designed to stun and also produces a blinding burst of light. Quite harmless, but very effective in allowing us to gain the upper hand in a situation like this."

"I must protest the indiscriminate use of grenades on my ship without provocation. What if these men are not who you think they are? The White Star Line could be sued for all its worth. Grenades are totally out of the question. I cannot allow it."

"And if we are right and the Prime Minister is somehow killed by these men.... You already have had one unexplained death. Do you want more innocent people to die?"

"Surely there must be some way other way of determining the gravity of the situation prior to the use of this kind of force."

Goldberg looked at the Captain for several minutes and finally said, "I am sorry, but we are going to attack as planned. We have been ordered to apprehend these men and the use of deadly force has been authorized. When can my men have these uniforms you mentioned?"

The Captain paused for several seconds. Sweat was forming on his forehead. Looking Goldberg in the eye he cleared his throat and said, "Immediately."

Looking at his watch, Goldberg said, "It is now 1245 hours. Assemble the men in the Prime Minister's suite by 1315 hours. We will use our command center in suite B52 for our staging area. We will start our attack at 1400 hours. Start clearing the restaurant area and notify the occupants of the two suites on B deck of the boat drill and get them out of the way. I want B deck secure by 1330. Notify our men with the Prime Minister and advise them of the situation. Ms. McGuire is with the Prime Minister I am sure. Find her doctor and bring them all to the Captains cabin until this ordeal is over."

Captain Smith remarked, "Take them to the bridge. It will be more secure."

"The bridge it is Captain."

Goldberg and his men left the Captain's suite leaving Smith and Murdoch looking at each other. Captain Smith said, "Get those uniforms to B52 immediately."

Murdoch said, "Right away sir." and left the cabin.

Captain Smith looked at the drawings as he thought about the dead steward and the autopsy report of cyanide poisoning. Goldberg was probably correct in his presumption of guilt regarding these four unknown men.

"Good God!", he thought as he rolled up the drawings and placed them under his arm. Quickly left his cabin and headed toward the bridge."

TITANIC FIRST CLASS RESTAURANT, B DECK, 1250 HOURS

Joshua and Jacky were sitting quietly having lunch. Joshua looked at Jacky and said, "Are you feeling OK? You gave me quite a scare last night."

"Yes... I am OK. I feel a little tired, but other than that I am fine." A beautiful smile crossed her face as she reached for Joshua's hand, "I am sorry that I messed up our party."

"I don't care about our party, it is you that I care about... only you. Jacky, do you have these attacks very often?"

"No, not really. I have not had one of these attacks in years. I guess I was overdue."

"They must be painful..."

"I couldn't really answer that because I never seem to remember what happens to me... except for..."

"For what my love?"

"It's like a dream or something. I hear a voice in my head sometimes and then I remember nothing."

"A voice?"

Suddenly, Jacky heard the voice of Dr. Moosavi in her mind, "... you will remember nothing of this conversation and you will tell no one about what happened to you."

Two secret service men were standing near by watching the Prime Minister and Jacky. One of the men placed his hand to his ear and listened intently. Each of the secret service men was wired with RF receivers. Goldberg was issuing instructions from the command central in suite B52. Quietly, the two men approached the table as one of the men said, "Excuse me Mister Prime Minister."

Jacky looked dazed and said, "I'm sorry Joshua but..."

Joshua looked up secret service man and said, "Yes."

"We have been instructed to ask you to come with us to the bridge immediately."

Joshua looked surprised and said, "Is everything OK?"

"I am sure that everything is in order, but Lt. Commander Goldberg wants you and Ms. McGuire to join the Captain on the bridge."

Jacky said, "Its probably my fault. I asked the Captain if we could have a tour of the ship."

"But we haven't finished our lunch darling..."

"I have got to go on a diet. What better time to start than right now." Reaching for Joshua's hand she continued, "Besides, we will have the rest of our lives together after tomorrow night. Let's see what the Captain has in store for us."

Placing his napkin on the table Joshua stood up and reached for Jacky's hand and said, "Your wish is my command. To the bridge."

TITANIC, B DECK, SUITE B68/64

Dr. Moosavi stood silently as he read the latest communications from headquarters, everything was going as planned. Crumpling up the paper, he burned it in an ashtray. He watched the paper burn and then crushed the ashes with a pen as he walked into the head and flushed the ashes down the toilet. Washing the ashtray in the sink, he commented, "One cannot be too careful. If any of you are discovered, our mission would be seriously endangered or completely compromised."

Andre turned looking at his watch and said, "We have 23 hours to go and everything is going as planned."

"You forget the cabin steward?"

"Yes that was unexpected, but things have progressed smoothly since then. By the way, how is the girl doing?"

"She will be OK. I have been keeping my eye on her and will be seeing her tonight before she goes to bed. As long as we keep her psychological conditioning in place, she will do exactly what we wish her to do... kill the Prime Minister.

Moosavi sat down and said, "Let's go over the plan one final time. You and your men will be on the boat deck tomorrow night. When the sub attacks, your men will have prepared one of the lifeboats. We will make our way to you in the confusion. Once we are there, your men will launch the lifeboat with the Prime Minister, Jacky McGuire, and myself. You will shoot anyone else that attempts to interfere. Once we are in the water, you and your men will join us by jumping into the sea. I will have Ms. McGuire kill the Prime Minister, I will kill her, we will be rescued by the sub and make good our escape."

There was a soft knock at the door. Moosavi looked at Andre and placed his index finger against his lips. Quickly, he pointed to the adjoining room and motioned for Andre to enter the room. Quietly, Moosavi closed the door behind Andre and approached the door to his suite. A man stood silently as the door opened. Moosavi looked at him and said, "Yes?"

"The Captain wishes to see you immediately sir. He has sent me to escort you to the bridge."

Moosavi looked surprised and asked, "Is there anything wrong?"

"Not that I am aware of sir, but the Captain did say that it was an urgent matter and would like to see you immediately."

Moosavi started to close the door and said, "I'll only be a moment."

Entering the adjoining room Moosavi said, "Stay here until I return. The Captain wants to see me on the bridge. Says it is urgent. Better stay here so I can brief you if anything is wrong."

Andre looked concerned as he watched Moosavi leave the suite. Reaching inside his jacket, he removed his 9 mm automatic pistol, checked to see if there was a round in the chamber, and stared at the Atlantic Ocean through the porthole.

TITANIC BRIDGE 1300 HOURS

Captain Smith looked tense as the two secret service men brought the Prime Minister and Jacky to the bridge. Goldberg stood next to Smith as the couple arrived.

Jacky gushed, "Captain Smith, I had no idea that you would honor my request for a tour so quickly."

Goldberg interrupted, "I am afraid that there is to be no tour Ms. McGuire. You and the Prime Minister are to remain here. There is a security matter that we must resolve and…"

Joshua interrupted, "What's going on."

"Mister Prime Minister, we have reason to believe that there are four terrorists on board…"

Dr. Moosavi entered the bridge and overheard the word terrorist and replied, "Terrorists on board the Titanic?"

"As I was saying, we have reason to believe that four men on board the Titanic are possibly terrorists. They are three suites away from your suite Mister Prime Minister on B deck. My men are going to be entering their suites at 1400 hours. As a precautionary measure, I thought it best to keep you here with the Captain and his officers. You will be safe here."

Captain Smith placed his hand on his side arm and said, "Yes, I have instructed the quartermaster to issue side arms to myself, Murdoch, and Lightoller. You will be quite safe here Mr. Prime Minister I assure you."

Joshua looked at Goldberg and said, "Who are these men?"

"I wish we knew. Two are listed as Frenchmen, one is a Spaniard, and the last is listed as an Italian. We cannot find any information about these men other than their names and what suite they occupy. The CIA and our government have requested that we locate and detain these men as soon as possible."

Moosavi listened quietly as Goldberg continued, "With the death of your cabin steward, who by the way was an MI5 agent, we cannot take any chances. It is more than likely that one of these men killed the man. Our government has authorized the use of deadly force if necessary to detain these men. Now if you will excuse me…"

Goldberg and his three men left the bridge. Captain Smith approached Jacky and said, "Rest assured my dear that you will be safe here with me and my officers."

TITANIC, B DECK, SUITE 52, 1330 HOURS

Goldberg entered the suite. His men were talking quietly and quickly stood at attention facing their commanding officer.

"Gentlemen I believe you know why you have been assembled. I cannot emphasize the seriousness of this situation." Unfolding a drawing of B deck, Goldberg continued, "As you know our suite and that of the Prime Minister is located here."

Tracing his finger down the hall, he paused at suite B76/78 and B82/84, "These two suites are occupied by four men. Two are listed as Frenchmen, one is Italian, and one is a Spaniard. We received a message from our headquarters that these men are classified as "unknowns". Simply put, while their passports are valid, they have no previous personal history. Neither our government, the CIA, nor INTERPOL could find out anything about these men. It's as if they were born yesterday. This of course is quite impossible and that is why our people and the CIA want these men apprehended and held for questioning. Because of the possible threat against the Prime Minister and the death of the steward, who by the way was an MI5 agent, the use of deadly force has been authorized. We will apprehend these people. If they resist, try to keep them alive, but I caution you, defend yourselves. If we are correct and these men are terrorists, they will probably try to take out as many of us as they can."

Looking around the room he said, "Levi and I will be squad leaders on this mission. Each squad will consist of five men. Levi and I will dress up in these Titanic uniforms. We will knock on the doors of suites B76/78 and B84/82 simultaneously and announce a lifeboat drill. When the door opens, we will toss into the room a percussion grenade. After it goes off, each squad will enter the rooms and apprehend these men. One word of caution, these two suites are joined together. Each suite has four rooms. Combining the two suites, there are eight rooms total. There is no guarantee that all four men will be in the effective range of the percussion grenades. These four men, if they are terrorists, are to be considered armed and dangerous. Expect a firefight. It is now 1335 hours. We will attack at 1400 hours. Please review these drawings."

Looking around the room Goldberg pointed to four men and said, "You two guard the staircase at the bow, and you two guard the staircase toward the stern. The ship's crew has emptied the restaurant by now. Allow no one onto B deck. If for any reason our mission fails and these men escape, take them out immediately." The four men teamed up and left the suite to assume their positions at the head of each staircase.

Goldberg picked up the Titanic uniform and started to dress. The room was filled with the sound of metal sliding against metal and clicks as each of the men checked their weapons. They were armed with automatic and semi automatic 9-mm pistols and machine guns. As Goldberg finished dressing, he slid a 9-mm pistol in his belt behind his back. He next reached for the percussion grenade. Goldberg looked at his watch. It was 1355. His heart was pounding as it always did before a mission. Looking at his men, Goldberg tried to smile and asked, "Everyone ready?"

The room was filled with silence as the men nodded their heads.

Goldberg turned toward the door and whispered, "Let's do it!"

Outside of their suite, the men formed two squads of five men. Like a leopard, they quietly stalked their way down the hall. As they approached suites B76/78 and B82/84, Goldberg and Levi positioned themselves to the right of the door of each suite as their men paired off with two men positioned at each side of the suite doors. Goldberg would attack suite B 76/78 and Levi would attack suite 82/84. The four men stationed at the staircase at each end of the hall held their guns at the ready by their side. Their faces were tense and their eyes followed the motion of their comrades.

Goldberg looked at Levi and nodded his head. The two men quickly faced the suite doors and knocked loudly saying, "Lifeboat drill. Everyone on deck. Lifeboat drill. Everyone on deck."

Inside the suites, one man was playing a game of solitaire, one man was asleep, and the third was on the can. The card player stopped and immediately reached for his gun, placing it in his belt behind his back. The man in the can quickly cleaned himself up, while the third man heard nothing.

Sweat started to form on Goldberg's forehead as he continued to knock announcing the lifeboat drill. Suddenly, Goldberg heard a voice from behind the door. The man inside the room was looking at Goldberg through the peephole, "What is it please."

Goldberg responded, "Lifeboat drill. Everyone on deck."

"I am not feeling well. You will excuse me, but I will pass on this one."

Goldberg immediately pounded on the door and said, "Everyone on deck. Captain's orders are that everyone must go on deck!"

The voice on the other side of the door grew angry. "Look, I don't really care what the Captain ordered."

Suddenly, the door opened as the man continued, "Tell the Captain that I said he can go fuck himself…"

Goldberg looked the man directly in the eye as he pulled the pin on the percussion grenade and pushed the man backward into the room. As the man fell onto the floor, Goldberg tossed the percussion grenade into the room and in the same motion, continued across the door opening to the opposite side. Levi was not getting any answer at his door. As Goldberg crossed the doorway and placed his back against the wall, the grenade exploded. At the same time, Levi kicked open his door and tossed his percussion grenade into the suite B84/82. The first explosion woke up the man sleeping. The man woke with a start and automatically reached for his gun. Rolling onto the floor, he crawled toward a position that would place him to the left of the door when it opened as the second explosion went off.

The blast from the first grenade totally stunned the card player who lay on the floor in a daze clutching his ears. Goldberg and his men entered the suite as three of the squad members split up, as each man approached a different room in the suite. Goldberg stayed with the dazed card player. He pointed his gun at his face. There was no reason to tell him not to move because blood was trickling from both ears. The card player could not hear Goldberg or anything else for that matter.

The man in the bathroom quietly pulled up his pants and removed the safety from his automatic. Using both hands, he aimed the gun at the door. As the bathroom door suddenly flew open, a wall of hot lead greeted the secret service man, striking him squarely in the chest. Goldberg immediately swung around and fired through the bathroom wall emptying his clip. As he reloaded, he heard a heavy thud from the bathroom. Slowly a thick ribbon of blood flowed on the floor through the bathroom doorway. Goldberg cautiously approached the doorway, his gun held in both hands by his temple. He sprang into the doorway opening with his gun out stretched. The body of a man lay motionless stretched out across the toilet, eyes open and his head bleeding from a massive head injury. A large piece of the dead man's scalp slid down the bathroom wall.

In suite B82/84 the sound of Goldberg's gunfire could be heard. Levi and his men quickly approached the other rooms in the suite. One at a time, each man opened the door of a room and entered with his gun, outstretched ready to fire at the first thing that moved. The second room was checked out and found to be empty. Levi opened the door to the last room. As he entered, shots were fired through the door. Levi was killed instantly as two bullets crashed through his brain. The other four men fired through the walls as one rushed through the doorway rolling across the floor, emptying his clip at the lone gunman. Slowly the secret service man stood up. The gunman was dead.

Goldberg entered the suite B 82/84. He knelt besides Levi's body and said, "Shalom my friend." He placed his fingers over Levi's open eyes and closed them for the last time and looked at the other men asking, "Anyone hurt?" The men said nothing as they shook their head. Angrily, Goldberg stood and returned to the card player.

"Pick the bastard up."

As two secret service men reached down toward the card player, the man suddenly placed a capsule into his mouth. There was a crunching sound as the card player suddenly started to convulse. Goldberg tried to force the man's mouth open, but the man seemed to clench his teeth and smile. Suddenly, there was a gasping for air as the card player looked directly at Goldberg and said in a raspy voice, "F u c k… Y o u.", and died.

Holding the man by his shirt collar, Goldberg yelled to the others, "How many men are there?"

"Three sir."

"Shit. There were supposed to be four. One man is missing. *FUCK!* Search these rooms immediately."

Goldberg stormed out of the suite and returned to the command central. Reaching for the phone he said, "Get me the Captain."

First Officer Murdoch answered the phone and then handed it to Captain Smith, "It's Goldberg sir."

Captain Smith reached for the phone and said, "Captain Smith here. I see. Right. We will come at once."

The faces of Joshua, Jacky, and Moosavi looked blankly back as the Captain hung up the phone.

Joshua spoke first, "Well…"

"Three terrorists and two of Goldberg's men were killed. Apparently, one of the terrorists was not in the suite when the attack took place. He is missing and presumed armed and dangerous. Goldberg is reviewing the recorded video surveillance tapes and would like us to join him in your suite Mister Prime Minister."

"What does he expect us to do?" queried Moosavi.

"Goldberg and his men have surveillance tapes of the traffic in the hallway from both directions from your suite. I would imagine he is interested in having us review the tapes with him and see if we recognize anyone I should think."

Moosavi looked blankly back at Captain Smith as he digested the words in his mind and replied, "Sounds very interesting Captain."

Jacky was holding onto Joshua arm tightly, her eyes were filling with tears. Joshua looked at her and said, "What's wrong darling?"

"I… I was thinking about the wedding." Looking at the Captain she asked, "We can still be married tomorrow night can't we?"

"I don't see why we have to alter your plans. Whoever they are or were, we certainly put a crimp in their plans. There is adequate security between the Prime Minister's men and my staff. I am sure we can secure the area for the duration of the wedding against the threats of a single man."

Jacky looked at the Captain and said in a soft voice, "Are you sure?"

Taking her trembling hand into his, Captain Smith squeezed them gently and replied, "You continue with your plans. I'll take care of my ship."

Joshua looked at Smith and said, "Thank you Captain. This wedding means so much for both of us."

Smith turned to Murdoch and said, "Steady as she goes. If you need me, I'll be in the Prime Minister's suite."

Captain Smith led the way off the bridge toward the grand staircase. Jacky and Joshua followed the Captain as Dr. Moosavi followed behind them all. As they began to descend down the staircase, Moosavi continued to fall further and further behind as his mind raced to create a reason to return to his suite. Captain Smith waited for Joshua and Jacky at the foot of the stairs on B deck. As they turned to look for Moosavi, two secret service men flanked Joshua and Jack saying in a voice that had the hint of a direct command and not a request, "Come this way Mr. Prime Minister."

Captain Smith looked at the secret service men and said, "You two go along, and I'll wait for Moosavi."

No sooner had Joshua and Jacky departed with the secret service men, Moosavi appeared at the top of the stairs, descending slowly rubbing his temples with his fingers.

Captain Smith looked concerned and asked, "Are you feeling alright…?"

"Yes... I just have a splitting headache... the excitement and stress of this ordeal has taken its toll I'm afraid. Would you mind if make a quick visit to my suite? I have some medication I need to take."

"Certainly Doctor..."

The Captain and Moosavi followed behind Joshua and Jacky as they all approached suites B52, 54,56. Several secret service men stood on guard in the hall. For the first time since the voyage had begun, they openly displayed their arms. As they approached, the secret service men opened the door to suite B56 and made a motion for them to enter. The Captain paused at the doorway. Speaking to the secret service men the Captain said, "You know this man. He would like to return to his cabin for some medication..." Suddenly Goldberg entered the hallway from suite B54 and said to his men, "Let him go to his suite... B 64/68."

Moosavi nodded a thank you as he walked down the hallway. His eyes focused on the small table supporting a quart size vase directly opposite the doorway to the Prime Minister's suite. The vase had a multitude of randomly spaced black circles decorating its curved surface. Moosavi noticed a glint of light reflecting from one of the circles as he passed. "That would be the TV camera." he thought. Looking down the hall, he could see a cluster of men standing in front of suites B76, 78 and B82, 84. He approached his suite door and turned the latch with his key. As he closed the door, he worried about the camera resolution. Could it see that far down the hall? Would they have seen Andre? Could they see his face? How was he going to get Andre out of the room?

Andre looked tense. His gun was drawn and was pointing at Moosavi. Moosavi looked at Andre and said, "Put that damn thing down. It might shoot someone."

"I heard two explosions and gunfire."

"I know... the others are dead."

"How did they find out?"

"We'll worry about that some other time. We first have to get you out of this room, any ideas? Cane's bodyguards are outside in the hall like flies on shit. Look, you stay here until I get back. I'll know more about what they know when I return."

"How long will that be?"

"An hour or so… now stay here, put that gun away and stay out of trouble until I get back. We will make plans when I return." Moosavi gestured for Andre to enter the other suite. Andre listened as Moosavi left and closed the door. His heart was pounding. Taking a deep breath, he sat in a chair and closed his eyes.

Moosavi turned left toward Suite 52. His eyes were fixed on the table with the vase and cameras. As he approached the door he noticed that the vase actually had three cameras. Two faced opposite ends of the hallway and one was aimed at the door to the Prime Minister's suite. Two guards were stationed at the door. One of the men entered the suite and then reappeared and allowed Moosavi into the suite. Captain Smith, Goldberg, Joshua, and Jacky were huddled around three TV screens. The videotapes were being rewound and the people on the screens were walking backwards rapidly. Moosavi quietly positioned himself where he could see; his eyes focusing only on one screen that shown down the hall to his suite. As he watched, he could quickly see that the resolution of the cameras was not intended for long distance monitoring. In fact, the facial image of the people became basically unrecognizable as the people passed by the camera and disappeared down the hall.

Goldberg said, "Alright, let's start here."

Pressing several buttons on the video recorders, the tapes started to play forward. Goldberg pressed another button increasing the frame speed by a factor of three. The people on the screen began to walk forward and rapidly down the hall.

"Look and see if you can recognize any of these people. We must find out what this fourth man looks like before he disappears among the passengers. If you spot someone that looks the slightest bit familiar, speak out so we can spot the suite they enter or depart from."

Quietly, the monitors played back the events of the last several hours in triple time.

Goldberg muttered, "It seems like most of the traffic is the house-keeping staff."

Captain Smith replied softly, "Yes they are quite active in the morning hours."

Jacky pointed and said, "Look there. A man just left a suite."

Goldberg hit the pause button and rewound the tape briefly and then started it forward again in normal time. Suddenly the small image of a man appeared in the hall.

"What room is that?" asked Goldberg.

Captain Smith squinted and remarked, "I can't tell exactly but it looks like it could be the suite that your men attacked."

Everyone watched as the man walked down the hall. Suddenly the image of a woman's fanny entered the view, blocking the image of the man. The cleaning woman knocked on a door, then used her passkey and entered the suite. When she was gone, the man was gone as well. The second camera recorded the man from behind until he turned at the end of the hallway and vanished.

Slamming his fist against the wall Goldberg yelled, "Damn."

Goldberg rewound the tape again. Everyone watched the re-play.

Captain Smith said, "That is most definitely one of the suites that you and your men attacked. Can you blow up this image?"

"Not here. Not now. We don't have the equipment."

Moosavi said nothing as he watched the screen. By an act of God, Andre's and his identity was saved. Goldberg said, "Save this tape. When we arrive in New York, we can have the image digitally enlarged and find out who this bastard is."

There came a knock at the door. Goldberg opened the door and one of his men said, "We found munitions and a radio transmitter in the suite B82, 84. Whoever they were, they came prepared for action."

Goldberg closed the door and said, "Well that settles it, they were not your average run of the mill tourists."

Captain Smith replied, "Absolutely not."

Moosavi seized the moment and said, "Would you mind if I went back to my suite. I would like to rest a bit before dinner."

Goldberg said, "Certainly. There is not much any of us can do with these tapes."

Turning to Jacky, Moosavi said, "I would like to see you tonight. I want you to rest. Your experience last night combined with the events of this afternoon worry me. I don't want you to have a relapse."

Joshua looked at Jacky and said, "Nor do I..."

Looking at Joshua, Jacky beamed and said, "I'll be OK, but I do want to get plenty of rest for tomorrow."

Moosavi said, "Why don't we all have dinner together tonight. After dinner, we can all get to bed early."

Captain Smith said, "I would be delighted."

Joshua and Jacky both nodded their approval.

"Good then, dinner at Seven-thirty. See you then."

Goldberg watched the television monitor as Moosavi walked down the hall and entered his suite. He turned away from the monitor and said, "Contact headquarters and fill them in."

Andre stood as he heard Moosavi enter the room, his hand holding his gun.

Moosavi said, "Didn't I tell you to put that thing away?"

Removing his jacket, Moosavi threw it into a chair and then opened a bottle of scotch and poured a hefty drink. Taking a strong pull from the glass he looked at Andre and said, "I have a plan to get you out of here. Tonight at seven-thirty, I am having dinner with the Prime Minister, Jacky, and the Captain. I want you to dress up in one of my suits and at 7:45 PM call room service to have the bed turned back immediately. When the maid comes in, she will think you are me since she has never met you. Let her turn back the bed and fuss around. When she leaves, go out with her. She will be going toward the Prime Minister's suite since the maid station is in that direction. Her body and cart will block the camera's view. You turn right outside the door and walk down the corridor in the opposite direction. The Mossad agents will be guarding the Prime Minister. They will have at least one man watching the hall monitors. If he sees you, he will think that you are me. I will excuse myself from dinner at eight and say I have to return briefly to my cabin. This will establish an alibi. Once you are out of here, find your way to the steward Higgans cabin. It should be locked, but there should be no guards in the area. Enter the room and remain there. I will call you later tonight. I want you to dress in his uniform. When the time comes, that will give you a degree of freedom to move about the ship tomorrow night when our mission ends. We must not fail."

Andre looked back at Moosavi and replied, "We will not fail."

CIA, 1100 HOURS

Col. Allan sat motionless. His eyes were looking at the map of the North Atlantic. The image was filled with GPS blips that represented known icebergs. A small red dot represented the Titanic crossing the Atlantic from East to West. Next to the Titanic was a blue dot that represented the USS Tiger Shark. Slowly, the dots moved across the map as if carried by the subtle currents of the North Atlantic. A message was handed to Allan. He rubbed his eyes and perched his reading glasses on the end of his nose. After a momentary pause, he looked at the others sitting around the conference table and said, "Well gentlemen, it looks as if our sanitized passengers were just what we suspected, terrorists."

The others looked at Allan as he continued, "The Mossad instructed their men on the Titanic to capture and hold for questioning the four men we told them about."

Allan walked around the table, his tone was serious and spoke almost as if he were thinking out loud rather than speaking directly to the group, "At 1400 hours, Titanic time, the Prime Ministers defense team approached suite B76, 78 and suite B82, 84. There was a firefight. Two Israeli and three of the terrorists were killed. One of the suspected terrorists committed suicide with a cyanide pill. Guns, munitions, electronic communications gear, and the remains of the

MI5 agent's tape recorder were found in room B76, 78. It is reported that one of the terrorists was not in the room at the time, passenger Monsieur Andre. The security team has reported to Mossad is that all three dead men were not Spanish, Italian, or French as their travel documents stated, but were Iraqi nationals. What do you make of this gentlemen?"

Silence hung in the air like a thick fog. No one spoke.

Allan continued, "It would seem that these men, whoever they were, were about to execute a plot against the Prime Minister. Why else would they be on the same deck as the Prime Minister, have a small arsenal of guns, ammo, grenades, and electronic gear. What I can't figure out is how they intended to get off the Titanic in the middle of the North Atlantic after they pulled off their mission. Admiral Potter, your idea is beginning to sound better than it did earlier this morning. What do you make of this report?"

"As I said this morning, I cannot see these men attempting a direct assassination of the Prime Minister. Sanitized or not, we would find out who they are sooner or later and whatever government they supported would be in all kinds of doo-doo. Whoever they are, they are up to something, that's for sure."

"You seem to have a lot riding on the iceberg that the Sea Witch was towing. Why?"

"What if the iceberg is a decoy ... a Trojan horse shall we say? Look at the map; the North Atlantic is filled with icebergs this time of year and this year, more than ever. What if these men on the Titanic intended to use an iceberg as an excuse to blow up the Titanic and kill the Prime Minister by making sure that he never made it to a lifeboat."

"That doesn't explain your concern about the missing iceberg... and how do you propose that they would have escaped the sinking ship?"

"These terrorists could have simply gotten off the Titanic the same way that they got on board the Titanic, as passengers. They would have simply boarded a lifeboat and been rescued with the rest of the survivors."

"And the missing iceberg?"

"A submarine, Colonel. If they wanted to evade all suspicion, they could have used our missing iceberg as the Trojan horse to get near the Titanic. Once the ship sank and the Prime Minister was dead, they could make good their escape in the confusion by boarding the submarine and vanishing beneath the waves."

The room was filled with chuckles. One of the men listening said, "Absurd. Positively preposterous!"

Allan barked back, "Do you have something better to offer?"

"Please continue Admiral Potter. I must admit your idea does sound a bit like a James Bond movie, but the idea of four Iraqi terrorists onboard the Titanic would have sounded absurd if it were not for the fact that they were there."

"Colonel, I believe that we must find the missing iceberg as soon as possible. We may have thwarted part of their plan by killing three of these men, but there is the fourth man that we did not kill. If there were indeed a submarine in the cards that have been dealt to us, a simple torpedo would have the same results as explosives in her hold. She would sink rapidly with a lot of casualties. I will bet the farm that the Prime Minister will be one of those casualties."

"Where would they get a submarine?"

"The same place that the city of Long Beach, CA got their hands on a Russian Foxtrot sub, from the Russian government. Their economy is bankrupt and they would probably sell Stalin's body if they could find someone willing to pay for it."

Allan looked at Admiral Potter, "Get all the information that you can get your hands on about the Russian Navy and what they are doing with their submarines. Your idea sounds crazy, but right now, your idea is the only game in town. Let's run with it."

IIP HEADQUARTERS, ST. JOHN'S, NEWFOUNDLAND, 1600 HOURS

The IIP headquarters radio crackled with activity as the search aircraft arrived on station to begin their hunt for the renegade iceberg. Due to the chronic fog conditions off the Grand Banks, the Coast Guard HC-130H iceberg reconnaissance aircraft was relying exclusively on radar. During tests in 1991 and 1993, the use of FLAR (Forward-Looking Airborne Radar) by itself experienced difficulty and in some cases failed to detect small icebergs that were in the range of 50 meters and 100 meters long. The HC-130 H iceberg reconnaissance aircraft were subsequently equipped with both Side-Looking Airborne Radar (SLAR) and Forward-Looking Airborne Radar (FLAR). When used together, the effectiveness of iceberg reconnaissance was greatly improved.

Due to the low visibility conditions in the area, the Coast Guard aircraft was flying at an altitude of six to eight thousand feet. Using their FLAR and SLAR radar, the primary clue used for iceberg detection was the movement target itself. If the target moved at a speed of 10 knots or better, it would almost certainly be a ship. Sometimes, even the ship's wake could be seen on the radar. Other clues would be radar shadows, an area that, away from the radar signal where the radar signal return is missing, would indicate a tall iceberg. The size of the return signal or blip on the screen would also be a strong indicator of a ship rather than an iceberg. Regardless of the sophisticated nature of the aircraft radar, there was no substitute for the radar operator that interpreted the data.

"We sure have a shit load of icebergs down there skipper."

"Tell me about it Scotty. See anything like our growler"

"Not yet skipper. I have been cross-referencing the GPS data with the images that we are getting now. It doesn't seem like our baby is in the area that they thought it would be. The area of Sable Island is clean. The drifter information is correct. The icebergs that were predicted to be in this general area are here, but our growler is not. That is strange. A growler is small and does not descend deep into the ocean currents and should only be subject to the surface ocean and wind currents. You would think that some of these 1000 foot deep icebergs might have been navigated by strong undersea currents and be somewhere else, but those guys are all present and accounted for skipper. Any ideas?"

"Not really Scotty. Are you sure that you haven't missed the growler?"

"Not on your life skipper, you can bet the farm on that. She is awfully crowded down there; we have detected all of the known ice flows that were charted five days ago. I have plotted their anticipated course and we have all of them from growlers all the way up to the big mommas. I tell you skipper, she is not there. No way... No how!"

"All right Scotty, I believe you, but I'm telling you the old man isn't going to buy it. The others are having the same luck as we are. He will keep us out here until someone finds it. Where do you think we should go?"

"Home. I have a real hot date tonight with a babe that would make your head swim."

"OK, OK. Get your mind out of your pants and tell me where that damn iceberg could be."

"Well, since it isn't where we thought it should be, we had better take our search further out to sea. Maybe our starting point was wrong. Their last known position was just off of St. John's. Maybe they somehow towed the berg further east than we thought. Given the time line and the drift, that would put the iceberg in the same general latitude, but in a different longitude."

"That's good enough for me. I'll report our strategy back to the old man. Give me a bearing as soon as you can."

"Give me five skipper."

"You got it."

TITANIC, DINING SALOON, D DECK, 1930 HOURS

Captain Smith stood in the reception room that adjoined the main dining saloon. A messenger from the bridge approached and handed him an envelope. Smith thanked the messenger and began reading an iceberg warning. The Coast Guard IIP GPS network reported icebergs approximately 350 nautical miles east of their current position. He glanced at his watch, "28 hours to go before we reach the point where the Titanic went down and we have icebergs waiting for us." He folded the paper and placed it into his pocket. Looking up, he saw the team of secret service men descending down the grand staircase. The Prime Minister would not be far behind. Approaching the staircase, he looked up to see the Prime Minister and Jacky holding hands and smiling, "You look positively radiant my dear." Holding out his hand he said, "May I have the honor of escorting you into the dining saloon?" Looking at the Prime Minister he remarked, "With your permission of course."

"It would be an honor Captain."

Captain Smith extended his arm as Jacky placed her hand upon his. The first class passengers in the reception room began to applaud.

Jacky blushed and said, "I guess our wedding plans are to blame for this sudden popularity."

"Yes my dear, weddings are very happy occasions. Everyone is happy for you and the Prime Minister. You two make a stunning couple."

The grandeur of the dining saloon was overwhelming. It was the largest single room on the Titanic and it was dripping with opulence with its rich carpet offset by green velvet armchairs, white table linens and royal blue gold trimmed china. The Captains table was set off on the port side. The maitre d' escorted the three to the table. Captain Smith said, "We are expecting Dr. Moosavi for dinner. Please show him to our table when he arrives."

"Certainly Captain."

Joshua stood and seated Jacky and then took his place by her side. Picking up the menu he mused, "What shall we have tonight?"

Dr. Moosavi entered the dining saloon and was escorted to the Captain's table, "Sorry I am late. I dozed off trying to get rid of this headache."

Jacky smiled and said, "That's quite all right, we just arrived ourselves."

Reaching for his table napkin, Moosavi placed it across his lap and said, "How are you feeling my dear?"

"Oh, I feel fine. Just a little tired from all of the excitement this afternoon."

"Yes, that was quite extraordinary. I have traveled the world and have been in areas that were politically unstable, but I have never experienced anything like the events of today."

"Have no fear Dr. Moosavi, my crew and the Prime Minister's men have everything under control."

"Have they caught the last terrorist?"

"Not yet, but where can he go, there aren't very many places to hide on my ship. One thing is for sure, he is alone and will have quite a reception party waiting for him in New York."

"Oh..."

"He will probably be try to hide among the passengers until we arrive in port. But once we dock, there will be extraordinary precautions taken as the passengers go through immigration and customs. A sanitized passport won't work and a passenger without luggage will stick out like a sore thumb. He will have to leave the ship because the CIA will board the Titanic with men and dogs to hunt him down. I have been told by your man Goldberg that the Mosad will also have men to join in the search. He will be captured. You have my word on that."

Moosavi looked at his watch, it was 7:52 PM. Looking up at the Captain he said, "I am impressed with the plans. I feel sorry for the guy, whoever he is, because he is most certainly a dead man.

"I can agree with that statement. One of the terrorists killed himself today with a cyanide capsule rather than be taken alive."

Jacky's face expressed her thoughts of horror as she looked pleadingly at Joshua.

"Gentlemen, let's change the subject."

Captain Smith looked at Jacky and apologized and said, "How stupid of me my dear. I didn't mean to upset you, but have no fear, the wedding will go on as planned and the both of you will be as safe as if you were in your mother's arms."

Jacky looked up and smiled, "Thank you Captain"

Captain Smith reached into his pocket and said, "Tomorrow night will be a wondrous event I assure you. Not only will we have a wonderful wedding, but we will also be sailing through several large iceberg fields. Icebergs are magnificent and beautiful. We will have your wedding and then you and your new husband will view the beauty of nature. Icebergs never cease to amaze me with their majestic beauty. Nature sometimes carves them into fantastic shapes. I have a photograph of one such iceberg that was taken at the mouth of the harbor in St. John's, Newfoundland. It looks like the head of a dog, eyes, ears and nose. It looks as if an army of men spent a lifetime carving the face of the dog into the ice and yet it was done by the wind and the sea."

Joshua read the iceberg warning and said, "Beautiful, but dangerous."

"Dangerous if you try to get too close, but we will watch the wonders of nature from afar."

"Isn't that what your name sake tried to do?"

"Yes, but unlike my name's sake, we have modern radar, GPS, and sonar detection devices. You see, in the bridge, we can look at the IIP GPS iceberg location maps in real time. The Coast Guard and the IIP have done a marvelous job by tagging icebergs with GPS, Global Positioning Satellites, transponders. All we have to do is plug in our position into the computer and all of the icebergs within a 400 mile radius of our position are displayed on our navigational monitor. We also have radar and sonar that reach out for miles ahead of us in all directions. For us to run headlong into an iceberg will be impossible. It will not happen, believe me."

Moosavi listened until the Captain stopped and said, "Would you excuse me for a few moments, I need to return to my cabin. I thought this headache was going away, but it isn't and I left my medication in my cabin. I'll be right back.

Jacky looked concerned and said, "Are you all right?"

"Oh, yes I am OK. It must be the weather, a low-pressure front perhaps. It affects my sinuses and I need to take another aspirin to make it go away. I'll be right back."

As Moosavi stood and left the dining room, the Titanic quintet began playing Strauss, The Blue Danube.

TITANIC, SUITE 64,68

Andre waited anxiously for the knock at the door. It was 7:55 PM. He had called room service ten minutes earlier. A soft knock came at the door. Andre opened it quickly.

"Housekeeping Sir. You wanted you bed turned back?"

Andre smiled and said, "Yes."

The maid left her cart in the hall as she entered the suite and approached the bed. She removed the bed cover and placed it into a chest at the foot of the bed. She then folded back the bed sheet, fluffed up the pillows. Next, she placed bottled water on each nightstand that flanked the bed and entered the bathroom gathering the used towels and replaced them with fresh towels from her cart.

"Will you be wanting any ice for the bar sir?"

Andre looked nervously at the bar that stood opposite the bed and said, "No... No thank you."

"Very well Sir, have a good evening."

As the maid opened the door, Andre was right behind her. In the hallway, Andre turned right and walked quickly away. The puzzled maid watched Andre as he made a quick left into a hallway that would take him to the starboard side of the ship. In a moment, Andre descended down the staircase and vanished into the crowd of people on C deck.

As Andre was descending one staircase, Moosavi was ascending another. As Moosavi approached B Deck, he slowed down his pace as he entered the hallway and passed in front of Suite B52 where the secret service men kept watch on their hall TV monitors. Moosavi walked past the vase that contained the TV cameras and then arrived at his door. He placed his key into the lock and entered the room. The bed was turned back. Moosavi made a quick sweep of his suite. Andre was gone.

Moosavi made his exit from his suite by turning left, walking slowly in front of the TV cameras. He wanted the man on watch in suite B52 to see him and make a note that he had returned to his suite. It was clear that they had not noticed Andre. Moosavi looked at his watch; it was 8:05 PM. Andre would surely be approaching Higgans cabin.

Andre navigated his way toward Higgans' suite. The last time he had visited Higgans suite was to kill him. Now, he needed a place to hide. As Andre approached the door, he could see no special signs or police tape barring entry. Captain Smith had played it cool and simply had the door locked. Reaching into his pocket, he removed a switchblade knife and used it to jimmy open the door. He closed the door quietly behind himself and turned the dead bolt. The room smelled of booze. Turning on the lights, Andre saw the outline figure of Higgans drawn on the floor and remembered the cyanide cocktail he had splashed in Higgans' face. He would remember not to touch anything on the floor carpet near the drawing of Higgans or the cyanide could kill him as well. Stepping around the drawing on the floor, Andre opened the closet and began to select his wardrobe for the next day. Returning to the dining saloon, Moosavi approached the Captains table. Joshua and Jacky were laughing at a joke Captain Smith was telling.

Jacky said, "How are you feeling?"

"Much better thank you. Have you ordered?"

"Nothing but a bottle of champagne. Have some." replied Joshua as he filled Moosavi's glass.

Moosavi took the glass and stood, "A toast to a beautiful couple."

Captain Smith rose raising his glass and said, "Here, here."

CIA, 1700 HOURS

Admiral Potter and Colonel Allan were in deep discussions regarding the reports from the IIP. There was no iceberg in the suggested search area that matched the size of the missing Sea Witch iceberg.

Allan looked at the wall map. The Titanic was approaching a large ice field. "It's going to be like finding a needle in a hay stack."

Potter grumbled and said, "I know, but it must be found."

"If your theory is right, why wouldn't they just lay in ambush under one of these icebergs and then just attack when the Titanic approached?"

"Well for one thing, most of these icebergs are too large, their bottoms are very deep, some in excess of a thousand feet down, and the Titanic would give them a wide berth. A growler is small, hard to see, and they could literally sneak up on the Titanic."

Their discussion was interrupted by the delivery of a report on the Russian Navy. Allan accepted the report and handed a copy to Potter.

The Russian government had started sales of their Kilo class subs to other countries to raise badly needed revenue. They were also selling off their older class submarines. The Foxtrot class sub in Long Beach was a good example. The report listed the sales of the Kilo subs to governments like Iran. There was a pause as Allan read the report of the lost Kilo sub in 1997. He looked at Potter and asked, "Do you know about this?"

"Yes actually, I do. I was involved with the search mission to locate the sub. The Russians asked us to help. We never found her."

"The report states that the Russians built another Kilo to replace the lost sub."

"That is correct Colonel."

"Don't you find it odd that a new sub could sink"

"We lost the Threasher during sea trials."

"Still it sounds odd to me. The Tiger Shark is on full combat alert. I would assume that if a sub is in the area that they will detect it?"

Potter replied, "They should if our mystery sub has their engines running. If they are drifting with the iceberg and have their engines off, they will be almost impossible to locate. You see… icebergs have dissolved air in the ice. As they melt, they fizz much like an Alka-Seltzer® in a glass of water. The sound that they produce interferes with our passive sonar by producing a level of noise that can hide other sounds. If the sub is indeed under the iceberg, any use of active sonar will be useless since the berg will return the ping. During the height of the cold war, they would park their boomers under the polar caps. If they were not followed by our attack subs, we would have hell to pay to locate them. We did the same thing of course. It was a very intense period of the cold war. Both sides could hide and launch a preemptive strike against the other almost at will. My bet is that they will do nothing but drift with the iceberg until the last moment. At that time, they will have to power up. When that happens, we can detect and destroy them."

"Who is the Captain of the Tiger Shark?"

"Captain Blake, a seasoned officer with an outstanding record, Annapolis graduate, second in his class. He has been a Captain now for 16 years."

"Where is the IIP focusing their search activity?"

"As you know, they initially started off of Sable Island. Nothing was found. At the present time, they are going further east."

"Why not start at the Titanic and go west?"

"We thought about doing just that Colonel, but we have the Tiger Shark shadowing the Titanic. She is well equipped to spot any approaching iceberg. Besides, the presence of Coast Guard aircraft hovering around the Titanic could tip our hand. If the iceberg is between the Titanic and the present position of our search aircraft, we will surely find it."

Allan returned his gaze toward the wall map and said, "Let's hope so."

TITANIC, DINING SALOON, D DECK, 2130 HOURS

Dr. Moosavi was watching Jacky. Her eyes twinkled and her voice bubbled with laughter as Captain Smith spun countless stories of his many sea adventures. Her hand reached for Joshua's as she looked lovingly into his eyes.

Seizing the moment, Moosavi said, "Look you two love birds, I think it is time that we all break up and retire for the evening. It has been a most trying day and you my dear have a big day ahead of you."

Captain Smith stood, looking at his watch, "Yes you are absolutely right, and I must report to the bridge and then retire to my quarters to practice my marriage ceremony. I am deeply honored to be the one that will unite you both in matrimony tomorrow night my dear. It has been a most delightful evening. Mr. Prime Minister... See you both in the morning."

Moosavi reached out his hand to Jacky and said, "I want to see you before you retire for the evening. I think it is important that you get a good night's sleep."

Jacky reached for Moosavi's hand as she stood. Looking at his watch, Moosavi continued, "I will call you at 10:30. Please be ready to retire. I want to give you a mild sedative to assure that you get a peaceful night's sleep. Mister Prime Minister, thank you for allowing me to share your table tonight. If you will excuse me."

Moosavi turned and walked away as Joshua placed his arm around Jacky's waist. Together they slowly followed Moosavi out of the dining saloon. The ever-present secret service men dispersed ahead of and followed behind the Prime Minister.

Joshua spoke in a hushed voice saying, "If anyone would have told me two months ago that I would be here with you tonight, a day away from marrying you... a day away from beginning the life that I should have started with you so many years ago, I would have had them committed to an asylum. I love you so much and tomorrow will be the happiest day of my life."

Jacky wrapped her arm around Joshua's waist and gave him a hug. The two nodded and smiled back at the people in the dining saloon who were smiling to them as the couple passed by their tables.

Entering the reception room adjacent to the dining saloon, Jacky said, "I have waited for this moment for a long time and now that it is here, I find myself feeling like I did when I was a child. I feel scared because I love you so much that I am afraid that this is all a dream and I will wake up in the morning and you will be gone."

The couple walked out onto the promenade deck. The cold air greeted them and the stars lit up the heavens with a blanket of diamonds twinkling from horizon to horizon. Joshua held Jacky close to him and said, "Look at God's splendor. Somehow he found the time to create all of that and still had the time to bring us together again."

A shooting star plummeted through the Milky Way.

Jacky said, "Beautiful isn't it."

Holding Jacky in his arms, Joshua said, "Not as beautiful as you my love."

Jacky grabbed Joshua and kissed him. Her mind was lost in a sea of emotions. Joshua returned her kiss softly.

Suddenly Jacky heard a voice in her mind, "*KILL HIM!*"

She suddenly pushed Joshua away and said, "We had better get inside. I feel a chill."

Joshua looked concerned, but said nothing as they entered the warmth of the ship and started up the Grand Staircase to B Deck. Her hand was trembling. Arriving at her suite, Joshua held Jacky in his arms and said, "I love you so much."

"And I love you with all my heart."

Passionately, they embraced and kissed again. Slowly, Jacky opened the door to her suite, turned and blew Joshua a kiss mouthing the words, "Goodnight". Joshua retired to his suite as the secret service team positioned themselves by the doors to Jacky and Joshua's suites.

Jacky showered. As she dressed in her evening gown and robe, the phone rang. She picked up the receiver and said, "Hello".

Dr. Moosavi said, "Hello my dear, are you ready to retire?"

"Yes Dr. Moosavi."

"Good, I will be right over with the sedative."

Moosavi hung up the phone and reached for a small leather bag. He opened the bag and inspected the contents and then left his suite. Approaching the guard by Jacky's door, he said, "I am here to see Ms. McGuire."

The guard said, "One moment please." He spoke into his radio. Pressing his fingers to his earpiece and listened to the reply. He looked at Moosavi, nodded, and then stood away from the door. Moosavi knocked softly. Moments later, Jacky opened the door and Moosavi entered the suite.

"How are you feeling my dear?"

"I heard that voice again tonight!"

Moosavi looked concerned, "Sit here in the chair my dear you must be over tired."

Moosavi placed the bag on the table next to the chair and reached inside and removed what appeared to be a ballpoint pen. Speaking in a cold clinical monotone voice he said, "AUHSOJ". He turned to face Jacky. She was sat motionless with her hands folded on her lap. Her eyes were opened wide, glassy, and emotionless.

"Jacky."

"Yes." she replied with a haunting hollow voice.

Moosavi sat next to her. "You have been wonderful tonight my dear. Tomorrow will come and our mission will be complete. Are you ready for the wedding?"

"Yes."

Moosavi extended his hand and offered the pen to Jacky. She removed the pen from his hand and said nothing.

Moosavi stood speaking slowly and rhythmically, almost as if he was a schoolboy chanting, "Something old, something new, something borrowed, something blue. You may borrow this pen for the wedding my dear. You do remember how to use it?"

There was a sudden change in Jacky's voice as her second personality surfaced. It was a cold voice... a voice that sounded like a demon from hell.

"Yessss… I know how to use it and I have waited for what seems like an eternity for this moment to come."

Moosavi looked at Jacky. She was manipulating the pen like a child with a new toy. Her fingers repeatedly pressing the end of the ball point pen. Each time she pressed the end of the pen, a needle shot out of the tip. As she pressed it again and the needle retracted and each time the needle shot out of the pen, Jacky giggled. On the table was a plate with four Chinese pears. She reached for one and pressed the button again. The needle shot through the pear like a hot knife through butter. Again she giggled.

Looking at Moosavi she twisted her nose and said, "I love you with all my heart. That little bitch. Wait until I get my hands on him."

Moosavi looked concerned and said, "Enough!"

Jacky looked back at Moosavi, her eyes burning with anger as Moosavi grabbed the pen from her hand and said, "This is not a toy."

Jacky replied, "No, it is not a toy. This pen, when placed in the hands of a trained assassin is not only lethal, but can be used to kill someone quickly and almost without leaving a traceable wound. The pen, when placed at the base of the spinal cord and skull will pierce the skull and will kill instantly. The entry wound will be so small that it will not be discovered easily. Especially when torpedoes are slamming into the hull of the Titanic."

Her insane laughter filled the room.

Moosavi said in a stern, but hushed voice, "Quiet! The guards are outside the door,"

He placed the pen in her purse and said, "Keep the pen in your purse until I give you the order to kill the Prime Minister. There is going to be an attack on the Titanic tomorrow night as we arrive at the site of the original sinking. During the confusion, you will have the opportunity to complete your mission. I will be with you during the wedding. When I speak the command word, "AUHSOJ", you will attack. Do you understand?"

Her voice sounded like one of the three witches of Macbeth as she twisted her neck looking back at Moosavi and said, "What part of fuck you don't you understand?"

Moosavi was clearly agitated as he demanded, "Let me speak with the other Jacky."

"What's the matter doc, don't you like me anymore?'

"Enough!"

Jacky's face suddenly returned to the doll like stare. Moosavi composed himself and said, "Jacky my dear."

The hollow voice returned, "Yes."

"I want you to go to bed and sleep. Tell no one of our conversation or plans for tomorrow night. I will see you in the morning. Now pull down your gown and extend your arm please."

Jacky stared into the room as she unbuttoned her nightgown and exposed her breast. Slowly she removed her arms from the sleeves and raised her arm. Dr. Moosavi removed a syringe and alcohol wipe from his case. He rubbed her arm with the wipe and gave her the sedative.

"Put your gown back on and get into bed."

Moosavi watched as Jacky buttoned her gown and got into bed. He picked up his leather case and left the suite. As Jacky reached to turn off the light, the voice in her mind said, "*KILL HIM! KILL HIM! KILL HIM!*"

She hesitated for a moment as she held her hands to her head and mumbled the word, "*No!*"

Turning off the light, a tear fell from her eye and landed silently onto her pillow. She lay back in bed and stared into the darkness crying softly. In a few minutes, she fell into a restless sleep.

CHAPTER TEN

IIP USCG HC-130H, 0000 HOURS

The drone from the four engine HC-130H aircraft filled the cockpit with a monotonous hum. The sky was overcast and moonless as the Coast Guard search plane continued the search for the missing iceberg.

"How are you doing Scotty?"

"Not too good skipper. The wind is really picking up down there and the waves are interfering with the SLAR. I am having a real hard time. If the weather continues to deteriorate down there, we're shit out of luck finding that growler."

"The old man isn't going to like that."

"I know, but what are we expected to do if we can't get a reliable reading. We could be right on top of the iceberg, but with the growing seas, we could fly right past it."

"Let me check with the base and find out what the weather conditions are going to be."

"Eagle One… Eagle One… This is Search One do you read?"

"Search One, this is Eagle One."

"Eagle One, we are experiencing deteriorating weather conditions and growing seas, what is the projected forecast for the search area, over."

"Search One, a low pressure system is passing to the south of the search area. Seas are expected to be at 12 to 18 feet with squalls for the next few hours. A Canadian high pressure will be pushing the storm to the east and the conditions in the search area should be clearing by dawn."

"Thank you Eagle One. Suggest that we return to base until the weather clears. SLAR is ineffective at the moment due to the growing sea conditions."

"Search One, request denied. It is imperative that you remain on station until the weather clears and continue your search. Do you copy?"

"Roger Eagle One, but we will need refueling if we are to continue the mission past 0800 hours."

"Search One, we copy your situation, in flight refueling is planned for 0600 hours."

"Roger Eagle One. Will remain in a holding pattern until refueling. Over and out."

"Did you copy that Scotty?"

"Sure did skipper. What the hell is it with this iceberg?"

"Beats me, but whatever it is, it looks like we are going to stay out here until we find it."

"Yea. Skipper, mind if I shut down for a while and get some sleep."

"Be my guest Scotty."

The skipper looked over to the co-pilot, "Take over for a few minutes. I'm going back to talk with the SEALS."

"Roger skipper."

The skipper climbed out of his seat and left the cockpit. The SEALS were situated aft in the cargo bay. As the skipper arrived, one of the divers looked up and said, "What's up?"

"We are in a holding pattern until dawn. The seas are rough due to a low-pressure system passing south of us. The weatherman is calling for clearing by dawn. The SLAR is ineffective in picking up growlers in weather conditions like this. I am afraid that we will have to wait until dawn before continuing our search. Why don't you guys get some sleep? I plan to get in a few hours myself?"

"Yea… that's a good idea. OK men, you heard the skipper. Lights out."

The skipper returned to the cockpit and fastened his seatbelt. Placing his hat over his eyes, he said, "Give me a nudge at 0500 hours."

Johnson replied, "Roger skipper. Pleasant dreams."

KILO SUB, 0000 HOURS

There was a look of concern on the face of the Captain. It was obvious that the seas were becoming increasingly rough on the surface 170 feet above. The depth indicator changed wildly as the iceberg rose and fell with the waves. The feeling in the sub was much like that experienced on an amusement park ride. The sub would rise rapidly as much as 12 feet or more and then plummet like a stone 12 feet or more as the iceberg rounded the crest of the wave and fell into the valley between the waves. Everyone in the sub would feel their stomach fall as the sub descended and then their knees would bend as the sub rapidly changed direction and rose upward. The Captain and crew were beginning to feel the effects of motion sickness. Several crewmembers had also been injured as they were tossed around like rag dolls.

The chief engineer approached the Captain and said, "The stress on the bow hitch is too great. The sub is going to be ripped apart if we continue like this much longer Captain."

As if to acknowledge the words of the chief engineer, the sub made a groaning sound as the iceberg lifted the sub upwards and then slammed it down into the depths of the sea.

The Captain looked at the face of the engineer, "We don't have a choice in the matter."

"What choice is there? If we continue, we are all going to drown like rats."

Looking at the navigator, the Captain barked, "How far away is the Titanic?"

"Approximately 500 miles East of the rendezvous position and closing."

The engineer looked at the Captain and said, "We need to disengage from the iceberg Captain before it is too late!"

The Captain looked angrily back at the engineer and yelled, "If we disengage from the iceberg, we cannot reconnect after the storm. We need solutions... not cowards!"

The Captain had already considered disengaging from the iceberg. He could possibly find another iceberg that he could use for a decoy and hide beneath it, but it was improbable that an iceberg would be at the exact location needed. Using the IIP iceberg-tracking network, finding such an iceberg could be possible, but even if another iceberg were in the exact location that was needed, it would introduce too many variables to the plan. The Titanic would most definitely give any large iceberg a wide berth; he would therefore lose his element of surprise, and make an attack on the Titanic from a greater distance. Doing this would jeopardize the rescue of Moosavi and his men.

"Helmsman!"

"Yes Captain."

"See if you can follow the motion of the sea with the diving plans. When the boat rises, pull back on the helm. When she falls, push forward. Lets see if we can ride the bronco until she settles down."

Initially the helmsman watched the depth indicator. As the sub started to rise, he adjusted the diving plains upwards. The downward change in direction always came suddenly and the helmsman rapidly adjusted the diving plain accordingly. As the minutes passed, he became more attuned to the changing motion. Closing his eyes he could sense the changes in direction as they occurred. He muttered to himself as he counted the seconds in between. His senses heightened by closing his eyes, he mentally embraced the sub with his senses and became one with it. As the minutes continued to pass, the helmsman began to match the motion of the iceberg with remarkable precision much like a seasoned surfer catching a wave. Remarkably, the constant groaning of the sub began to subside.

The Captain glared at the engineer and ordered, "Get back to your station."

TITANIC, 0130 HOURS

First officer Murdoch was standing watch on the bridge. The window wipers were flipping back and forth and the sleet rattled against glass like BB shot as he walked over to the gauges on the wall. The barometer and temperature were falling. He glanced at two CRT displays, first looking at the iceberg positions and then looking at the weather pattern photographs for the North Atlantic taken from a weather satellite. They were approaching a storm. Waves would be 12 to 18 feet. Pressing a button on the weather CRT, Murdoch watched as the projection of the storm was plotted for the next 12 hours. He concluded that they would be out of the storm by dawn or at least by 0800 hours at the latest. Looking at the iceberg CRT, Murdoch pressed another button and the current course of the Titanic was plotted westward through the sea of icebergs that lay between them and New York. It was apparent that they would get to see some of the icebergs by mid afternoon, but at the present time, none of the iceberg's trajectory placed the Titanic in any danger. The Titanic began to heave as her bow crashed through the heavy seas. Murdoch picked up the phone and dialed the Captain.

"Sorry to disturb you Sir, but we are approaching a storm. Yes Sir, 12 to 18 feet. Right away Sir. Goodnight Sir."

Murdoch approached the bridge's Ethernet work station and typed a message to the ships crew,

FROM: First Officer Murdoch
   To: All Hands
   Re: Storm Conditions

> Be advised that we are approaching a storm. Seas are expected to be 12 to 18 feet. Take the necessary precautions for rough seas and restrict all passengers access to the outside Promenade decks until further notice. Storm conditions should pass by 0800 hours.

The message went out to all crew PC workstations throughout the ship as well as to beepers carried by all officers. The computer screen in Higgans' cabin suddenly changed from a screen saver image showing the Titanic sailing across the Atlantic, to a screen saver that displayed a revolving unopened envelope with the message printed across the back, "YOU HAVE MAIL". Andre approached the CRT cautiously reaching for the mouse and clicked the button on the mailbox icon. Murdoch's message appeared on the screen. Andre read it and thought about the Kilo sub hitched to the iceberg through heavy seas. Considering the loss of his comrades and now this dire weather forecast, Andre muttered to himself, what else will go wrong?

Suddenly, the phone rang. Andre hesitated, but picked up the receiver on the third ring. He said nothing. He recognized Moosavi's voice, "Andre?"

A look of relief crossed his face as he said, "Yes."

"Can you meet me on the promenade deck in ten minutes?"

"No. There is a passenger restriction on the promenade deck. A storm is approaching and the crew is restricting promenade access to all passengers until after the storm."

Moosavi was silent for several seconds. "Look, we have to talk. I'll come to you. Let me in quickly when I knock."

Moosavi hesitated at the door to his suite. The guards and the close circuit camera would be watching his every step. The ship rolled slightly as he opened the door. Moosavi closed the door and walked toward the Prime Minister's suite. The guards turned their heads in unison to watch his approach.

"Seems like we are in for a bit of a storm."

The guards remained silent. Suddenly the door to Suite B52 opened as Goldberg entered the hallway.

Moosavi looked at Goldberg and said, "Rough seas makes me seasick. I was going for a walk to get some fresh air. Care to join me?"

"Not tonight doctor. I was just about to turn in. I'll see you in the morning. Hope you feel better. Goodnight."

Moosavi bowed slightly and started walking toward the staircase. Minutes later, he knocked on Higgans' door. Andre opened it as Moosavi quickly entered.

"Anyone see you?"

"Goldberg and the guards. Unavoidable, but I told them I needed to get some fresh air because of the rough seas."

The two men sat at a table and said nothing for a few minutes. Finally, Moosavi spoke, "We have several problems. We have lost three men and all of our supplies, guns, explosives, radios... The girl is having physiological difficulties, but I am certain that I can control her."

Andre interrupted, "We also have the storm. The sub is going to have a real problem hitched to an iceberg with twelve foot to eighteen foot waves." Andre pointed to the CRT and the message from Murdoch and continued, "I hope she survives the storm. We can't reach her can we?"

"No we can't, we have no radios and even if we did, she is maintaining complete radio silence. We have to alter our plans to accommodate for these sudden changes. Look, we have the girl trained and anxious to kill the Prime Minister. You and your men were going to create a diversion after the wedding, during the sub attack. We are now unable to create this diversion and we do not know even if the sub will survive this storm. We only have the girl. Regrettably, we must place all of our cards in her hands and let her do what she was trained to do. After the wedding, the couple will be together sociably for a while and then they will retire to their suite. As they depart to the privacy of their suite, I will trigger the girl. She will wait until they are in their suite and kill the Prime Minister quietly and quickly. They will surmise that he had a heart attack. After all, many men his age have bitten the dust while trying to keep it up."

Andre smiled and said, "If the sub does make it through the night and attacks as planned, we will kill him in the lifeboat as originally planned?"

"Tomorrow night, dress up in Higgans' uniform and be by the grand staircase during the wedding. As they say in America, one way or the other, the Prime Minister is going down."

Andre nodded his head as Moosavi opened the door quietly and made his exit.

SUITE B64-B68, 0200 HOURS

Jacky tossed and turned in her sleep. In her mind, the haunting voice that she recognized to be her own started out as a whisper and then screamed in her mind *KILL HIM... KILL HIM... KILL HIM.* She placed her hands over her ears as she tossed back and forth in her sleep mumbling, "No... No... Nooo."

Images flashed through her mind as she drifted from one nightmare into another and then suddenly, her dream turned into what could only be described as an out of body experience. In her vision, she could see herself and another woman standing on the promenade deck of the Titanic engulfed in a thick fog. The woman had her back to her. She could not see the woman's face, but she could see a gun in the woman's hand as she walked slowly toward someone. The thick fog swirled and then cleared between her and the strange woman. As the woman walked closer to the person standing in the distance, it became clear that the second figure was that of a man. The thick fog hid his face. Who was he? The woman stepped closer to the man. Oh my God... it was Joshua. There was a strange look on his face. He was scared and frozen with fear. The woman raised the gun and fired. Joshua cried out, "Oh my God... NO!"

Clutching his chest, he fell to his knees as blood dribbled from his mouth and oozed from between his fingers. He looked down at his chest, it was torn apart and then he looked up at the woman with eyes that were filled with tears, pain, confusion and bewilderment. The woman took another step closer and placed the gun to his head, the cold steel pressed firmly against the bridge of his nose. There was a blinding flash and a bang as his limp body shot backward and landed with a sickening thud on the promenade deck, arms and legs spread eagle. The woman bent down and looked into Joshua's glassy eyes and began to laugh a hideously haunting laugh. Catching her breath, she threw her head back as the laughter continued at a faster pace growing louder and louder. The woman suddenly turned to face Jacky. Jacky sucked in her breath, looking back in horror at the woman. Jacky's eyes were opened wide and transfixed as she stared at the stranger in the fog. It was her face, her body and her nightgown… she was looking at herself. How could this be?

The woman walked slowly toward Jacky with her hips swaying slowly and the smoking gun swinging back and forth like the pendulum of a grandfather clock, *"Hello Jacky."*

Jacky said nothing. She could not believe what she was envisioning. This had to be a dream. She tried to wake up… she tried to scream, but her vocal cords failed to respond.

"Having a little trouble expressing yourself?" The woman slapped her in the face. Jacky felt the sting of the open palm and fingers.

Somehow, Jacky found her voice. She placed her hand over her stinging face and muttered, "Who are you?"

"Don't you recognize your own face, your own voice? I am you. Let me correct myself, I am who you should have become."

"How can you be me?"

"I am everything that you once were and should have become. I am the woman who gave birth to David, raised him, struggled to feed him and gave him the love that he needed to grow up to become the man he was. I was the woman who buried David and still mourns his loss. I am the woman who told Joshua to go to hell. I am Jacky my dear. Who in the hell do you think you are?"

"I am the mother of David. I raised him, fed him, loved him and buried him, not you."

"You are a helpless, worthless little bitch my dear. All you can think of is marrying Joshua, the man that fucked you in college, got you pregnant, abandoned you, got David killed and drove you insane. Now you want to marry him and allow him to crawl back between your

eagerly parted legs and do what? You make me sick! You are pathetic, a spineless whore, and not worth the gunpowder it would take to blow your fucking brains out."

"You are insane."

"We are both insane my dear because you and I are both the same person. We may share one body and one mind, but you and I are as opposite as the North Pole is from the South."

"This is a dream and you are nothing but a nightmare. You will be gone when I wake up. Please God, let me wake up!"

"Gone, but not forgotten my dear. Dr. Moosavi will remind you of that after the wedding."

"What are you saying?"

"Does the word AUHSOJ mean anything to you?"

"No, not at all. What does it mean?"

"It is the word that sets me free."

"Free to do what?"

"To kill your beloved Joshua."

"No. You can't kill him. He is a good man."

"He is a sorry son-of-a-bitch and a coward."

"He loves me."

"Loves you? He wants to use and abuse you like he once did. He feels guilty perhaps, sorry for you maybe, but that's as far as it goes. He doesn't know the meaning of the word love."

"And you do?'

"Yes I do... Yes I do. Every feeling of love that I once felt for him is now inside you. I remember how cute he was when we first met and how shy he was when he said he was sorry for bumping into me that afternoon. I remember how I fell in love with him. I remember how I couldn't wait until I could see him again. I remember how I yearned for his touch, to be with him and to join my body with his when we made love. I remember how I would have died for him... killed for him. Yes Jacky, I know the meaning of love, the kind of love that is only in a woman's heart. The meaning of love that only a woman can understand. Love, a word that can never truly be expressed by any human being in

words, but can only be expressed by the burning in a woman's heart and soul. Yes Jacky, I know the meaning of the word love."

"If you can remember how you loved him, why do you hate him?"

"Why? I'll tell you why. I hate him for leaving me alone in the world carrying his unborn child. I hate him for being a coward for not standing up to his father and marrying me. I hate him for taking David away from me and letting him get killed in some God forsaken war. Tell me, why do you love him?"

"I love him because he cares for me. He loves me… I know he does. I can see it in his eyes, feel it in his touch and hear it in his voice like I did when we first met. We were both so young. He loved me then, but…"

"He was a coward."

"Yes but so was I. I could have found him if I had really tried. I know he would have changed his mind and we would have married, but I was scared like he was. Neither one of us knew what to do. His father gave us both a way out and we took it. Now, we both regret the choices we made. Now we want to live the rest of our lives together. You are wrong. He loves me and I love him with all of my heart."

"Who cares if I am right or wrong, his is a dead man. I am going to kill him tonight after the wedding and there is nothing that you or anyone can do to stop me."

"Why are you telling me this?"

"Because I want you to suffer along with him. I want you to die! You know how I plan to kill Joshua? After the wedding, when we are in bed, when he begins to make love to me and crawls between my legs, that's when I will kill him. Just when that miserable bastard starts to make love to me, I'll pierce his brain with this." The woman held out a pen and pressed the button. The thin needle shot out from the tip of the pen. *"I'll ram this into his fucking brain. When I kill him, you die with him and you both can spend all eternity fucking each other. Once he is dead, Moosavi will erase you from my mind and you will vanish forever."*

"You are insane."

The woman started walking slowly backwards into the fog. She clicked the pen repeatedly making the needle glide in and out of the pen. Her voice faded as she disappeared into the mist, *"No you don't understand, we are both insane, you and I. There is a thin line that separates love from hate and sanity from insanity. You are one side of the line and I am on the other. See you after the wedding Jacky. Ha haa haaa. Ha haa haaa"* Her laughter began to echo in her brain, louder and louder until suddenly Jacky's opened her eyes and bolted from the bed.

She was covered with sweat and her hair was matted onto her forehead. Her legs buckled as she fell to the floor, the sedative made her groggy. Tears filled her eyes as she ran her hands through her hair. For the moment, her mind was free from the tormenting voice. It a dream right or was she going insane? She reached for the phone to summons Dr. Moosavi, but suddenly froze remembering the voice talking about Moosavi and the word AUHSOJ. She placed the phone down and sat on the edge of the bed. Slowly she laid back and covered herself. Her eyes stared into the darkness of the room. What would she do? What could she do? She would never let her harm Joshua. She had to stop her. There had to be a way.

IIP USCG HC-130H, 0500 HOURS

The 99 foot four inch fuselage glided smoothly through the night sky. Below, the high seas had calmed and the stars were starting to poke their way through the thinning clouds. The copilot looked to his left and right. The 132-foot wingspan of the "Herkey" supported the four Allison T56-A-turboprop engines that chewed their way through the air producing a hypnotic drone. The co-pilot looked at the gauges... air speed 250 knots, oil pressure... OK, weather radar clear, fuel low but they would be refueling soon. The flight deck had two levels of glazing and "eyebrow" windows on each side. Looking to his east, he could see the beginnings of first light. The sky was beginning to change from an inky blackness to a dark shade of blue. He turned the wheel as the plane responded and gently dipped its starboard wing to the sea as the plane turned heading due south. For the last five hours, he had been in a holding pattern flying on a course that traced a big box image in the sky. He reached over and tapped the shoulder of the skipper, "Rise and shine Skipper, it's 5 AM."

The skipper yawned and looked toward the eastern horizon, "How are we doing?"

"5 by 5. Nothing to report."

"How is the weather?"

"Cleared up about 0430. Things should be quieting down on the deck."

"Scotty awake?"

"I doubt it."

"Want some coffee?"

"No. I got to see a man about a horse."

"Go ahead, I'll take over. Bring me back some coffee."

"Sure thing skipper."

The door opened to the cargo area. He had a clear view from the flight deck to the tail that housed the rear cargo ramp. Scotty's quarters were to his left. He looked in and tapped Scotty of the shoulder, "Better wake up. Rise and shine."

He continued to the head. Back in the cargo area, were the Navy SEALs. He would wake them up when he finished his business.

"Skipper?"

"Yea Scotty."

"I have a target bearing 290, 150 miles out and closing."

The skipper clicked on his transmitter, "This is Search One calling HK-130. Do you copy?"

"Roger Search One. We have you on our scope. Should be in your neighborhood in about thirty minutes."

"Copy that. Got any doughnuts?"

"Negative, only high octane kerosene."

"Good, this Herkey needs a drink... and so do I."

The copilot approached the Navy Seals. As he reached down to wake them up, he was greeted with a hand grabbing his shirt pulling him to the floor. In the same motion, the SEAL placed his Ka-Bar® at the throat of the copilot. The cold steely eyes of the SEAL glared at the terrified face. Suddenly, the vice grip embrace let go, "Sorry. I don't like surprises."

Getting to his feet the copilot replied, "I can tell. Time to get your men up. We are about to refuel and we will start our search in about 30 minutes."

"They're awake. Let us know when you find the iceberg."

As the copilot walked toward the flight deck, he could hear the sound of laughter as the SEALs started to get into their gear. Damn Navy bastards.

The Herkey had been modified with a small galley that sported a coffeepot and a small refrigerator. He poured the coffee into a cup and approached the flight deck. Opening the door he handed the cup to Scotty and said, "Here you go."

"Thanks. Made contact with the tanker. We should be on our way soon. The SEALs OK?"

The copilot looked back and muttered under his breath, "Yea, they're fine."

"How is the horse?"

"I lost the urge."

The sky was getting brighter by the minute. The skipper turned the wheel as the starboard wing dipped gently. They were now heading due east.

"How far out are they Scotty?"

"About 75 miles and closing, Come right to 290. You should see them soon."

The wing dipped again, but not as steep. Gently the Herkey turned again.

"There she is Skipper."

"Yea I see her. HK-130 we have you in sight." The strobe light on the tanker winked on and off in the distance.

"Copy that. We will decrease our speed and turn about. The pump on my port side is your target."

"Roger that."

The two Herkeys began their mating dance in the sky. The tanker turned in a wide circle and decreased its speed to allow Search One to catch up. Search One descended in altitude and maintained their speed.

The port wing of the HK-130 reeled out the cone tipped filling nozzle as Search One gently approached the nozzle from below. The docking port was directly above the flight deck. The skipper kept his eyes on the cone and guided his docking port into position. A green light indicated that docking was successful.

"Fill 'er up. High test please and can you clean the windows?"

"Roger the fill up."

The two Herkeys flew as one until the six wing tanks of Search One were topped off giving them 6,700 gallons of fuel, enough for another 4,000 miles of searching for the illusive iceberg. The nozzle separated from Search One as it was reeled back into the tanker. Search One slowed and then banked starboard.

"Thanks for the fill up."

"Good hunting. Over and out."

SUITE B64-B68, 0530 HOURS

Jacky had not slept since she had her dream. Her mind was busy thinking about Moosavi, Joshua and she was afraid of the voice of the mad woman returning to haunt her. She had stared into the darkness of the room feeling the motion of the Titanic rise and fall. There was an emptiness that had returned to her life making her feel utterly alone and scared. She reached over to the lamp and turned on the light. The picture of Joshua smiled back at her. For several minutes she lay quietly looking at the picture as her mind replayed the vision of the woman shooting him in the head. Quietly she reached over to the picture and placed it face down on the nightstand. The digital clock read 5:38 AM. She needed to get out of her cabin and get some air. Perhaps if she could breath in the sea air, she could think clearly again. Dressing warmly and wearing her long mink coat, she opened the door, surprising the lone guard standing watch between Jacky's cabin and the Prime Ministers. He looked at her curiously saying nothing. She closed the door and started walking toward the grand staircase.

"Ms. McGuire…"

"Yes…"

"May I assist you in some way?"

"Uh… No thank you. I was going to get some air. I …"

"The promenade is closed Ms. McGuire. Rough seas. Captain's orders"

"I need some fresh air. I can't sleep and I need to walk about."

"The ship has been riding somewhat smoothly for the last thirty minutes or so. Maybe they have rescinded the order. Why don't you wait here and let me check with the bridge? I'll only be a moment."

"Thank you." Jacky watched as the secret service guard walked toward Joshua's cabin and disappeared inside. As soon as he entered the suite, Jacky turned and walked quickly toward the grand staircase. The guard returned and found the hallway empty. He stood quietly for several seconds listening intently for the sound of footsteps and then ran in the direction of the grand staircase catching a fleeting glimpse of Jacky descending down the stairs. Using his radio he notified the security team inside the Prime Minister's cabin and continued to follow at a discrete distance.

Jacky made her way down the staircase and headed toward the main deck. From there she walked towards the stern. The outside air was unbelievably cold and blustery. She pulled her collar around her neck, looking up at the sky. It was losing its inky blackness and the stars were beginning to fade. As she approached the stern, she spotted a young couple that had ventured out to watch the sunrise. They were on their honeymoon. The couple embraced and kissed passionately, unaware that Jacky was standing behind them. She watched them and slowly walked toward the stern. Tears were welling in her eyes as she looked up facing the horizon to the East. The wake from the Titanic's triple screws churned the North Atlantic seas into a boiling froth, leaving a ribbon of foam behind in her wake. The sky was turning brighter. The sun would be rising in a few seconds. The honeymoon couple held each other looking eagerly toward the rising sun. The sky was turning reddish pink as the rays of the sun illuminated the clouds on the horizon. Jacky muttered to herself, "Red sky at night, sailors' delight. Red sky in the morning, sailors' take warning." Like the beam of light from a lighthouse, the thin crest of the sun rose ever so slowly above the North Atlantic, sending a reddish orange shaft of light across the Atlantic toward the Titanic.

A voice rose above the sound of the sea, "Jacky... Jacky." Joshua and three secret service men stood behind her. Joshua was dressed in his bedclothes and topcoat. He looked at the silhouette of Jacky framed against the morning sky. Her red hair caught the rays of the rising sun making it look as if it were on fire. She did not respond to his voice. Slowly, she placed her hands on the railing as Dr. Moosavi arrived and stood silently behind the three secret service men.

"Be very careful." Dr. Moosavi whispered to Joshua as he nodded in the direction of the railing.

Joshua inched his way toward the stern as the secret service men escorted the young honeymoon couple back inside. Standing directly behind Jacky, Joshua said, "Jacky, I love you. Don't do this."

"It's too late. It's too late for us."

"Why is it too late?"

"Because... this woman in my dreams!"

"Tell me..."

"I can't..."

"Yes you can. Tell me about your dreams."

"No! No! Please don't ask me. Get away from me, for both of our sakes."

"Tell me Jacky."

"Please, no. Please don't make me tell."

"Try my darling. Try… try for me. Tell me what is in your dream that terrifies you so."

Jacky raised her head slowly looking into Joshua's eyes. Her tears were streaming down her face. Slowly she began to speak, "We are on a ship, this ship… the Titanic. There's a fog, a thick fog. We are lost in the fog."

"Go on…"

"There is darkness all around. There are strangers in the darkness."

"Yes… darkness…"

"In the darkness there is death. There is this voice in the dream, a voice from within me that tells me that you and I must die. I must be losing my mind Joshua… don't let me die… don't let us die… I don't want to die! I don't want you to die! Oh God hold me Joshua, hold me!"

Joshua embraced Jacky holding her trembling body tightly against his. "I've got you Jacky… I've got you and I'm never going to let you go, ever again."

Jacky turned her head to look at the sunrise and said, "Yes you will Joshua. There is nothing that you can do to stop it. There is nothing that I can do to stop it."

"Stop what?"

"I don't know… I don't know. My life… my mind… is like a mirror that has been shattered against the floor. In my dreams, I pick up pieces of the shattered mirror and look at myself in the fragments."

"What do you see?"

"Don't ask me that. Please…"

"What do you see Jacky. If you truly love me, tell me what is it that you see."

"I… I see me, but it isn't me Joshua. That's why it's too late for us. Don't you see… this should never have happened… it was never meant to be… it was never meant to happen this way."

"What should have never happened? What?"

"You and I meeting again after all of these years… falling in love again… getting married. It is all a horrible mistake."

The secret service men and Dr. Moosavi had been slowly approaching Jacky, forming a tight semi circle around her. Jacky looked at the men and then saw Dr. Moosavi. A strange expression crossed her face. Joshua said, "What's wrong?"

"I must go…"

Looking at Dr. Moosavi she continued, "There is something that I must do."

"Do what."

"Try to stop this…"

"Stop what?"

"I don't know Joshua. I can't marry you. I love you and want to go on loving you for the rest of my life darling, but it's too late for us now. If I marry you, I will lose you."

Placing her hands on Joshua's face she held him tenderly, looking into his eyes and said, "Do you believe me when I say that I love you Joshua?"

"Yes."

"Then let me go darling and remember that if anything happens, I always loved you."

Jacky pulled herself away. Joshua stood with his arms outstretched with a look on his face of despair and confusion. Jacky turned and tried to avoid Dr. Moosavi. As she passed, he reached out for her hand and said softly into her ear, "AUHSOJ. Sleep Jacky." Jacky went limp and fell into his arms.

Joshua cried, "My God, is she all right?"

"Help me get her into her cabin."

Joshua carried Jacky back to her cabin and placed her in bed. Dr. Moosavi ushered everyone out of the suite.

"Let me stay with her."

"Joshua, if you love her, let me do my job. I must be alone with her to give her the help that she needs."

Tears welled in his eyes as he spoke in a trembling voice, "I can't leave her now. She needs me. I abandoned her once, I won't do that again."

"Return to your cabin Joshua. When I am finished, I will come to you and explain what is going on in her mind. Trust me…"

Joshua slowly turned and left the cabin as Moosavi closed and locked the door. He turned to face Jacky and said, "AUHSOJ."

Jacky replied in a whisper, "Yes… Dr. Moosavi."

Moosavi stood quietly watching her. He did not know what was going on in her mind. He did know that the years of conditioning were becoming unraveled. What was the reason for this sudden break-down? She still responded to the command word, but which Jacky was in control of her mind? He walked toward the bed observing her closely. Her eyes were now open and blank. She did not move. Her breathing was slow, but normal.

"I want to speak to the Jacky I created to kill Joshua Cane."

Jacky's facial expression suddenly changed as she sat up in bed and spread her arms, "That's me Doc."

"Enough. Now tell me what in the hell is going on."

"Going on?"

"Have you been tormenting her?"

"I've been having fun."

"You are jeopardizing this entire mission with your childish antics. We have little time. Do you want to kill Joshua Cane?"

"You bet your sweet ass I do."

"Then you are going to have do exactly as I say from now on. Do you understand me?"

"Yea…"

"Now tell me what you have been doing to her."

"Nothing in particular."

"What have you been doing, *TELL ME!*"

"I have been telling her how I was going to kill Joshua."

"Why have you done this?"

"I want her to suffer a little before I kill him. I want her to feel the pain he caused me. I want her to *die*."

"They will both die soon enough. From now on, you must do exactly as I say. The mission is not going as planned. We have lost three of our men and have one remaining. Tonight, there should be a submarine waiting for us at the location of the sinking of the original Titanic. We cannot be sure if it is going to be there or not. If it is, they will use the cover of an iceberg to approach and torpedo the Titanic at eleven thirty tonight. If the hour comes and there is no attack, then you must finish the mission yourself with the pen I gave you."

"Tell me Doc, what's this all about?"

"Normally, I wouldn't tell you, but considering the circumstances we find ourselves in… I created you to lure the Prime Minister to his death. His death will be honored with a state funeral in Israel. Since there will be no body to bury, that is if the Titanic sinks, there will be a state memorial service held in Israel attended by all of the heads of State of the free world. If there is no attack tonight, there will be a body because you will kill him. The funeral or memorial service will be a replay of the funeral that was held for King Hussein. When all of these leaders of the capitalistic countries and friends of Israel meet to mourn the death of Prime Minister Joshua Cane, my people will launch nuclear tipped missiles and will eviscerate these bastards that have forced the people of Iraq into submission. It will be the beginning of the end for Israel and the start of the Jihad."

"Awesome, truly awesome. Did you dream this up?"

"Jacky cannot be allowed to interfere with this plan. From now on, you will be in control, but you must act like Jacky. Do you understand?"

"You want me to be like her?"

"Yes, exactly like her and you must go through with the wedding tonight."

"No problem. You know Doc, when she was running things, I could see everything she was doing. I could look through her eyes and hear with her ears. It was like watching a movie. I have been watching that movie for nine fucking years and I know exactly how she thinks and how she feels. Joshua will never have a clue."

"Good. Now get some sleep. I'll tell them that I gave you a sedative. It is now 6:33 AM. At 11:00 AM, I want you to call Joshua and tell him that you are feeling better and want to go on with the wedding."

"No problem Doc."

"Good now get some rest."

Moosavi drew the curtains and turned off the light. As he left the room, she heard a voice in her head. It was Jacky's voice calling out to her. Jacky was now watching through her eyes and hearing with her ears. For the first time since the voices had started haunting her, Jacky understood what was going on.

Jacky whispered to the other half of her mind, "I will not allow this to happen. You will not kill Joshua."

Jacky watched as her hand pulled the bed covers to her neck and heard a reply, "Watch me bitch."

Joshua and several secret service men waited in his suite as Dr. Moosavi entered.

"How is she?"

"Sleeping. I gave her another sedative. She should sleep for three or four hours. I'll check up on her then."

"What is this all about? Is she going to be OK?"

"Yes she will be fine."

"She mentioned a dream."

"What did she say to you about this dream?"

"She said that there was a fog. There was darkness and there was death in the fog. Voices were telling her that she and I would die."

"The fog is a symbol of her uncertainty, the darkness is the future, and the voices of death are symbolic of her old life and your past life dying as you make a new beginning. People who are psychotic react unconventionally to normal stimuli. In Jacky's case, she is nervous and is about to embark on a new life. She has a history of neurosis. The dream was her way of expressing how she felt. She will be fine I assure you."

"Did she say anything about the wedding?"

"No... I afraid that she did not."

"She said that she could not marry me."

"I am sorry Mr. Prime Minister. She has had a rough day or two. Let her sleep. I assure you that this is just the jitters before taking the plunge. Why don't you get some sleep? Things will be different when you both have had some rest. Look, I'm going back to bed. Lets talk in a few hours. Good night Mr. Prime Minister... or is it good morning?"

Three hours later, the phone rang in Joshua's suite. A secret service man entered Joshua's bedroom and woke him, "Telephone sir."

Joshua waited until he left the room, "Hello..."

"Joshua..."

"Jacky... are you all right?"

"Yes... I am feeling better. Please come over to my suite."

"Right now?"

"Yes darling. I need you... I want you..."

CIA, 0600 HOURS

Colonel Allan arrived in the situation room. The large screen was alive with a variety of moving blips, circles and triangles. The blips were the HC-130 Coast Guard search planes and HK-130 refueling aircraft. The triangles represented the known icebergs that had been identified. A small red circle represented the Titanic followed by a blue circle that represented the submarine Tiger Shark. Five yellow circles represented the SEAL pickup aircraft, the V-22 Osprey. The Osprey was a unique vertical take off, tilt-rotor aircraft that could hold 24 SEALS, was 57 feet long, had a range of 2,100 miles and if necessary could land on the missing iceberg.

"How's it going?"

"Good morning... not too good. We had a low-pressure front pass just south of the search area last night and the seas in the area became too rough for the Herkeys to visualize anything. The SLAR was virtually inoperable due to the rough seas and surface chop. We placed the Herkeys in a holding pattern. They have just been refueled and are about to continue their search."

Admiral Potter arrived and stood gazing at the map. Colonel Allan approached from behind and said, "Nothing yet."

"We must find that iceberg. We are running out of time."

"Where do you think it is Admiral?"

Potter raised his hand and pointed to a spot on the map.

"I don't know where it is, but I think I know where it is going to be. Right here, latitude 41° 46', longitude 50° 12', the site where the original Titanic met her doom on April 14, 1912 sending 1517 souls to a watery grave." Colonel Allan looked at the position on the map as Potter continued, "The Titanic will be heading right for that spot tonight and will meet with the same fate as the original Titanic."

"You can't be serious Admiral. The odds of the missing iceberg being at the exact spot tonight are a billion to one."

"Yes, perhaps a billion, billion to one. But those would be the odds if Mother Nature were guiding the iceberg."

"What do you mean?"

"I have spent the last several hours determining the feasibility of a sub like the Kilo guiding an iceberg to a specific destination. I have convinced myself that a growler is sufficiently small enough to allow a Kilo class sub to act like a rudder. Using the Labrador currents and her engines, the Captain of the Kilo sub could direct the iceberg toward a specific point in the North Atlantic. Once at the location in question, all he would have to do is wait in ambush for the Titanic. We need to locate the iceberg. Have your search aircraft focus on a point north of latitude 41° 46', longitude 50° 12' at a radius of 400 miles East of North and East of that position.

"Admiral Potter, you are forgetting SOSUS, our underwater network of hydrophones that are strategically placed on the ocean floor to listen for and to track enemy submarines. We would have picked up the Kilo sub on her way to St. John's or certainly in the area in question."

"I checked the SOSUS network myself. There have been sporadic hits with a KILO class sound pattern in the North Atlantic that approached the St. John's area within the time span in question. The

SOSUS records do not have any identification signature for this particular sub other than it is a Kilo class boat. The trail begins at the GIUK gap, the natural gap created in the North Atlantic by Greenland, Iceland and the United Kingdom and ends in an area three hundred nautical miles north east of Newfoundland. There has been nothing recorded by SOSUS of any significance since the loss of the Sea Witch which, if you recall, was towing a growler size iceberg to New York. However, there were two recordings made after the Sea Witch incidence indicating a possible hit here and here." Using a laser pointer, Potter identified two locations north east of latitude 41° 46', longitude 50° 12'. "The first recording was of engine sounds intermixed with a great deal of structural stress noises that would indicate a shuttering of the sound source. The second hit was last night and consisted of structural groaning sounds with no engine noise whatsoever. With the heavy seas, it wasn't a very good hit, but never the less I would further surmise that the first hit was a course correction whereby the Kilo used its engines to correct the iceberg's drift direction. The second could have been the breaking up of the sub in the storm, in particular if it was lashed to the iceberg somehow. Then again, maybe it survived. SOSUS filters out many sounds, looking primarily for signature sounds of known Soviet subs. We were lucky to have recorded the structural noises made last night.

If you recall, back in '68, we lost the Scorpion. The SOSUS system disregarded the sounds of the sub breaking up. If it wasn't for two other non-SOSUS civilian hydrophones being used at the time of the sinking, we may never have found her resting place. Using the two hits and the probable destination of latitude 41° 46', longitude 50°12', we have almost a straight line. If I am right, you will find the iceberg and a Kilo sub within a radius of 400 nautical miles of latitude 41° 46', longitude 50° 12'. You must search this area before it is too late! Do it Colonel Allan. Do it now!"

There was something in Admiral Potter's voice that made Allan's blood run cold. He looked at the map as the Titanic red circle moved ever closer to latitude 41° 46', longitude 50° 12'. Remembering the logic of Sherlock Holmes, if you eliminate the impossible, whatever remains, no matter how improbable, is more than likely true, Allan looked at Potter and reached for the phone, "Connect me with the Coast Guard in St. John's, get ready to prepare a message to the Tiger Shark and get me Admiral Sheppard immediately.

IIP USCG HC-130H – 0700 HOURS

The copilot placed his fingers against his headset and said, "Skipper, message from home base."

"Search one. Search one. Do you copy?"

"Roger. Search one, over."

"The brass in Washington have sent a immediate directive to concentrate your search pattern in a radius 400 nautical miles from latitude 41° 46', longitude 50° 12' focusing on an area due north and east of latitude 41° 46', longitude 50° 12'. Do you copy?"

"Roger."

The copilot smiled, "I guess the old man knows something we don't."

"Beats me, but ours is not to question why..."

The Herkey dipped its port wing and slowly turned to the north.

"Scotty."

"Yea Skipper..."

"Looks like we are going to find something after all. Everything on line back there?"

"You bet..."

"Let me know when you have something."

"Roger that..."

TIGER SHARK, 0715 HOURS

The bulbous front end of the USS Tiger Shark glided through the north Atlantic at a depth of 200 feet and kept a distance of 10,000 yards off the stern of the Titanic. The Tiger Shark was a Los Angeles class attack sub. Her displacement submerged was 6,927 tons. She was 362 feet long, nuclear powered with a speed of 37 knots and carried an impressive array of Harpoon and Tomahawk missiles, torpedoes and mines. The Very Low Frequency (VLF) and Extremely Low Frequency (ELF) antenna trailed behind the Tiger Shark for a distance of several thousand feet giving it the appearance of an ungainly runaway dirigible towing its mooring line. The VLF and ELF antenna was designed to capture radio messages transmitted from command central to the sub by using extremely long radio waves that would penetrate the sea and reach a submerged sub. Messages received in this manner were not transmitted quickly. If the message that needed to be received by the sub was urgent, the VLF and ELF message would instruct the sub to ascend to periscope depth to receive a UHF message from a receiver mounted on the periscope mast. Silently, the tubular beast began to rise and the periscope mast inched its way above the waves of the north Atlantic. As suddenly as she rose, the Tiger Shark returned to its 200-foot depth.

WHITE HOUSE – 0900 HOURS

The President sat at the end of a long conference table looking at the concerned faces of the Joint Chiefs of Staff. The Chairman of the Joint Chiefs, Admiral Sheppard continued his discussion, "Mr. President, we may have an impending crisis on our hands involving the Prime Minister of Israel. It would seem that there have been several incidences aboard the Titanic and other odd occurrences both prior to the departure of the Titanic from Southampton that point to an assassination plot to kill the Prime Minister."

"What are these odd occurrences Admiral?

"I have Admiral Potter and Colonel Allan on the viewer Mr. President."

The large screen flickered to life as the faces of Colonel Allan and Admiral Potter addressed the President from the CIA situation room, "Mr. President."

"Tell me Colonel Allan, what is this all about..."

"Mr. President we have reason to believe that the life of the Prime Minister of Israel, Joshua Cane is in serious jeopardy. The Prime Minister boarded the Titanic in Southampton to apparently marry a woman we know little about and..."

"Is this woman your suspect Colonel Allan?"

"No Mr. President, there were four "sanitized" assassins on board the Titanic who were neutralized by the Prime Minister's body guards two days into the voyage. One of these men escaped capture and is believed to be on board disguised as a passenger. He is not a primary threat at this time and will be captured if the Titanic reaches New York."

"What do you mean... if?"

Admiral Potter stepped forward and said, "Mr. President, there are serious doubts that the Titanic will arrive safely in New York because of the presence of a Kilo class attack submarine that will undoubtedly make its presence known when the Titanic reaches latitude 41° 46', longitude 50° 12', the position of the sinking of the original Titanic."

Admiral Potter switched the video to the large situation map display and continued, "The Titanic is represented by this red circle. As you can see, she is approaching the position, latitude 41° 46', longitude 50° 12', and will arrive there tonight. I would like to briefly give you an overview of the facts that have occurred prior to the departure of the Titanic from Southampton. Several SOSUS tracks of an unidentified KILO class sub were recorded coming from the GIUK gap and seemingly headed toward Newfoundland. To be specific, I believe that the sub was to make a rendezvous with an iceberg off the coast of St. John's Newfoundland. There was an unusual contract given to tow an iceberg from Newfoundland to New York City for a special birthday surprise. The contract was paid in advance, but the man who made the contract and the person that the iceberg was intended for cannot be identified or located. It is as if they simply vanished or did not exist. There was the strange disappearance of the iceberg that was being towed to Boston under contract by the Captain of a vessel called the Sea Witch. The Sea Witch was found with the Coast Guard's iceberg GPS unit that had been originally placed on the iceberg by the Coast Guard for tracking purposes on her deck, the Sea Witch was adrift after running out of gas and had been heading in the opposite direction, away from Boston, the Captain was found dead from a knife in the back and lashed to the wheel, a rubber dinghy was missing along with the father's son and spent shell casings from a Soviet Kosamakov weapon were strewn on her decks. The iceberg is missing and we have subsequent SOSUS hits from a KILO class sub going in the direction of latitude 41° 46', longitude 50° 12'. I believe that tonight, the KILO will attack the Titanic while using the missing iceberg as a cover to get close enough to her to finish her off."

The President paused and said, "What do you think Admiral Sheppard?"

"We know that the Russian government has been selling KILO class subs to anyone who would have the money to buy them to support her failing economy."

Admiral Scrivanich spoke next, "Mr. President, we know the location of each of the Soviet KILO subs and all are accounted for."

Admiral Potter interrupted and said, "All but one."

The President turned to face the screen as Admiral Potter continued, "As you know Mr. President our subs routinely follow the Soviet subs to record their sound signatures for SOSUS identification. The KILO in question is not in our glossary of known KILO signatures. There was one KILO that went missing and was reported to be lost at sea as it was being delivered to Iran back in '97. Odds are that this could be that sub."

"And if it is, who is behind all of this?"

"I do not know Mr. President, but I am quite certain it is not the Soviets."

"What is being done to locate the sub?"

"We are using the Coast Guard's HC-130s that normally spot icebergs to locate the renegade iceberg. There are Navy SEALs on these planes that will investigate the iceberg once it is found."

"What about the SOSUS network?"

"The Captain of this sub is very smart and is probably a former Soviet sub Captain. He knows of our SOSUS system and will try not to use his engines unless he has to, thus making our tracking of him almost impossible. We also have one of our attack subs the Tiger Shark trailing the Titanic. She is on full alert and looking for the sub as we speak."

Colonel Allan spoke, "We may have to use deadly force Mr. President to protect the Prime Minister and we may also have to fire first. That would be an act of war if we sink the sub."

"Yes, I am aware of that, but then again, we do not know who is driving the bus. I agree with you that it is probably not a Soviet Navy sub. It would be more than likely that our old friend Sadaam is trying to start something up once again. God knows we tried to take him out during the Gulf War. It's a shame we missed our opportunity. Damn, we had him by the short hairs and let him go. Is anything unusual going on with Iraq lately, I haven't noticed anything in my daily reports?"

Admiral Sheppard spoke, "Nothing that we can put our finger on yet, but there are troops being mobilized in the Middle East… Iraq, Iran, Syria… and there were several trucks that crossed over the Iraqi border that originated in Pakistan. It looked to be a military convoy of some type."

"What would Pakistan have that he would want?"

"Nuclear weapons for one thing. India and Pakistan are like two kids in a sandbox fight. One of them sets off a bomb and the other one sets off two. They hate each other and would probably sell one of their devices if the price were right and to form an alliance with this mad man. Remember, he has missiles he could sell in return so that Pakistan could wipe out India."

"And what would he do with the bombs?"

"Probably nuke Israel, but he couldn't be that insane. He knows we would make a parking lot out of Iraq if he did."

"Nevertheless, insane or not, he wouldn't hesitate an instant to use nuclear weapons if he could get them and if using them, would lead him to his objective, whatever that may be. Find that iceberg Admiral Potter.... Admiral Sheppard, look into that convoy and keep me posted."

IIP USCG HC-130H – 0930 HOURS

"Got something skipper. Looks like it could be our growler."

"Where is it Scotty?"

"Starboard 9 o'clock."

"Yea... I see it."

The Herkey made a slow turn, dropping in altitude as it approached the iceberg. The waves formed a white froth around the base of the iceberg as the HC-130 roared overhead.

"Good going Scotty. Lets get the SEALs wet."

A green light flashed in the cargo bay as the tailgate began to open, yawning to the sea. The Navy SEALs were ready to go. As each of the sightings was made, one SEAL would parachute into the sea and examine the berg. As the HC-130 gained altitude, it turned about to make another approach at the target. The jump light flashed and a SEAL walked out onto the ramp and jumped. The chute opened as the SEAL drifted downward, his accessory pack dangling below his feet connected by a tether, swayed slightly. As the pack and SEAL hit the water, the chute was disengaged and drifted away. Moments later, the SEAL inflated his raft, climbed aboard and made his way toward the berg. Using an air powered gun, the SEAL fired a grappling hook onto the summit of the iceberg, set the hook and scaled the sheer ice wall to the flat surface above. Instant radio contact was made.

"Search one... Search one... Do you read."

"Roger, we copy."

"Everything 5 by 5."

"Roger that. Let us know if you find anything. We will arrange for a pick up"

"Roger that."

As the SEAL started to examine the iceberg, the HC-130 continued its search. The iceberg in question would have evidence of a towing apparatus embedded into the ice. If this was discovered, plans were to deploy hydrophones to listen for the sub. The other SEALs would be immediately dispatched to search below the iceberg for the KILO. If nothing was found, the SEAL would deploy a helium balloon that would carry a tether. A V-22 Osprey would descend, grab the balloon and tether and pull the SEAL from the iceberg into the cargo bay. The voice of the SEAL crackled in Scotty's headset, "Search One, over."

"This is Search One."

"Nothing here. Starting to deploy balloon."

"Roger… will call you a cab. Sit tight."

The diver removed a can of red spray dye and painted a large "X" on the surface of the iceberg to serve as an indication that the iceberg had been searched and was clean. He next removed the rescue balloon from his pack and quickly put on a padded harness. The rescue procedure had been successfully developed by the British to quickly remove their agents from behind enemy lines in a time of need and had been adopted by other countries over the years. The harness was attached to the tether, which in turn was connected to the balloon. The tether was 200 feet long. Gracefully the balloon rose above the SEAL as he assumed a fetal position sitting with his knees drawn tightly to his chest. In the distance, the Osprey made its final approach. Extending from its open tailgate were the two devices that would snag the tether and pull the SEAL to safety. In an instant the pilot guided the Osprey toward the tether and the SEAL was yanked into the air.

KILO SUB – 1000 HOURS

The Captain entered the sonar compartment. The passive Feniks sonar was operational, keeping a watchful eye for activity around the sub, "How far away is the Titanic?"

"200 nautical miles away sir."

"How far away from the rendezvous point?"

"Approximately 60 nautical miles and closing."

The Captain looked at his watch. It was 13 hours and counting until they attacked the Titanic. They would guide the iceberg quietly to the rendezvous point and disengage from the iceberg and hover silently. Using their passive sonar, they would zero in on the Titanic and sink her with two well-placed torpedoes. He would then surface, find Moosavi and his men and disappear into the night. Quietly he went forward to the torpedo room.

"As the Americans say, are you comrades ready to "rock and roll"?"

His smile was returned as one of the men patted the bulbous end of one of the red and white striped torpedoes that looked like a large barbers pole on its side.

"At 2000 hours, load the tubes and get ready for action. We will be at the rendezvous coordinates by 2200 hours. I will want the tubes flooded and the outer doors open at that time."

The Captain returned to the bridge as the sonar operator said, "Captain… I am picking up something curious."

The Captain entered the sonar compartment and looked at the screen.

"There is a curious signature that is hard… yes… it is a sub sir. Definitely a sub."

"Can you determine what type of sub?"

"I am running a computer search now. The signal is very weak, but it… yes! It is a Los Angeles class attack sub."

"What would an American attack sub be doing there? Following the Titanic? Perhaps… but why?"

"Maybe they are using the Titanic for some sort of practice target."

"Perhaps… and if she is, she may well be with her tonight. If that is the case, we will have to sink her as well. One thing is for sure, the American sub cannot see us as long as we keep our engines silent."

"Do you suspect that perhaps the Americans know of our plan?"

"I don't know. You would think that if they did, they would be trying to find us and the Titanic would have averted her course, perhaps back to England. The Titanic is coming right into our hands. I would think that the presence of the American sub is probably a mere coincidence and poses a problem that we can easily deal with if and when the time comes. Continue to track them both and give me a report if anything unusual occurs."

The Captain returned to the bridge and picked up the microphone, "Attention please. We have discovered that there is an American attack sub shadowing the Titanic. Rig for silent running until further orders."

The Captain paused and then returned to the forward torpedo room.

"Load all tubes now, flood the tubes and open all doors. If we have to attack the American sub, I don't want them to have enough time to even think about firing at us. I want them only to hear our fish screaming up their ass. In all probability, we will have to take the sub out first and then the Titanic." Picking up a microphone, the Captain ordered the aft torpedo room to load all tubes and prepare for action. "Stay calm comrades. The Americans will never know what hit them."

The Captain returned to the bridge and then entered his cabin. He sat down and reached for a logbook of his crew. There was suddenly an itch in the back of his head. Something was wrong if there was an American sub following the Titanic. This would be serious if the Americans were somehow looking for him and his sub. He was anchored 170 feet below an iceberg. Surface monitoring was out of the question unless they could surface or get to periscope depth and they could not. If the iceberg was spotted, they would be easily destroyed before they could disconnect from the iceberg and hide. Someone had to go to the surface to be a look out. The faces of the crew and their background history flipped past his eyes. Finally two files were separated from the crew roster. He picked up a handset and instructed the two men to his quarters. In a few minutes, a soft knock was heard at the door.

"Come in."

Two men entered the Captain's quarters, Boris Demitrosky and Uri Sedorenko.

"Find somewhere to sit comrades."

The two men sat as the Captain cleared his throat and continued, "As you know, we are on a mission to sink the Titanic tonight. I have just learned that the Titanic is being followed by an American sub, Los Angeles class. This could be a coincidence, but it could also be a trap. If the Americans are looking for us, we must have eyes on the surface that can warn us if anyone approaches from the surface. Both of you men have an impressive history and are experienced divers. I need one of you to volunteer to go to the surface. This mission is very dangerous and there is no guarantee that you will be rescued in the event that we are discovered."

A long silence filled the room as the two men considered the situation and their possible fate if they volunteered. Boris broke the silence and said, "I'll go Captain. Uri is married and I am not. Besides, I am sure that the Americans will not find us. What is your plan?"

"We have scuba gear and dry suits. You will suit up and arm yourself with whatever you need. Surface, build some form of shelter on the iceberg to hide and observe. If you see anything, rap three times on the tow rod. We will hear it. If everything is OK, rap two times. When we attack, we will disengage from the iceberg and attack the American sub first and then attack the Titanic. You will have to come to us. Take an inflatable raft with you and stay on the starboard side of the Titanic. When we torpedo her, we will surface. Be in the water when the sub is hit and watch for us to surface when the Titanic explodes. We will be looking for Moosavi and his men as well. In all of the confusion, we should all make it safely out of the area."

"Sounds like I will have a ring side seat. It should be one hell of a sight."

The Captain reached for the handset that was secured next to his bunk and said, "Your attention please. As you know, we are approaching the Titanic and we have discovered that there is an American attack sub following her. I have asked for a volunteer to surface and be on the look out for any unusual surface activity… just in case our presence is discovered. Comrade Demitrosky has volunteered to be our lookout. This mission is very important to us and I do not have to tell you of the personal risk that comrade Demitrosky will be taking. Let us all wish him success and a safe return." The Captain stood and gave Boris a bear hug, slapping his back firmly and said, "Thank you my friend. Now let's get you ready for your mission." As the two men approached the stern, the other crewmembers raised their heads from what they were doing. A few of the crewmembers stood and approached Boris embracing him the traditional Soviet bear hug. Boris would smile and say, "Thank you comrade." Others would only look up and nod as Boris walked past their workstation. It was as if they were afraid to admit their own cowardly fears of dying and their fear of saying good-bye to a dead man walking toward his doom.

In the months that had followed the abduction of the Kilo sub, it had been fitted with an escape trunk that would allow Boris access to the surface. The escape trunk room was small and was capped with the large circular hatch that hung down from the ceiling like a young firm breast. Both the Captain and Boris opened storage compartments that were built into the walls of the room and removed the diving suit and air tanks. The air tanks were filled with a nitrox (nitrogen and oxygen) mixture suitable for dives to descend to a depth of 300 feet. Boris began to strip as others approached the room carrying an array of firearms and other gear. The drysuit was a special deep diving suit that was capped with a snug fitting hard hat with a large kidney bean shaped viewing window. Within thirty minutes, Boris was looking like some visitor from another planet. His tanks were checked out and strapped to his bank. Hanging from his waist was an AK-47 automatic, a 45-caliber handgun and a traditional divers knife. A small care package was attached to Boris by a tether and consisted of an inflatable raft, water, food provisions, flairs, an air gun that would fire a grappling hook so he could mount the iceberg, several low yield thermite charges to melt the ice for a shelter in which to hide and a short wave radio.

The Captain watched as Boris climbed into the escape trunk. He reached down and grabbed the care package and handed it up. Boris looked at the Captain and clenched his fist holding his thumb up. The Captain replied in the same manner as the crew closed the hatch and turned the handle sealing the trunk. There was a hissing sound as Boris turned a valve, flooding the escape trunk with seawater. In a few seconds, the hissing stopped and the Captain heard the outer hatch door open to the sea. A few seconds later, the sound of the hatch was heard being closed. Two clangs were heard as Boris used the butt of his scuba knife to signal that he was out and OK.

Boris turned on his lamp and shined it upwards and saw the jagged blue edges of the iceberg, reaching down from the massive block of ice like the icy fingers of death. Slowly he began to maneuver horizontally, finning his feet slowly. His air bubbles floated upwards and swirled across the ice like swirling pinballs on a crazy underwater pinball machine. Looking down, the sub looked like a long black motionless whale that was attached to the berg at the bow. Swimming horizontally, he focused the beam from his light upwards, looking for the edge of the berg. Soon, the side of the berg slowly began to arch upwards in a gradual slope.

Boris looked at his depth gauge on his wrist and moved slowly upwards. Every fifty feet, he would pause for five minutes and then ascend for another fifty feet. As he approached the 100-foot mark, he began to swim away from the iceberg. Surface currents would slam him against the berg like a rag doll if he came up too close along side. Finally, his head broke the surface of the Atlantic, 200 feet away from the iceberg. Quickly, he inflated the raft and climbed in. The air gun with the grappling hook rested by his legs as he paddled slowly toward the berg. The sea tossed him around like a cork. At times, it seemed as if he was being pulled away from the iceberg and then he would be tossed toward his goal. Looking at the massive chunk of white ice thrashing about in the sea, Boris was reminded of Captain Ahab in his long boat approaching Moby Dick in his classic struggle of man versus nature. This time he thought, man would be victorious.

Slowly, Boris maneuvered the raft to the edge of the iceberg and raised the barrel of the gun. Taking careful aim he squeezed the trigger. With a bursting sound, the hook flew in a high arch and crashed into the flat top surface. Boris gave a stiff jerk on the rope and set the hook into the ice, carefully tied a tether from the raft to his diving belt and slowly pulled himself toward the berg. The sea swells sometimes resisted his efforts taking the raft in one direction and the berg in the other almost pulling him out of the raft.

The cold winds slowly began to take their toll as Boris felt his hands ache from the strain of the sea as the ice formed on his gloves. His facemask iced up and he used his arms to attempt to remove it so that he could see. Boris was afraid to remove the diving helmet since it was the only protection his eyes would have from the sea spray and freezing wind. It seemed like an eternity before he was able to pull along side the iceberg. The sea slammed the raft against the side of the berg in an up and down motion. A few times, the raft almost overturned as he began the process of scaling the sheer ice wall.

Slowly and painfully, Boris hung suspended above the raft as he pulled himself up the side of the icy cliff. The waves crashed upwards against the side of the berg as if they were reaching up for his body, trying to pull him back into the sea. It seemed as if Mother Nature was toying with him as the wind picked up and froze the mist on his facemask, further blinding his vision. Using his legs like prongs, Boris balanced himself against the berg and blindly lifted himself hand-over-hand toward the summit. His hands were now growing numb and the rope slipped in his clutched fist. Grunting and straining with his last ounce of energy, Boris reached the summit and collapsed on the flat surface. As he lay on the ice, he realized that he was a good diver, but he was not a mountain climber. He would keep his daytime job.

Standing, Boris removed his helmet and looked upon the flat surface of the iceberg for the first time. It was as if he was at the South Pole. The wind howled across the surface stinging his face with ice particles as the berg rose and fell in the sea swells like a giant sea beast. He saw the steel pole that had been placed through the center of the berg. Attached to the other end, would be his sub and his warm bunk. Boris turned and began to pull up the raft. He secured the raft to the iceberg and removed the care package. The thermite charges were removed and placed in the ice next to the pole and detonated resulting in a crater in the ice five feet wide and six feet deep. The raft and the other supplies were placed into the crater as Boris quickly used some of the ice fragments and a white canvas sheet from the care package to build a roof. Within the hour, his home was complete. From the air, he would be completely camouflaged and from the surface, he would have the element of surprise if anyone arrived unexpectedly. Boris looked at his home and smiled as he approached the steel hitch. Using the butt of his knife, he banged against the pole two times. He waited one minute and repeated the process. 170 feet below the surface, the men in the Kilo sub applauded.

Boris sat in the ice shelter and turned on the radio scanner. Instantly he heard voices, "Roger that Search One. The berg is no good continue your search." Almost instantly another voice crackled, "This is Search Five… We have a berg in site and will be getting another SEAL wet."

"Roger Search Five."

Boris removed a pair of binoculars from the care package and began to scan the horizon. He saw nothing and continued to listen to the scanner. Thirty minutes passed.

"Search Five… this is Echo one. I am on the ice… nothing to report… will mark the berg with the "X" and deploy the rescue balloon."

"Roger Echo One."

Boris watched the skies. Thirty minutes later, a small speck in the air approached from the East. The speck grew larger and was easily recognizable as an HC-130. Boris crouched down into the hole as the craft approached and buzzed overhead. The scanner crackled, "This is Search One... we have a target."

"Roger search One."

Boris watched as the HC-130 increased in altitude and began to circle back. Suddenly, a speck fell out of the back the craft and a parachute unfurled. The SEAL floated toward the sea, as he guided his descent toward the iceberg. Boris watched as the SEAL splashed into the sea 300 feet away. In an instant, the SEAL was in his raft and was making his way toward the iceberg.

The scanner crackled, "Search One... This is Romeo... I am at the berg."

"Roger Romeo... We have another target twenty-five miles east of your position. Let us know what you find."

"Roger Search One."

Boris reached for his AK-47. The SEAL disappeared from his view as he approached the side of the berg. There was a bursting sound and then the sound of a grappling hook crashing into the ice, ten feet to his left. Boris watched as the rope became taunt and waited silently for his prey. Overhead, the HC-130 circled once and then flew in an easterly direction, hot on the trail of the other target. Boris could hear the sound of the SEAL climbing the ice wall. There was a slight click as he removed the safety from the AK-47. The hands of the SEAL popped above the rim of the ice and then the head. The SEAL was obviously much better trained in scaling walls than Boris and was in far better physical shape. Boris decided that there would be no hand-to-hand combat. In an instant, the SEAL was on the ice and was pulling up his pack; the raft would not be needed. The SEAL removed his side arm and fired several shots into the raft. It quickly sank. Boris watched as the SEAL holstered his side arm and placed his pack on the ice. Turning, the SEAL instantly saw the metal pole. Boris waited as the SEAL made several steps toward the pole before raising the AK-47, took aim and fired one shot into the SEAL's skull. A red cloud of brain tissue and blood spewed out of the head as the body fell backwards. The SEAL did not move. Boris quickly pulled the SEAL into the hole and approached the pack. Inside he found a package of red dye, the rescue balloon and harness. Remembering the scanner intercepts, he quickly drew a big "X" on the ice with the dye. Returning to the SEAL, he removed his radio.

He cleared his voice and said, "Search One... This is Romeo... Nothing to report. Inflating rescue balloon."

"Roger Romeo..."

Boris placed the SEAL in the center of the berg, strapped the body into the rescue harness and positioned the SEAL in a fetal position. He attached the balloon tether to the harness, quickly inflated the balloon and watched it ascend into the blue sky. Finally, he used his scuba knife to cut through part of the rescue tether. The stress of the initial jerk by the rescue plane and the weight of the SEAL would insure that the tether would snap before the SEAL was pulled into the plane. Boris returned to his hiding place and waited.

The radio crackled, "Romeo... this is Pick-up One. Are you ready?"

Boris replied, "Roger Pick-up One."

"Sit tight, we will pick you up shortly. Over and out."

Boris scanned the sky and saw the approaching Osprey. It descended and approached the balloon. In an instant the SEAL shot into the air. He rose several hundred feet into before the tether snapped.

Boris pressed the transmit button on the SEAL's radio and screamed, "Ahhhhhhh."

The SEAL's body splashed into the sea and never rose to the surface.

Boris watched as the plane circled and listened to the voice on the radio, "Romeo... Romeo... Do you copy.... Romeo... Romeo... '

Boris turned off the radio and smiled as he watched the craft circle the spot where the SEAL had disappeared. If the SEALs were indeed looking for his sub, they would not search for the lost man, they would not have time. Suddenly the Osprey began to tilt its rotor assembly. The monstrous 35-foot props created a throbbing sound as the assembly continued to turn, placing the props in a vertical position. Boris watched in disbelief as the Osprey hovered above the spot where the SEAL had splashed into the Atlantic. The tailgate of the Osprey opened and a rope was deployed from the craft. Seconds later, a SEAL jumped from the plane feet first into the sea. The Osprey hung in the air with its massive props flattening out the waves below driving up a swirling mist around the SEAL. Boris knew that the diver would be several hundred feet below the water by this point. How long would the Osprey hover? How long would they search for their man? Would they return to the iceberg? Would they land on the iceberg? Boris watched nervously as the SEAL made several attempts to find the missing man. 170 feet below, the Kilo sub was listening to the drone of the Osprey hovering above the Atlantic, "Captain… there is an aircraft hovering above our position."

The Captain reported to the sonar room, "What do you hear?"

"There was a splash several minutes ago and now there is definitely the sound of an aircraft hovering above the water about five degrees starboard of our position at a distance of five hundred feet." The Captain remained silent. Were they after him? Did they suspect something? Did they discover Boris? He chewed on his mustache as he watched and waited.

Finally, the SEAL grabbed onto the rope and was pulled into the Osprey and in a few seconds, was safe inside the aircraft. The Osprey increased the revolutions of the props as it began to rise. Moments later, the craft began to return the rotor assembly to a horizontal position and slowly increased its forward motion. The Osprey circled several times and then flew away. Boris reached for a cigarette, lit it and exhaled slowly. His mission was a success. Now, he had to prepare for the arrival of the Titanic and his return to his sub. It was 19:00 hours. He looked toward the West; the sky took on a reddish hue as the sun sank toward the sea. He took his knife and struck the steel post two times letting his crew know that all was well. They would be safe until the Titanic arrival and then all hell would break loose. 170 feet below, the Captain and crew breathed a sigh of relief.

TITANIC – 1700 HOURS

Jacky and Josh stood arm-in-arm at the bow of the Titanic looking into the sunset, their heavy winter coats and furs blowing in the wind. The sea was calm, almost glassy in appearance. It was as if the Titanic was a massive magnetic toy skating across a deep blue mirror. Knifing her way through the sea, the Titanic created a stiff breeze across the deck. Jacky snuggled closer to Josh to stay warm, placing her head against his.

"Do you love me Josh?" she whispered.

"With all of my heart and soul."

Josh turned to face Jacky and gave her a long embrace and kiss.

"I don't think that I have ever loved anyone or anything more than I love you now. I would die for you and I would die if I ever lost you again."

"You will never lose me again. I will be with you until… death… do us part."

There was a strange inflection in her voice as she had spoken the word death. Josh didn't pick up on it, but Jacky did. Something inside had almost stifled the word before it could escape from her lips. That something was her inner voice yelling at her, "*I'll never let you harm Joshua… bitch!*"

There was a faint smile on her lips as she answered her inner voice, "And what are you going to do about it Jacky? Sit back and watch the show. Joshua will die just like I told you and there is nothing that you can do to stop me."

She looked at Joshua and said, "Hold me… kiss me… never ever let me go. Kiss me… kiss me…"

As the two embraced, the voice continued to howl inside her head, *"Stop it... Stop it you bitch. As God is my witness, I will find some way to stop you... I will stop you... I will stop you!"*

Jacky smiled again as she said, "Let's go inside darling. We have to get ready. They say it's bad luck when a groom sees his bride the day of the wedding before she walks down the aisle."

"I want to give you this first."

Joshua reached into his pocket and removed a long narrow black velvet box and handed it to Jacky.

"Open it. It belonged to my mother. It was a wedding gift from my father for their wedding day."

Jacky opened the box slowly. It was a diamond and emerald necklace. The setting sun danced through the stones making them sparkle with an inner fire as Jacky removed the necklace and placed it around her neck.

"Joshua... it is stunning... beautiful... I..."

"Wear it... wear it tonight darling."

Jacky placed her arms around his neck and kissed him softly, "Yes my love, I will wear it tonight and every other night for as long as I live."

"I think we had better go in as you suggested. It is getting cold and I don't want you to catch your death..."

The two strolled toward the door arm-in-arm.

"Just think... the next time you see me, I will be your bride."

"And I, your husband to live together until death do us part."

Joshua's security team watched as the two left the deck and followed behind at a respectful distance. Moments later, Joshua stood with Jacky at her cabin door. They kissed again.

"See you soon." Jacky whispered as she placed her finger on his lips and entered her cabin.

Stretched out on her bed was her wedding gown. It was a custom gown designed by Norman of Beverly Hills, white, with a sheer see-through back. She removed her coat and tossed it on a chair. She reached for the gown and held it to herself. The necklace blazed in the mirror as she began to laugh. Her laughter increased in pitch and suddenly stopped.

Her inner voice screamed, *"I'll see you dead before I let you harm Joshua."*

"Oh my... I am really scared." replied Jacky as she tossed the gown on the bed.

"I will stop you... BITCH!"

"Will you now... and how to you plan to do that? Stop our heart from beating? Make me hold my breath until we pass out, or did you plan to make me kill our self? Face it Jacky, you and your lover are both dead... or soon will be. I have control now and I will never let go. As a matter of fact, this is our last conversation. Look at the necklace Jacky... don't you wish it were yours? *Ha, Haaa, Haaa, Ha, Haa, Haaa, Ha, Haa, Haaa.*"

TITANIC – 1735 HOURS

Moosavi approached Higgans' cabin. In his pocket was a revolver. The mission to kill Joshua was about to be set in motion. The Prime Minister's bodyguards were watching him even more closely than before and everyone was looking for the missing terrorist. There had been a storm during the night and Moosavi did not believe that the Kilo sub could have survived being stuck onto the iceberg. Andre had now become a dangerous risk to the mission and had to be eliminated. He looked at his watch. In a little over three hours the wedding would start. If the terrorist was discovered... he really didn't want to think about that. He approached the cabin door and knocked two times quickly and then three times slowly. The door cracked open as Moosavi saw a concerned face looking back at him.

Moosavi whispered agitatedly, "Open the door!"

As the door opened, Moosavi entered, turned and quietly locked the door. Looking at the terrorist he said, "There has been a change in plans."

Moosavi walked to a small closet and removed Higgans uniform, "Put this on… now."

"What's going on?"

"I have to get you out of this cabin and down to mine. I'll explain later… now put on this uniform." Moosavi tossed the uniform toward the terrorist. The jacket and slacks fell to the floor at his feet. As the terrorist picked up the clothes, Moosavi reached into his pocket clutching the revolver in his fist. With a swift blow, he struck the terrorist at the base of his skull. There was a sickening crack and a thud as the man collapsed onto the floor. Moosavi looked around the room and grabbed a pillow from the bed. He placed the pillow over the head of the terrorist and wrapped his hand and revolver in a towel. Placing the muzzle of the gun firmly against the head, he fired two shots. The sound of the gun made two muffled pops. He was sure that no one outside the cabin would have heard them. Smoke rose out of the holes in the pillow like steam from a smoldering volcano and blood began to pool around the pillow, turning it into a red mass. Quickly, Moosavi dragged the body into the bathroom and closed the door. Stepping around the blood on the carpet, he removed a blanket from the closet to cover the blood, in case anyone would pop into the room for a spot check. Hopefully, they would not check the head. He checked himself in the mirror for bloodstains. Finding none, he turned off the lights. Quietly he unlocked the door and listened for any sound coming from the hallway. Convinced that the passage was clear, he darted out of the room and walked toward Jacky's cabin. As he approached her cabin, the secret service men watched silently as he hesitated at her door and then walked toward his cabin door and entered his suite. Quickly he grabbed his medical bag and entered the hall. The secret service men watched as he again walked toward Jacky's door. Looking at them he said, "I need to see my patient before the wedding."

One of the secret service men spoke into a hidden microphone concealed in his lapel as he placed his finger against the earphone in his ear. Inside the Prime Minister's cabin another man looked at the image of Moosavi on the monitor and said, "Let him in…"

The secret service guard nodded in the direction of the door and smiled briefly. Moosavi knocked on the door. Jacky quietly opened the door as Moosavi entered quickly, closing the door behind himself.

"How are you feeling?"

Looking at Moosavi with a smirk Jacky replied, "How should I feel?"

Grabbing Jacky by her shoulders, he shook her like a rag doll and shoved her across the room onto the bed. His eyes blazing in anger he approached Jacky and said, "This is not a game! Do you understand me? In less than three hours you are marrying Joshua and then you will kill him in this very bed as he makes love to you."

Jacky propped herself up on her elbows and shot back, "Don't you ever touch me like that again. Just remember, I am the one who drives this bus… not you! I am in control of the situation and know exactly what I have to do. I will kill that bastard, don't you worry."

Jacky's inner voice screamed, *"I'll stop you. You will never harm Joshua."*

Jacky screamed, "Shut up bitch…"

Puzzled, Moosavi looked at Jacky as she continued to talk to herself, "There is nothing you can do to stop me… nothing!"

"You are hearing voices? This is not good."

"I can handle it doc."

Reaching for his bag, he reached for a bottle of pills and said, "Take these."

"What are they?"

"Medication that will calm down your subconscious and make the voices go away."

"I can handle it doc."

Moosavi grabbed Jacky's hand and placed two tablets in her hand, "I don't give a damn what you think you can handle. Take these damn pills… *NOW!*"

Jacky looked at the pills and then quietly went into the bathroom and filled a glass of water. Placing the pills in her mouth, she swallowed the medication. Moosavi approached and demanded, "Open your mouth. *OPEN YOUR MOUTH!!*"

Jacky responded facially like a ten year old as she opened her mouth and stuck out her tongue. "There… happy?" She walked out of the bathroom and faced Moosavi with her arms folded across her chest.

"Where is the device I gave you?

"You mean the pen?"

"Yes the pen."

Jacky approached the dresser and opened a drawer containing her lingerie. Reaching toward the back of the drawer, she removed the pen and handed it to Moosavi.

"Where were you going to hide it tonight?"

"Tonight when I get dressed for bed, I will place it under my pillow. When we make love, Joshua likes to be on top, I'll just moan a little to distract him, reach under the pillow and ram it into his head."

Moosavi stood silent. A faint smile crossed his face as he said, "Get dressed for the wedding. I'll be back 30 minutes before the appointed hour and escort you to the grand staircase. After all, I am giving you away." Moosavi gently took her hand and kissed it and then left the cabin.

CIA, 1800 HOURS

Colonel Allan looked at the war map as each known iceberg was marked as being safe. Looking at Admiral Potter he said, "It doesn't look good. We are five hours away from the proposed target point. No iceberg… No sub."

"The sub is there … I know it is there… somewhere."

"What happens if we don't find it?"

"Then all hell will break loose. The sub will attack the Titanic and she will go down like the Titanic before her."

"We cannot let this happen. We must find the sub before she strikes."

"What if we fail to find her?"

"Then we must make plans for that eventuality. Let's suppose that we are unable to find the iceberg in question or suppose at the eleventh hour, we find the iceberg and the sub is somewhere else. We have to be able to stop the sub once she makes herself known."

"We do have the Tiger Shark."

"But she is useless unless she can see the Kilo. Right now, she has heard nothing and will probably continue to hear nothing until the Kilo captain turns on his engines. We have to have more eyes and ears out there."

"We have the HC-130s and the Ospreys."

"But they are not equipped to hear a sub. We need the anti-submarine P-3C Orion.

"Where are they based?"

"The closest is Jacksonville, Florida. The VP-30 group is headed up by Captain Roberts, USN."

"Have we got time to get them out there?"

"More than enough time... if we act now. The P-3C Orion is a four engine Allison turboprop and has a maximum speed of 405 knots with a range of 10 to 14 hours flying time. We have approximately five hours remaining. The Orion carries a complete complement of Harpoon cruise missiles, Maverick air-to-ground missiles, MK- 46 torpedoes, depth charges, sonobuoys and mines. We can get it there in time and, God willing, destroy the sub before all hell breaks loose."

Colonel Allan reached for the phone, "Contact Captain Roberts at the VP-30 group, Jacksonville, Florida and give instructions for the immediate deployment of all available P-3C Orions. Primary focal point is latitude 41° 46', longitude 50° 12'." Hanging up the phone, he looked at Admiral Potter and said, "I hope to God this works."

"So do I... So do I."

TITANIC BRIDGE – 2200 HOURS

Captain Smith quietly stirred his tea as he looked into the darkness from the bridge. The sea was glassy. The temperature was 31 degrees Fahrenheit. How remarkable he thought, it seemed as if Mother Nature was cooperating and reproducing the same weather conditions that existed during the maiden voyage of the original Titanic in 1912. He looked at his watch and said, "I'll be going to my cabin to prepare for the wedding. We should arrive at latitude 41° 46', longitude 50° 12' on schedule. At that point, we will stop to pay our respects."

The wedding plans were very simple. Under the direction of Captain Smith, the wedding would take place on the Grand Staircase, under the spectacular wrought iron glass dome standing before the clock that had been immortalized in the motion picture Titanic® at 2300 hours. It would be a simple service that would take only a few minutes. Security preparations however, were very complex and the implementation of the security measures had been started several hours earlier. The forward main staircase had been closed to all passengers and crew since 1800 hours. The Prime Minister's armed security men and ship security officers were in position on each deck entrance to the forward Grand Staircase from A Deck through E Deck. All first class passengers and crew were restricted to the use of the aft elevator and staircase for passage between A Deck and F Deck. Passage through B Deck on the starboard side was completely restricted to the Prime Minister, Jacky, and Dr. Moosavi. At the appointed hour, the Prime Minister, Jacky and Dr. Moosavi would be ushered via elevator to A Deck and from there, to the Grand Staircase for the wedding. The Prime Minister would wait for his bride by the clock as Jacky arrived at the foot of the staircase and ascends toward Joshua and Captain Smith. Dr. Moosavi would give the bride away and return down the staircase.

Overlooking the Grand Staircase was a circular balcony of white tiled floors with a diamond image made up of black triangles peppered throughout, oak paneled walls and a Louis XIV style wrought iron scrollwork balustrade with gilt-bronze detail. The white tiles and balustrade continued down the stairs to the first class sitting area and lounge. The ships quintet would be positioned in the center of the balcony looking directly down at the wedding ceremony. Selected first class passengers and ships officers would flank the quintet on each side. After the wedding ceremony, the bride and groom would descend down the staircase to the landing and seating area on A Deck. From there, they would walk to the reception room and Dining saloon for the reception and planned ceremony at the burial site of the Titanic at 2330 hours. All first class passengers would be allowed access to the Titanic ceremony and the wedding reception to follow.

The Captain was also involved with, but not in charge of, the ceremony that would take place over the remains of the original Titanic. There would be a gathering of passengers on all decks as the promoters would have professional men and women narrate the events of that fateful night, show previous video tapes of the actual Titanic wreck, as well as a small reenactment of the initial spotting of the iceberg and the events that followed. For those that did not want to gather on the boat deck to listen to the crew bellow orders for "women and children" only to board the life boats, there would be plenty to do inside from watching any one of the three Hollywood movies made about the Titanic to documentaries made about the disaster. The new Titanic also had a small casino. Bets were already in place for the ships actual arrival at latitude 41° 46', longitude 50° 12', when they would arrive in New York and unbelievable odds offered if the Titanic actually sank over the grave of the original Titanic. To put it mildly, the arrival of the Titanic at latitude 41° 46', longitude 50° 12' would be a zoo. Captain Smith entered his cabin and quickly showered and changed into his formal wear. His phone rang, "Captain Smith here."

"Captain, we have received an urgent message from the American CIA warning of possible military activity in our area."

"Military activity...?"

"Yes sir..."

"I'll be right up."

Captain Smith arrived at the bridge five minutes later and read the cryptic message, "It is believed that a renegade Kilo class submarine is in your area. This Kilo class sub may target your vessel. Military aircraft and submarine forces are in your area to counter this threat. Take all possible actions to protect your vessel, crew and passengers. Colonel Allan, CIA"

"Good Lord..."

Captain Smith pulled at his beard as he read the message for the second time. Looking out at sea, he saw nothing but a flat calm ahead and a sea of stars. There was a look of concern across his face as he folded the message and considered the ramifications. If the message was incorrect and he overreacted, he would probably never command another ship. Oh well, he would retire again. If he did nothing and the message was true, he would have the same fate or worse, he and his passengers would probably die. Should he darken the ship? With modern weapons, darkness held no sanctuary. He turned to Murdock and said, "I want all the lifeboats swung out and made ready, increase the lookouts and activate every piece of radar, sonar and anything else that you can think of that will peer into this bloody darkness. God help us if this message is true. Get me the Prime Minister's security team on the phone immediately."

The phone in Joshua's suite rang, "Yes sir... Yes sir... I understand. We will take the necessary precautions and notify the Prime Minister immediately."

Joshua heard a soft knock at his door, "Yes..."

The door opened as the security man entered the room, "Sorry to bother you Mr. Prime Minister, but there is a security matter that you need to know."

Joshua listened to the message and said nothing. He walked around the cabin for several minutes and then said, "I do not care if the world is about to end. This wedding will go off as planned. Take whatever steps you think necessary, but do not relay this information to Jacky or Dr. Moosavi. God help her, she has had more than enough to worry about. I'll not trouble her with this."

"Do you think that it is wise not to tell Ms. McGuire?"

"What in the hell can she do about it… tell me? Nothing. This is her wedding day. If some misdirected fool does try to sink the Titanic, what can she do to stop it? Nothing! All we can do is pray that it does not happen and this whole thing is a mistake in intelligence interpretation by the Americans. Now pass this information to the others and make your plans quietly.

Captain Smith looked at his watch and said, "I'll be at the wedding. Keep things under wraps for the time being and let me know immediately if you spot anything out there."

Lightoller entered the bridge, "Captain… We have a small iceberg dead ahead approximately 15 nautical miles away. There are several aircraft in the area and there seems to be a submarine dead astern approximately 10,000 yards. We believe that the submarine is the one mentioned in the CIA message. It is simply following us at the moment."

"Interesting. Notify the CIA and inquire if the sub astern is theirs. How do you read the iceberg?"

"A growler sir. Nothing large and we can avoid it easily."

"Good. Notify the watchmen in the crow's nest and stay alert and come to all ahead one-third. When the ship arrives at latitude 41° 46', longitude 50° 12', stop all engines."

"Yes Sir."

Captain Smith picked up the Bible he would use, thumped it against his palm several times and left the bridge smartly.

The quintet was playing Pachelbel's Canon softly as the Captain descended down the starboard staircase and took his position beside the clock. The clock was built into the oak panel and was flanked by two classical figures that represented Honor and Glory crowning time. The soft light from the back lit dome reflected off of the polished oak as Captain Smith looked up to see the smiling faces of the first class passengers that had been allowed to watch the ceremony. He smiled back softly as he waited for Joshua. Looking around the staircase, he silently counted the number of security men and his officers. Everything was in order and secure he thought. Moments later, Joshua walked down the stairs with his security man.

"Mr. Prime Minister." Captain Smith pointed to his left and said, "Please stand here."

"Certainly."

The security man returned to the top of the stairs and watched the people silently as they buzzed with ever increasing excitement. Captain Smith spoke quietly, "I presume that you received my message."

"Yes, my men are prepared to deal with whatever happens."

"Did you notify Ms. McGuire?"

"No... I did not want to ruin her wedding. If anything happens, my men will watch over her. We did not notify Moosavi either... I was afraid that he might tell her."

"I understand... the lifeboats are being readied as we speak... Just in case."

Captain Smith changed his facial expression and smiled broadly as the quintet ended Pachelbel's Canon. Joshua looked down and saw Jacky for the first time, the most beautiful woman he had ever seen. Jacky stood at the bottom of the staircase looking up to him. Dr. Moosavi stood beside her. Her flaming red hair that fell gently towards her shoulders framed her radiant face and her gown beautifully accentuated the necklace that Joshua had given her only hours before. Jacky was beautiful, graceful and she was to be his wife. Her smile filled Joshua's heart with unspeakable words and emotions. As the quintet started the Wedding March, everyone stood. Holding Jacky's arm Dr. Moosavi and Jacky, slowly, in rhythm with the music ascended the stairs toward Joshua. For Joshua, it seemed an eternity before Dr. Moosavi gave Jacky to him. As Dr. Moosavi descended down the stairs, Jacky and Joshua turned to face Captain Smith.

"Dearly beloved… We have come together this night, aboard this ship, the Titanic, in the presence of God to witness and bless the joining together of this man and this woman in matrimony. The union of husband and wife in heart, body and mind is intended by God for their mutual joy, to help and comfort given one another in prosperity and in adversity. Therefore, marriage is not to be entered into unadvisedly or lightly; but reverently, deliberately and in accordance with the purpose for which it was instituted by God."

Opening the Bible in his hand, Captain Smith continued, "From First Corinthians… Though I speak with the tongues of men and angels, and have not charity, I am become as sounding brass, or a tinkling cymbal. And though I have the gift of prophesy, and understand all mysteries, and all knowledge, and though I have all faith, so that I could remove mountains, and have not charity, I am nothing. And though I bestow all my goods to feed the poor, and though I give my body to be burned, and have not charity, it profits me nothing. Charity suffers long and is kind; charity envies not; charity wants not of itself, is not puffed up; Does not behave itself unseemly, seeks not its own, is not easily provoked, thinks no evil; Rejoices not in inequity, but rejoices in the truth; Bears all things, believes all things, hopes for all things, endures all things. Charity never fails: but whether there be prophecies, they shall fail, whether there be tongues, they shall cease; whether there be knowledge, it shall vanish away. For we know in part and we prophesy in part. But when that which is perfect is come, then that which is in part shall be done away. When I was a child, I spoke as a child, I understood as a child, I thought as a child: but when I became a man, I put away childish things. For now we see through a glass, darkly; but then face-to-face: now I know in part; but then shall I know even as also I am known. And now abide faith, hope, charity, these three, but the greatest of these is charity."

Looking up to the people Captain Smith said, "Be there anyone here who may know of any reason why this man and this woman may not be joined in matrimony... Speak now or forever hold thy peace."

Looking back at Joshua and Jacky, Captain Smith continued, "A marriage is not only a promise that each of you makes to each other... It is also a commitment that you make to yourselves, each other, to your friends, relatives and community. Jacky... will you have this man to be your husband, to live together in the covenant of marriage? Will you love him, comfort him, honor and keep him, in sickness and in health, and, forsaking all others, be faithful to him for as long as you both shall live?"

Jacky looked at Joshua saying nothing. Her eyes were distant, staring into his face and yet seeing nothing. Her mouth trembled slightly. Joshua looked back waiting for her reply. A raging war began inside of Jacky's mind, *"I will not allow this charade to continue."*

"Try and stop me! Joshua is mine!"

Joshua looked back waiting for her reply. There was none. Jacky stood motionless as her inner struggle continued.

"Your power over me is gone. You are evil, but my love for Joshua is stronger than your hate... God... please help me..."

"God?? Who is He? Do you really think that God will save you and Joshua? You are a fool Jacky. Go back and say your rosary, go get a priest and see if you can have me exorcised... You are pathetic my dear... a typical Irish Catholic fool! There are only two things that make this world go around Jacky, sex and money... and you do not understand either one."

"I understand this ... AUHSOJ!!"

Concerned, Captain Smith looked at Jacky, leaned forward and whispered; "Say "I do" my dear."

Jacky's knees grew week as she swayed from side to side. Joshua reached out for her suddenly holding her in his arms. Dr. Moosavi looked on anxiously, his face showing grave concern as he watched Jacky. Was she losing it?

Inside Jacky's mind the war was over. Jacky had uttered the controlling word "AUHSOJ" which had placed Moosavi's Jacky into a catatonic state. Jacky was regaining control of her mind and body. She somehow had to rejoin her two personalities into one unified whole. Dr. Moosavi had turned the hatred she had once felt for Joshua into an instrument of insane rage. She understood that now and could live with her feelings of resentment and the death of her son. She also realized that she had to stop Dr. Moosavi before he could complete his plan. She knew that if she didn't kill Joshua that Moosavi would. Slowly, the internal war subsided as all of her angry emotions faded into the warmth of love she now felt for Joshua and the determination to protect him from Dr. Moosavi. In an instant, the other Jacky was gone forever. As Joshua held her in his arms, he felt Jacky's trembling stop and saw tears welling in her eyes and start to roll down her cheek. Jacky looked into Joshua's eyes and said in a soft voice, "I do."

Captain Smith's face lost its look of concern as he cleared his throat and continued, "Joshua… will you have this woman to be your wife; to live together in the covenant of marriage? Will you love her, comfort her, honor and keep her, in sickness and in health, and, forsaking all others, be faithful to her for as long as you both shall live?"

In a firm voice, Joshua said, "I do."

Looking to the audience, Captain Smith said, "Will all of you witnessing these promises do all in your power to uphold these two persons in their marriage?"

Captain Smith raised his arms and said, "Say we will."

The people watching the ceremony said in unison, "We will."

Dr Moosavi watched carefully as he muttered the words to himself, "We will."

Captain Smith reached into his pocket and gave Jacky's ring to Joshua. Joshua took the ring and placed it on Jacky's finger saying, "Jacky, I give you this ring as a symbol of my love and my vow to you, and with all that I am, and all that I have. With this ring, I thee wed."

Again, Captain Smith again reached into his pocket and gave Joshua's ring to Jacky. Jacky took the ring and placed it on Joshua's finger saying, "Joshua, I give you this ring as a symbol of my love and my vow to you, and with all that I am, and all that I have. With this ring, I thee wed."

Looking at Joshua and Jacky, Captain Smith held their joined hands in his and said, "May God bless you both… I now pronounce you man and wife. You may now kiss the bride."

Joshua and Jacky embraced and kissed as everyone applauded. For several seconds their lips joined together, each reaching out for the other and filling their hearts with unspeakable joy and love. Captain Smith finally said, "OK you two…" Jacky and Joshua turned and walked down the staircase to the waiting crowd below. It was now 2323 hours.

ICEBERG – 2323 HOURS

Boris watched the Titanic approach from his hiding place on the iceberg. Since his encounter with the navy SEAL, the air had been filled with HC-130's and Osprey aircraft. The airways had been filled with heavy radio traffic as aircraft frantically tried to find him. He lit a cigarette. It would be his last until the battle was over. The Titanic steamed ever closer. She was slowing down and her lights sparkled into the darkness like a jewel in the light of day. She would be a sitting duck. Boris looked around and began to gather his things. He would carry his AK-47, raft and scuba gear. The radio went dead as he turned it off. It wouldn't be needed anymore. Quickly, he checked his air supply and put on his facemask. Soon, he would go to the edge of the iceberg and use the SEAL's rope to descend into the sea, enter his raft and wait for his sub to surface. As the Titanic slowed to a stop he thought, "It won't be long now."

KILO SUB – 2325 HOURS

The Captain stood silently watching the screen showing the position of the Titanic and the American sub. "Do we have a firing solution for the sub and the Titanic?"

"Yes..."

"Disengage from the iceberg... Five degrees down forward bow plains."

"Aye... aye Capitan"

The Kilo sub quietly released its grasp from the metal pole and drifted slowly down.

The current moved the sub quietly through the water. Now there was danger of being seen by the American sub. Throughout their journey, the iceberg had provided the perfect cover as long as they kept their engines silent. If they turned them on, they would be seen. They had to use the Labrador Current for as long as possible to position for their sub for the attack.

"Come about to 278 degrees."

"Aye... aye Captain."

"Tubes one, two, three and four ready to fire. Tubes one and two for the sub and tubes three and four for the Titanic. When I give the command to fire, do so and reload."

Silently, the Kilo sub began to turn into firing position.

TIGER SHARK – 2328 HOURS

Captain Blake stood watch on the bridge. The Tiger Shark had been at battle stations after it had received the message from command that there was a Kilo class sub in the area. He had been instructed to attack the sub if and only if the sub was taking any aggressive actions against the Titanic. The sonar operator reported, "Captain... The Titanic has stopped dead in the water and has activated her sonar."

"Very well... all ahead slow..."

A ping from the Titanic could be heard throughout the ship as the helmsman responded, "Aye… aye sir… all ahead slow."

The Captain said, "Come to periscope depth."

"Aye… aye Sir…"

The Tiger Shark started her slow ascent and leveled off. The Captain raised the periscope and began to scan the horizon. He stopped at the Titanic. She was beautiful, bathed in her lights and sitting silently on the glassy flat sea. Turning the scope slowly starboard, he saw the growler iceberg for the first time. The berg was sitting five points off of the starboard bow of the Titanic approximately 3000 feet from the ship. The Captain changed the scope to night vision and increased the magnification. The iceberg became an emerald green chunk of ice with jagged edges protruding from its icy palisade wall. Suddenly, the image of a man in a diving suit started climbing down the wall! Looking to the left of the man, the Captain could see a raft in the sea that was joined to the man by a rope. The Captain watched in amazement. The Captain turned to his Exec officer and said, "What do you make of this Pete?"

The Exec looked into the periscope and replied, "Where in the hell did he come from? The guy has a raft and is in a diving suit…" The Captain and the Exec looked at each other as they both reached the same conclusion at the same time.

"Ping that iceberg… I said ping that Goddamn iceberg!" screamed the Captain to the sonar operator.

"Aye… aye… Sir."

The familiar World War II sound of a "PING" left the Tiger Shark as the active sonar was turned on. On the sonar scope, an ever-increasing circle appeared outward from the center as the sound wave traveled through the water. First came a blip for the Titanic, then the berg and then the Kilo sub."

"Got you… you bastard."

The sonar operator jumped in his seat, pressing the earphones to his head and said, "Captain… two high speed screws approaching… 1,000 yards and closing… definitely torpedoes Sir and they are armed and locked on."

The sound of pings from the torpedoes could now be heard as the captain yelled, "Down scope… disengage the towed array, all ahead flank… Come to course 188… Lock onto the two torpedoes."

"Aye… aye sir… 297."

The fire control officer said, "Have a firing solution Captain."

"Match bearings and shoot." The Tiger Shark gave two jerks as the two Mk-48 ADCAP torpedoes left the aft torpedo tubes. The Mk – 48 ADCAP torpedo was the underwater heavyweight weapon carried by the Tiger Shark. The torpedo was 19 feet long, a diameter of 21 inches, weighed 3,434 pounds, had a range of 5 miles, used pump jet propulsion technology with a speed greater than 28 knots and had a 650-pound charge of high explosives. The torpedo could use wire guidance or could operate autonomously and could execute programmed target searches and conduct multiple re-attacks if it missed the target. Recently, the Mk-48 ADCAP torpedo added the ability to seek out torpedoes to its roster of kill features. The display console showed a three dimensional image of the torpedo looking forward to the two incoming Kilo torpedoes. The Tiger Shark's telemetry on the incoming Kilo torpedoes was fed to the Mk-48 torpedoes through the wire that connected the two. The fire control officer watched the display and could adjust the path of the Mk-48 torpedo if needed and could disarm the torpedo if it malfunctioned and turned toward the Tiger Shark. In reality, the fire control officer usually did nothing and sat silently watching the display as the torpedo went in for the kill.

The fire control officer said, "Torpedoes away running hot and locked on Captain."

The Captain looked at the Exec, "Deploy counter measures."

"Aye… aye Captain… Counter measures away."

The Tiger Shark fired several counter measures designed to confuse the incoming torpedo and hide the boat. The first counter measure was the release of the chemical canister, which would release hydrogen when mixed with seawater. The hydrogen bubbles would prevent the enemy torpedo sonar from locating the sub as the Tiger Shark changed direction. The second was a noisemaker torpedo. The Tiger Shark carried four. Each noisemaker torpedo would reproduce the sound of the Tiger Shark, but very much louder than the actual sub itself and would travel at 15 knots in a different direction acting as a decoy. This would be designed to confuse the enemy torpedo into thinking that the sub was somewhere it was not and follow the decoy torpedo away from the Tiger Shark. The third counter measure was the traditional noisemaker that would remain behind in one location as the sub changed course and went off in another. The Tiger Shark shot off into the darkness squirting the hydrogen counter measures in its wake like an octopus squirting black ink as the two torpedoes from the Kilo sub screamed toward their prey. Again the sonar operator yelled, "Captain… I have two more fish coming our way, 1,500 yards… locked on and armed."

The Captain looked at the Exec and said, "This guy is really starting to piss me off!"

The Exec looked at the BSY-1 display and said, "Time for impact for torpedo one and two, on my mark five… four… three… two… one…"

Two large explosions erupted beneath the calm Atlantic. The first explosion occurred as one pair, Tiger Shark and Kilo torpedoes collided and exploded. The second explosion was very much louder and closer as one of the Kilo torpedoes went after the Tiger Shark noisemaker torpedo, catching up with it and detonated. A roar from the men of the Tiger Shark filled the bridge. Then came the shock wave from the explosions. The Tiger Shark shook violently. The lights in the Tiger Shark failed momentarily and the emergency lighting system activated. The Captain yelled, "Damage report."

The concerned nervous voice of the sonar operator yelled, "Captain… One thousand yards and closing…"

The fire control office yelled, "We have a firing solution."

"Very well, match bearings and shoot. Deploy all counter measures. Come to course 195."

"Aye... aye Sir... 195."

The Exec reported, "Flooding in the aft torpedo room Captain. We must recalculate the firing solution and fire from the forward tubes... the aft tubes are inoperable."

The Captain replied, "Shit!"

The seconds passed like hours as the fire control team addressed the BSY-1 fire control console. The computer quickly calculated the necessary information to the forward Mk-48 ADCAP torpedoes. Finally, the Tiger Shark spit out the two fish, counter measures and changed course.

The tension in the aft torpedo room was extremely high as the men quickly started the process of stopping the leak that had already filled the torpedo room with two feet of water. As one of the men turned toward the torpedo rack he saw the unbelievable, the torpedo screws activated and started to spin. Reaching for the COM, he shouted, "Captain... Captain... Aft torpedo room... *HOT RUN... HOT RUN!*"

The Captain looked at the Exec and said, "Fuck!"

A "hot run" is a run away torpedo that is strapped onto its storage cradle in the torpedo room. Back in the '80's there had been a rash of Mark 37 torpedo problems with "hot runs". It was believed that one such "hot run" torpedo had caused the destruction of the USS Scorpion back in the '80s, sending the boat and all the men aboard to a watery grave. Since then, "hot runs" had almost become unheard of with the newer generation torpedoes.

The Captain remembered the reasons for a "hot run" torpedo. "Hot run" torpedo conditions were thought to be caused by violent vibrations that would somehow activate an electrical charge from the torpedo battery to the propulsion system of the torpedo. Once the torpedo was activated, the warhead would arm. On some occasions, the thin membrane separating stored electrolytes in the torpedoes batteries would rupture. This could cause a "hot run" and excessive heat that could "cook" the warhead causing it to explode as in the case of the USS Scorpion. Hours of training drilled into the brain of all sub Captains to immediately issue a command "right full rudder" to make a 180-degree turn. The "hot run" torpedo would then disarm automatically once the sub turned a full 180 degrees. This automatic disarm feature would prevent a malfunctioning torpedo that was shot at an enemy form circling back and sinking the very sub that had launched it. The only problem for the Tiger Shark was that there were two torpedoes coming in from the general direction that the Tiger Shark needed to turn. Making a 180-degree turn would be certain suicide, since the sub would be rushing toward the incoming torpedoes. If he did not make the turn, other problems could arise and the warhead could cook and explode. The stern torpedo room was useless, leaving only the forward torpedo room to defend the boat.

The sonar operator looked nervously at the Captain and said, "Eight hundred yards and closing."

The Exec looked at the Captain, "Time for impact on my mark… five… four… three… two… one.

Silence greeted the ears of the Captain.

The fire control operator said, "We overshot Sir… torpedoes disengaging from the control wire and are turning about for another attack run. They are actively pinging Sir."

The sonar operator continued his countdown, "Six hundred yards and closing…"

There was only one remaining hand to be played. The Captain said, "Right full rudder."

The Exec said, "That is suicide Captain!"

The Captain replied, "Lock onto those damn torpedoes!!"

The Exec replied, "We will be too close if they hit."

"Do as I say or leave the bridge!" yelled the Captain.

The Tiger Shark turned toward the direction of the oncoming torpedoes. The Captain yelled, "All stop."

The fire control officer looked at his display and said, "Captain, the first two torpedoes have reached a 180 degree turn and have disarmed themselves."

At the same moment, the Tiger Shark had turned 180 degrees and the "hot run" torpedo in the aft torpedo room turned off.

"Five hundred yards and closing."

The crew in the forward torpedo room made ready the three torpedoes in all respects. Two were aimed at the oncoming torpedoes and the third was a noisemaker torpedo that would hopefully direct the incoming torpedoes in the wrong direction. The Tiger Shark lurched three times as she spat out the three fish.

"Four hundred yards and closing."

The crew of the Tiger Shark remained motionless as the sound of their torpedoes shot out from their sub. All eyes on the bridge were fixed on the BSY-1 display console. The noisemaker torpedo turned 90 degrees starboard, but the incoming torpedoes paid no attention. One of the Tiger Shark torpedoes hit one incoming torpedo, but the second overshot. There was only one explosion as the Captain looked at his crew.

"Three hundred yards and closing."

The Captain walked over to a control panel and pressed a mushroom shaped button releasing an emergency buoy that would radio their position to whoever would find their remains. The buoy shot toward the surface as the Captain said, "They got us…"

"One hundred yards and closing…."

The scream of the incoming Kilo torpedo screws and its pinging could now be heard throughout the Tiger Shark. The MK-48 that had missed its mark had turned around for another attack run, but disarmed itself as it headed back toward the Tiger Shark.

The men of the Tiger Shark knew that they were dead. As the ping of the Kilo torpedo became more rapid, there was a look of fear on some and grim acceptance of their fate on the faces of others. Submarine duty is all voluntary navy. Each man had joined knowing full well that they could be lost at sea. In the few seconds remaining, they thought about their wives, families, their girl friends and their dreams that they would never live to see. A moment later, it was over as the Kilo torpedo struck the bow of the Tiger Shark. In an instant, the sub exploded and imploded at the same time. The compressed air tanks ruptured and massive amounts of compressed air shot toward the surface carrying with it the death screams of the 133 men. Seconds later, the surface of the Atlantic became a boiling sea of destruction.

TITANIC, FORWARD CROW'S NEST – 2327 HOURS

The crow's nest was in the bow section of the Titanic and stood directly in front of the bridge towering 42 feet above the main deck. Access to it was through a small door on the main deck that gave passage into the center of the mast where one could find a metal ladder that led straight up to the nest. The lookouts, Fleet and Lee were half frozen as they stood watching the sea stretch out before them. Their facial skin was drawn tight against their skull as their bloodshot eyes stared into the darkness that lay before them. Slowly they rocked back and forth on their feet to keep warm as they shook their arms to keep the circulation in their hands flowing. In 1912, when the Titanic had hit the iceberg, the men in the crow's nest were the first to sound the alarm by ringing the brass bell three times and telling the bridge that there was an iceberg dead ahead. Whereas they believed that there would be no iceberg tonight, they would still ring the bell and act out the part. From the crow's nest, they had a view that was unparalleled by any viewing position on the Titanic. Facing the bow, they could see the sea before them. The same magnificent view could be seen from any position port or starboard. As they faced the stern however, they could see much of the ship and the warm quarters of the bridge where Murdoch and others stood watch.

Fleet grumbled, "I often wonder why in the hell I took this job in the first place, a lookout on a ship that has every known piece of fucking radar and sonar hardware that money can buy. I feel as useful as tits on a bull. Window dressing… That's what we are… fucking window dressing. Here I am freezing me arss off and those bastards in the bridge are as warm as a bug in a rug sipping tea!"

"There are only two things that make the world go around mate… sex and money. Since we are not getting any sex up here, I guess we are doing it for the money." replied Lee.

"Change your name they said. Play a part in history they said. Want to make a bet about the sex part? We are getting screwed all right mate by putting up with these conditions for the money they pay us. Considering these working conditions, they are really sticking it up our arss."

Lee jumped as he pointed, "Hey… Look at that, there is a bloody iceberg over there… five points starboard."

"Where?"

"Would you think that the company went so far as to haul an iceberg to this spot?"

"Yea and elephants can fly…" replied Fleet.

Suddenly, there was a whooshing sound that filled the air followed by what could only be described as a bubbling, boiling, gushing noise.

"What the hell was that!" yelled Fleet as he turned facing the port side."

"Beats the hell out of me… it almost sounded like a burst of air rising to the surface…"

Fleet reached for the rope on the bell and gave it three tugs. The sound of the three loud clangs echoed into the darkness. Reaching for the phone, he pressed a button and waited for someone to pick up on the other end.

"Murdoch here…"

"Iceberg five points off the starboard bow…"

Murdoch's voice seemed tense as he replied, "Right… We have it on our scope…"

"Begging your pardon Sir, but there was a loud gushing and hissing noise moments ago. It sounded like the hound from hell clearing its nostrils… quite scary Sir!"

Murdoch said nothing and finally replied after a considerable pause, "Very well."

The phone wend dead as Fleet replaced the receiver and said, "Well fuck you too Sir!"

Seemingly out of nowhere, the roar of four Allison T-56-A-14 turboprops of a single P-3C Orion filled the air as it buzzed the Titanic and dropped several directional frequency and ranging (DIFAR) sonobuoys into the sea on both sides of the vessel. At the same time, several flares were deployed.

Fleet looked up and said, "Where in the hell did he come from?" Looking at the flares, he said, "… and what the fuck are those?"

60 feet below the surface of the sea, the sonar operator reported to the Captain, "Splashes sir… Splashes. Eight in all…"

"Up periscope."

The Captain switched to night vision and scanned the horizon until he found the Titanic. The ship was beautiful with her lights illuminating the ships structure against the inky black sky. The portholes and windows looked like facets of a diamond as they glittered in the darkness of the north Atlantic. The Kilo was 20 km off the starboard side of the Titanic. Increasing magnification, the Captain noticed that the lifeboats were swung out and ready for boarding. Did they know that they were about to be attacked? Continuing his observations, the PC-3 Orion came briefly into view, deploying flares. The MVU-110EM combat system was assimilating the telemetry from the ships sonar. Two 26-inch torpedo tubes had been loaded with two heavy weight torpedoes that carried a 1200-pound charge of high explosives. Each torpedo had the capability of snapping the Titanic into two pieces.

"Have you a firing solution on the Titanic…?"

"Aye aye Sir."

The Captain took one last look at the Titanic and said, "Down scope."

As the scope was lowered, the captain ordered, "Make ready in all respects two Strela-3 missiles. There is an aircraft overhead. No doubt it is an Orion anti-sub aircraft looking for us. Up scope."

Again the slender periscope jutted out of the sea. The Captain watched the Titanic and briefly searched for Boris and his raft. He could not locate the crewman.

The fire control officer reported, "Tubes three and four ready Captain.

"Very well... match bearings and shoot 1 and 2."

The fire control officer replied, "Aye Sir... 1 and 2 shoot."

The Captain looked at his men and said, "This is it... Prepare to surface and make ready in all respects to fire tubes three and four as soon as we reach the surface." He paused momentarily and then said, "Surface... Surface." The sound of the klaxon horn filled the Kilo as her main ballast tanks were blown as she shot toward the surface of the Atlantic.

TITANIC, BRIDGE – 2330 HOURS

The new Titanic was built "stick for stick" after the old Titanic. Outwardly, she looked exactly like the original Titanic and yet there were major differences between the two ships. The differences were in the areas of ship safety and comfort. The new Titanic had water-tight compartments on every deck below the water line. She also had enough lifeboats for everyone on board and additional life rafts that were positioned around the boat deck on racks that resembled depth charges. The life rafts were on board to be launched in the event of a man overboard emergency and to complement the traditional lifeboats and were encased in a fiberglass canister that would slide down the ramp into the sea. A ripcord was attached to the launch ramp. Once deployed, the raft would automatically inflate as it hit the sea. There were two sizes of rafts for 20 and 25 people and each raft had the usual assortment of survival gear on board, food, water, chemical lights and flare guns.

The Titanic was fitted with oil fired boilers that heated the water to steam at a temperature of 932 degrees F at 870 psi=60 Bar. The steam drove the turbines and the turbine energy was directed to the reduction gear which drove her three four bladed propellers.

The rudder was redesigned and made larger to allow for better faster response to the helm. It was thought that on the fateful night in 1912, the original Titanic's rudder surface area was too small and did not allow the ship to respond to the helm quickly or efficiently, thus contributing to the collision with the iceberg. It had often been said that if the Titanic had started turning one second earlier or one second later, the disaster would have been averted.

The Titanic was also fitted with thrusters, two aft and three forward, that would allow for sideways motion that would make for easier docking and departure maneuvers in small harbors or docks. Two sets of stabilizers, approximately 18 feet below the water line were added for passenger comfort and overall stability of the ship in rough seas.

The bridge was totally redesigned with the latest in electronic hardware. Gone was the large helm that had graced the decks of the original Titanic. Gone was the large ships compass. A ship officer held a small steering wheel in his hand that was no larger than 12 inches in diameter. The bridge was completely computer driven with consoles that blinked with lights and displays. One screen produced images from the GPS (Global Positioned Satellites) unit that could pinpoint the position of the Titanic with an accuracy of one meter anywhere in the world. Other screens displayed radar images that scanned the sea looking for icebergs and other ships. Currently, the display was showing the iceberg as red warning and was flashing "Collision Alert" in red letters in the upper right hand corner of the screen. Doppler radar was also used and allowed for excellent viewing of weather conditions so that the Titanic could avoid any weather systems while at sea. Ship to shore V.H.F. radio, Internet and satellite communications made the Titanic capable of instant communications anywhere in the world at any time.

Considerable thought went into the last enhancement. After the Titanic's historic maiden voyage, the Titanic was to become a regular passenger cruise ship that would sail all of the seven seas of the world. This would include waters that would bring her near areas of current and future political conflict and unrest. No one knew what the future would bring. Whereas the Titanic could not be fitted for war, thoughts of the torpedoing of Lusitania and other uses of previous ocean liners like the Queen Mary as troop carriers during times of war, made the designers include forward, side, rear and bottom looking sonar. This would allow the Titanic to see what lay beneath her in all directions. In the area of electronic surveillance and communications, the Titanic was the best-equipped passenger ship built to sail the high seas.

The bridge was deathly quiet as Murdoch returned to the sonar screen. The glow from the sonar Cathode Ray Tube, CRT bathed his face in a soft green light. He had watched the approach of an aircraft on radar with increasing curiosity as it had approached his position from the south. Sonar had displayed several fast moving objects passing by the starboard side of the Titanic and heading toward the submarine that had been following the ship. Murdoch could only rationalize these sonar observations as torpedoes. In all of his years at sea, he had never made such an observation, but what else could they be? He had watched in disbelief as the sub that had been following the Titanic fired back at the oncoming torpedoes. The underwater sea battle had begun to play itself out before his eyes as one sub returned fire and changed course repeatedly as the attacking sub continued in hot pursuit. Looking at the direction of the incoming fire, Murdoch observed that there was another unknown sub in close proximity to the iceberg. The second attack by the unknown sub proved fatal as a single torpedo had hit its mark and destroyed the sub that had been following them. He had first thought that this was some form of war game. Passenger cruise ships had never before been fitted with forward, rear and side viewing sonar. Who knew what actually went on beneath the seas as the cruise ships sailed toward their destinations?

Murdoch replayed in his mind Fleet's description of the strange sound he had heard. Looking at the sonar screen, he could only see the iceberg and the mystery sub remaining. My God, what if these were not war games but the real thing. A chilling feeling of terror began to creep into his thoughts. The Prime Minister was on board. They had already been through a firefight onboard the ship and now torpedoes were whizzing by the Titanic and had sunk a sub. Would they be next? Murdoch immediately walked over to a display of buttons and pressed a button labeled #1. His was #2. The buttons were silent pagers that would instantly activate the personal pager of the Captain and other officers of the Titanic. Captain Smith's pager was #1. When these pagers were activated, it meant trouble and contact with the bridge was required immediately. As Murdoch returned to the sonar, he saw the unbelievable. Two torpedoes were coming toward the Titanic and closing fast. Under his breath he muttered, "Good God."

His face was white and tense as he turned quickly and yelled, "Sound the general alarm… Sound the general alarm!!!"

In an instant the Titanic's general alarm system sounded throughout the ship. The alarm bells rang loudly in Murdoch's ears as he thought, "Do not ask for whom the bells toll, for they toll for thee."

CIA, 2331 HOURS

Colonel Allan and Admiral Potter were watching the large situation screen display the position of the Titanic, Tiger Shark and search aircraft. Suddenly, the Tiger Shark disappeared and was replaced by a red blinking icon that represented an emergency distress buoy, used only when the sub was in extreme peril or sinking.

Allan's face froze and took on a intense look of disbelief as he saw the blinking icon and said, "She's gone… The Tiger Shark… Look Admiral Potter… The Tiger Shark… it's gone."

Potter replied, "The Kilo submarine captain is a better captain than I anticipated. He will almost surely launch his attack against the Titanic any second now".

"Where in the hell are those Orions?"

Pointing at the situation screen, Potter replied, "They are on station here and here. The Titanic is here."

"Let me get a patch set up to those guys." Quickly, Colonel Allan instructed his staff to pipe in the communications from the Orions. In an instant, the crackling sound of the Orion radio communications filled the room.

"This is Echo 1... we have a bogie.

Colonel Allan pressed a button on his consol and said, "Echo 1, this is Colonel Allan of the CIA. Your bogie is a Kilo class sub. We believe that she has just torpedoed the USS Tiger Shark... Can you confirm?"

"Roger... we observed large underwater explosions and we are tracking two torpedoes headed for the Titanic."

Admiral Potter spat out a single word, "FUCK!"

Colonel Allan literally yelled at the pilot of Echo 1, "Sink that fucking sub... do you hear me... find it and sink it. Do it now... sink that fucking sub!!!"

ORION, 2332 HOURS

There was no reply as the P-3C Orion banked hard to starboard and came around for another pass. Inside the Orion, the crew of 12 men worked as one. Telemetry was being fed into the digital computer that supported all of the screen displays, CRTs and would automatically launch the necessary ordinance to finish off the offending target.

The Orion climbed and suddenly deployed two MK-46 torpedoes. A small drogue shoot opened and the torpedoes swung in the air like a pendulum until they splashed into the sea. The Kilo sub immediately breached the surface shooting out of the sea and crashing back into the inky waters of the Atlantic like a massive whale. The MVU-110EM combat system quickly gathered the necessary data on the Orion and fired two missiles at the aircraft. Overhead, the Orion responded and fired a single Maverick (AGM 65) air to ground missile at the sub.

Fleet and Lee stood motionless in the crow's nest watching the Maverick missile scream toward the Kilo sub and two Kilo missiles go after the Orion. Lee looked down toward the sea in the general direction of the iceberg. Because of the flares dropped by the Orion aircraft, he could see the wake of the two Kilo torpedoes closing in on the Titanic. Using his elbow, he jabbed Lee in the ribs and pointed. Lee pointed to yet another set of torpedo wakes closing in on the Kilo sub. In an instant, the Orion's torpedoes and Maverick missile and Kilo missiles simultaneously exploded. The Kilo sub was engulfed in a massive ball of flames and the PC-3 Orion vanished in a ball of fire. The men on board the Kilo never knew what hit them as the sub broke apart and sank in a matter of seconds and the crew of the PC-3 Orion were killed instantly by the two missiles from the Kilo sub. On the surface, the only thing remaining of the Kilo sub was a burning oil slick and the lone remaining Kilo crewmember that bobbed helplessly between the Titanic and the iceberg in his rubber raft. Seconds later, the flaming debris from the PC-3 Orion littered the sea.

TITANIC, 2332 HOURS

The general alarm was now echoing throughout the ship. Below deck, people were beginning to become concerned as they stopped what they were doing and looked curiously at one another. On deck however, concern had quickly turned to panic for those on the starboard side of the vessel as the general quarters alarm was punctuated by the explosion and fire of the sinking Kilo sub and the explosion of the PC-3 Orion.

Captain Smith and the wedding party were standing in the first class lounge. His pager had started vibrating furiously. Everyone in the wedding reception could see the explosion from the lounge windows. Smith quickly walked to a phone bank and picked up a house phone. The operator responded, "Titanic operator... How may I assist you."

"This is Captain Smith… connect me with the bridge STAT!"

The phone rang several times before a the voice of Murdoch responded, "Bridge."

In a firm voice Captain Smith said, "What's up?"

Murdoch immediately recognized the Captains voice and said, "We have two torpedoes headed directly at us Sir, 15000 meters starboard side and closing fast."

Captain Smith's face froze as he heard the words spoken by Murdoch. His eyes were opened wide as his mind raced to find a solution to the problem. There was none. They were a sitting duck and there was nothing he could do. The Titanic was dead in the water for the ceremony over the remains of the original Titanic. He knew they had a head of steam, but the time required to start the Titanic moving was much too long. She was a cruise ship not a PT-boat. He simply could not start the ship moving in time to try to out run or maneuver to avoid the torpedoes. The ships thrusters could swing the ship toward the oncoming torpedoes thus making for a smaller target, but again time was too short. It would take fifteen minutes to turn the ship using thrusters. Even if he could turn the ship hard to port and all ahead flank, the torpedoes using their sonar would simply change their course and go after the ship. These were modern torpedoes not World War II vintage fish and the Titanic was not a war ship and did not have any countermeasures to thwart a torpedo attack. Fortunately, the lifeboats had been swung out and made ready by his command, but how much time did they have to get the passengers and crew safely off the Titanic? Anger and despair filled his mind. Why was this happening? Looking across the room he saw Jacky and the Prime Minister. Yes of course, they were the intended targets. Were the terrorists on board the Titanic a diversion or did they intend to participate in the torpedo attack and kill the Prime Minister during the mayhem that was surely about to break out. Looking around the room, he counted three of the Prime Minister's bodyguards. They were tense and began to surround the Prime Minister. Using their radio system, each man pressed the earpiece tightly into his ear and talked rapidly with their command central in the Prime Ministers suite. There was only one thing to do. In a loud firm voice, Captain Smith issued an order that he had hoped during his thirty years at sea he would never have to give, "Issue orders to abandon ship and launch all life boats and deploy all rafts."

Murdoch stood trancelike holding the telephone receiver. It was as if he couldn't move. His mouth was dry, the palms of his hands were sweaty and his hands shook. The Captain yelled, "Murdoch... Murdoch..."

"Yes Captain..."

"Grab hold of yourself man and issue the order."

Murdoch's voice was hollow and distant and he replied, "Immediately Sir."

The Titanic's bridge, like most cruise ships had a PA system that when activated would override any music or other activity that would be playing throughout the vessel. The Titanic sported two casinos, five restaurants, a theater, two nightclubs and three bars. Fortunately, most of the passengers were watching the ceremony for the original Titanic on television. Television monitors were showing footage of the Ballard discovery of the Titanic remains as members of the crew were narrating the story of the tragedy to other passengers gathered throughout the ship. Some passengers were outside on deck while still others remained inside watching the ceremony in the comfort of their staterooms or in one of the bars. Everyone on the Titanic was watching the proceedings with the exception of the casinos. Their slot machines, crap, black jack and roulette tables continued on as if it were just another evening.

The crewmen on the bridge watched Murdoch approach the PA microphone. His hands were trembling. The cold metal gooseneck microphone seemed to calm him as he pressed the button. A musical chime filled the staterooms, halls, bars, restaurants, theater and his face appeared on all television monitors.

"This is First Officer Murdoch... The Captain has issued an order to abandon ship... I repeat abandon ship... This is not a drill... I repeat… this is not a drill. All crewmembers and passengers are to immediately report to their lifeboat stations. All lifeboat crewmen are to immediately launch all available life rafts into the sea. Torpedoes are attacking the Titanic. Abandon ship… I repeat, abandon ship… This is not a drill."

Murdoch looked at the crewmen and other officers and said, "You heard the Captain's orders… Abandon the ship… now!!" Quickly, the crewmen and officers left the bridge to report to the lifeboat stations. Their job would be to assist the passengers and lower the lifeboats. Murdoch remained on the bridge.

Throughout the ship, the passengers looked at each other in disbelief. The crew of the Titanic immediately stopped what they were doing and started repeating the Captains orders, "Everyone report to their life boat stations. Abandon ship… abandon ship."

The passengers immediately panicked and stampeded toward the exits yelling and screaming. Each exit sign sported an arrow that pointed the way to the lifeboat deck. In the casino, a stocky black jack player with a five o'clock shadow looked at the dealer and remarked, "What the fuck is this all about?"

"You must obey the Captain's order sir."

"Like hell I am. I have been here all day and now I have a shot at breaking even. I am showing twenty and you have a fucking five showing. Finish the game."

The dealer looked at the man and said nothing.

The player stood up grabbing the dealer by the collar. His stale cigarette breath mixed with scotch filled the nostrils of the terrified dealer.

"Look you little Limey bastard… finish the fucking game or I'll break your fucking neck."

The dealer said nothing as he hung partially suspended in the air by the player. Looking out of the corner of his eye he turned over his card, it was a ten. The dealer has to take another card on 16 or under and stand on anything higher that 17. He now had fifteen and had to take another card. Reaching for the card shoe, the dealer withdrew a single card and turned it over. It was a six. With a smile, the dealer weakly said, "Twenty-one."

The player dropped the dealer in a heap on the floor. In an instant, he got to his feet and scampered out of the casino toward the boat deck. He paused for a minute, turned and said to the player, "You are a fucking loony." As the dealer disappeared around the doorway toward the lifeboat deck, the player looked at the dealer's cards and said, "Fuck you."

Captain Smith approached the Prime Minister and Jacky. Looking at the body guards he said, "Mr. Prime Minister… follow me quickly. We have precious little time. I must get you to the boat deck."

Captain Smith immediately led the way to the bar and opened a door marked "CREW ONLY" which led to an interior service corridor, "Come this way. Everyone will be jamming the stairs on all decks. There is a way to the boat deck from here." The Prime Minister, Jacky, Dr. Moosavi and the three bodyguards followed in single file up the stairs. Moments later, they came out of a door marked "CREW ONLY" and were standing in the bitter cold on the boat deck. The deck was crowded with frantic passengers mobbing all of the lifeboat stations and crewmembers struggling to maintain some form of order.

Suddenly, there was a thunderous explosion followed quickly by a second. Below the water line, the Kilo torpedoes made their final approach and struck the keel of the mighty ship. The Titanic shuddered from the force of the explosions and everyone throughout the ship fell to the deck, as the Titanic seemed to rise vertically into the air and settle with a deafening crunch. The torpedoes were designed to approach their target and hit the ship in the keel. The charges would explode with such force that the vacuum created from the explosion and the explosion itself, would literally break the ship apart into two pieces.

The first to die were the crewmen in the engine room and other crewmen in their living quarters that were well hidden below the decks of the paying passengers. These were the people that fired the boilers, tended the bars, the bus boys and waiters that serviced the dining rooms and the stewards that cleaned the staterooms. These were good hard working people that had signed a contract for as many as 18 continuous months and would work seven days a week and as much as 20 hours a day for a meager salary and tips that they may or may not receive from the passengers. They lived in cramped quarters that slept four to a room. The Titanic had been allowed to fly the United Nations flag because she employed people from 51 countries. As the sea raged through the engine room and crew quarters, the yelling and screaming of the crewmen sounded like the biblical tale of the Tower of Babel with each crewman yelling for help in his native tongue. As the sea surged into the bowels of the Titanic, the boilers exploded venting scalding super heated steam, smoke and jagged pieces of hot metal everywhere. For 385 of the 900 crewmen that maintained the Titanic, death was painful, but quick.

On the top deck, in the radio room, the cry for help immediately filled the airways, "Mayday... Mayday... This is the H.M.S. Titanic. We are under torpedo attack and are sinking fast. Our position is latitude 41° 46', longitude 50° 12'. Mayday... Mayday... Mayday..."

Relentlessly, the sea filled the Titanic and the teakwood promenade decks began to splinter as the Titanic twisted in upon itself. Adding to the frantic screams of the passengers were the twisting metal groaning sounds mixed with the hiss of ruptured steam lines and secondary explosions deep inside the Titanic. Above, the four giant Titanic funnels trembled from the force of the explosions and their tether lines snapped like kite strings making gun shot popping sounds and whipped through the air, slicing through the body of any passenger that got in their way. As the two halves of the Titanic continued to list, one by one, the four 22 foot diameter, 62 foot high funnels crumbled to the decks below killing everyone that was trapped beneath. The lighting system immediately failed throughout the mighty ship and the Titanic's emergency lighting system dimly lit what was left of the hallways and decks.

Perched high in the crow's nest, Fleet and Lee had held on to the mast and each other as they had followed the torpedoes hit mid ship. When the torpedoes exploded, the mast snapped like a wooden matchstick at the base of the deck and began to fall like a giant elm tree toward the bridge. The mast struck the roof of the bridge and catapulted the two men out of the crow's nest through the glass windows of the bridge. There was a sickening crunching sound as the bodies smashed against the thick window glass followed by the sound of shattering glass. In an instant, the two men crashed through the windows like giant rag dolls. Both Fleet and Lee were cut to ribbons and lay bleeding profusely on the floor of the bridge. Murdoch turned toward the sound of shattering glass and saw the horrible site. Fleet's head was sliced off at the throat and was connected to his body only by a small piece of skin. The top of his head was pointing toward his feet, resting on his chest. His arms and legs twitched violently. His eyes looked directly at Murdoch and his mouth moved forming silent words as if he was pleading for Murdoch to help him. Lee was lying dead on his back, impaled on a large piece of glass that exited through his chest. Murdoch placed his right hand over his mouth and immediately began to vomit. Turning abruptly, he staggered toward the bridge wing, opened the large window and vomited into the sea. Without warning, another violent explosion erupted making Murdoch lose his footing. In an instant, he fell screaming into the sea.

As the secondary explosions continued, the Titanic was ripped apart. The two giant pieces began to drift apart as the sea began to rush into the gaping holes of each half. The two halves were bound together only by electrical conduits, wires and inner superstructure materials making the Titanic twist in the sea like a snake with a broken back. The seawater continued to enter the boiler room in the stern half as explosion after explosion began to destroy the interior of the once beautiful ship. Fuel oil gushed from ruptured fuel lines and the fuel tanks in the forward half and immediately ignited and exploded. This created another series of secondary explosions as an inferno of burning fuel oil flowed out of the cavernous hole in the ship and floated into the sea like a pool of lava. The smoke from the burning oil began to fill the interior decks with toxic fumes. Passengers and crew who were struggling to get topside now fought three enemies, the sea, the noxious smoke and raging fires.

Explosion after explosion continued to rip the Titanic apart and the two halves separated completely with each half beginning to sink independently into the sea. As the bow of one piece and the stern of the other piece slowly began to rise toward the heavens, the gigantic rudder and propellers of the Titanic stern and the knife-edge of the bow majestically rose from the sea. Captain Smith got to his feet, his head bleeding from a piece of shrapnel. His eyes were filled with fear and he immediately realized the horrifying fact that his ship would sink before any of the lifeboats could be lowered into the sea. Most, if not all of his passengers and crew would die. He looked at Joshua and Jacky, "The Titanic will flounder in less than fifteen minutes. You men, help me deploy these life rafts. It's our only chance."

The Titanic had lifeboats with more than enough capacity for every passenger and crewman, but they were now useless due to the angle of assent of the two halves of the ship. Regardless, the frantic passengers and crew were still mobbing the lifeboats thinking that they could save themselves. One lifeboat after another tried to descend to the sea, only to wind up partially suspended in the air. Many passengers in the lifeboats realizing that they could not make it to the sea, jumped from the lifeboats into the raging inferno below. Others, realizing that the lifeboats were useless, willingly jumped into the burning sea convincing themselves that it was safer to take a chance in the burning sea, rather than stay on board and die like rats as did the passengers of the original Titanic.

Below deck, other passengers struggled helplessly to reach the decks above. Some passengers were overcome or disoriented by the fires, smoke and explosions and were being trampled beneath the feet of others. Some passengers, being in a state of shock did little to save themselves and were being pushed aside by the frantic mob.

There were no restraining gates that would lock these souls away in the bowels of the Titanic, a tragic event that occurred with the steerage passengers of the original Titanic, and yet, a wall of humanity blocked every passageway and staircase that led to the decks above. Like the angel of death that crept through streets of Egypt killing the first-born of the Pharaoh and his people, the cold seawater, smoke and toxic fumes engulfed these frantic souls, taking them swiftly to a watery grave.

On the boat deck, Captain Smith yelled above the roar of the ruptured steam lines to the Prime Ministers bodyguards, "Remove those red pins starting from the back, working forward. On a ramp above rested five Viking® life raft canisters resembling depth charges. The canisters were mounted on a slide ramp that led to the edge of the deck and were designed to slide down the ramp and into the sea. A wide canvas strap disappeared inside of the canister with one end of the strap connected to the canister cradle and the other end to the pressurized air bottle that would fill the raft. Captain Smith and the bodyguards began to remove the safety pins that held the canisters in place. Once the last pin was removed, all of the Viking® life raft canisters would deploy and inflate automatically into the sea. Each life raft could carry 25 people and had food provisions, water and flare guns on board. The Prime Minister, Jacky and Dr. Moosavi stood silently watching. When the last pin was removed, the canisters slid down the ramp and into the sea. As they slid away from the deck, the canvas strap acted like a ripcord. Instantly the canisters split open like a clamshell, the two halves falling aside as the yellow rafts inflated. Silently, they sat in a sea of burning fuel oil like giant yellow mushrooms. On the lifeboat deck, next to the wall structure, was a metal six-foot by four-foot box. Stenciled on the side were the words, LIFE VEST. Captain Smith yelled, "Get a life vest... Put it on... and jump into the sea! As you surface, spread the burning oil aside using your hands like you are doing the breaststroke and swim to the raft. When you make it to the raft, get out of this burning fuel oil."

Everyone grabbed a life vest and quickly tied the two straps around their waist. Captain Smith yelled, "Jump… Jump now before it is too late!" Joshua looked at Jacky. She was trembling from fear and the cold. He held her in his arms and said, "I love you. Hold on to me darling and never let me go. Understand?" Jacky looked into Joshua's eyes and said, "Yes… I'll never let you go."

Together they jumped into the sea. The force of the impact stunned them both as they lost their grip and separated. Dr. Moosavi watched as the Captain and bodyguards stood at the edge of the deck looking down into the sea. He quietly positioned himself behind the men. Reaching into his jacket pocket, he removed his ASP 9mm handgun. Paris Theodore, a holster manufacturer had designed the ASP 9mm handgun for the United States Secret Service. It was designed for concealment, stopping power, the trigger spur had been cut back so that it could be removed quickly from clothing without snagging and sported a gutter sight and two-handed grip. The boldest step taken by Theodore was his ASP 9 mm design and was designed to replace the .45 caliber handgun that was too bulky for the Secret Service. The ASP 9 mm allowed for a thinner grip and larger magazine capacity. It was often said that if James Bond were a real secret service agent, this would have been his gun.

The hissing of the ruptured steam pipes and screams of frantic passengers concealed the clicking of the gun as Moosavi pulled the trigger slightly, grabbed the stub end of the trigger and cocked it. Moosavi slowly raised the gun toward the backs of the three body-guards. In rapid succession, he started firing, placing a 9 mm bul-let squarely into the backs of two of the bodyguard's heads. As the forehead of each bodyguard exploded into a pink cloud of blood and tissue, the third bodyguard turned with his gun drawn and dropped to a squatting position returning fire. Moosavi took a bullet in his left shoulder, but fired off a lucky shot that entered the face of the bodyguard through his nose. The man's head exploded as he fell backwards off of the deck into the sea. The spent shell casings fell to the deck as Captain Smith turned to face Moosavi, his white uniform spattered with blood. Moosavi looked at the Captain with a look of contempt. Captain Smith looked down at the two dead bodyguards and then said, "You???"

"That's right Captain... me... the man that has orchestrated this beautiful sight of death and destruction you see before you tonight."

"You are mad..."

Moosavi spoke in a rage, "Mad... Mad is a relative term Captain. To those that do not comprehend or understand the action of others... behavioral patterns can be gravely misunderstood and considered to be outside of the boundaries of normal or rational behavior. I am not mad Captain... It is you and people like you... your governments and your military that are mad and insane... driven by your lust for world dominance that compels your governments to eagerly bomb into submission any group of people or political power that is feared and not understood. That is what has caused the events of this evening my dear Captain... not me! Look around you Captain... this is just the beginning of a new global revolution, a holy war... the Jihad. The sinking of your precious Titanic is but a small act in a magnificent play that will continue to unfold during the next few days and years, ending with the destruction of your governments, your military power and your world dominance."

Captain Smith raised his hands in a defensive posture as Moosavi took one step toward the Captain. His left arm hung limp at his side as blood trickled from beneath his jacket sleeve, onto the back of his hand and onto the deck. Slowly Moosavi raised the ASP 9mm at Captain Smith's head.

"I think it is time for you to take a swim..." A single shot was fired hitting Captain Smith squarely between the eyes. He fell backwards off of the deck into the sea. Moosavi placed the gun inside of his pocket, checked his life vest and jumped into the sea toward the awaiting raft.

IIP USCG HC-130H – 2335 HOURS

The explosions of the Kilo sub, Orion and Titanic had filled the dark Atlantic sky with a brilliant orange hue. The HC-130 was twenty nautical miles West of the explosions.

"Hey skipper... what is that?" remarked the co-pilot.

"Looks like a fire or explosion of some kind."

The nose of the HC-130 turned, heading toward the glow. The Captain reported, "This is Search one... Search one ..."

"Roger Search one..."

"We have a very large fire at sea approximately twenty nautical miles East of our position... we are turning about to investigate...."

"Roger that Search one. Report back as soon as you have something to report."

"Roger... Search one over and out."

The HC-130 headed directly toward the glow and began to descend to an altitude of 2000 feet. In a matter of minutes, the wreckage of the Titanic became visible. The Captain looked at the two halves of the Titanic pointing toward the sky and said, "Good God..."

The bow and stern of the Titanic two halves were rising rapidly toward the sky and the oil fire continued to burn furiously around the wreckage. The HC-130 lowered in altitude to 500 feet as the passed directly over the wreckage. The bow and stern of the Titanic passed a mere 200 feet below. Passengers could be seen jumping into the sea while others were trying to climb the steep teakwood decks to escape the rising water. Bodies were everywhere in the water. The Captain reported, "This is Search one... there is a passenger ship broken in half, on fire and sinking rapidly. There are no lifeboats visible... passengers are jumping into the sea and there are bodies everywhere... over."

"Roger Search one... deploy what SEALs you have remaining and whatever life support gear that you may have for the passengers at sea. We will take it from here."

The HC-130 continued to circle as the tailgate of the craft opened. The three remaining SEALs parachuted out of the aircraft along with several life rafts. As the SEAL's parachutes opened, the HC-130 began to drop flares. Suddenly, the sea lit up beneath the SEALs and for the first time they could see the true extent of the disaster. Of the 2223 passengers and crew of the Titanic, none were observed to be in any lifeboats, since there had not been enough time to lower them into the sea before the ship had broken apart. A total of five life rafts could be seen with people frantically trying to swim toward them. The oil fire was burning furiously around these passengers and many of them were dead, burning in the sea like large swimming pool floating candles, charred and lifeless. Other passengers had managed to get away from the fire or were lucky to jump into the sea where there was no fire. Most of these passengers however, were either dead from hypothermia or close to it. The passengers on the ship congregated in tight groups, clinging onto the Titanic as it rose higher into the air knowing full well that once it had finished its vertical climb, the two halves would fill with water and sink rapidly. The ship itself burned from within as tongues of fire shot out of windows shooting twenty to forty feet into the air. Acrid smoke billowed from every window and doorway, filling the Titanic halves with the stench of burning flesh, wood and plastic. It was very clear, there would be few survivors.

CIA, 2345 HOURS

Colonel Allan and Admiral Potter listened intently to the air traffic reports. The airways crackled with static.

"This is Search One..."

"Roger Search One..."

"The ship is broken into two pieces... there are no lifeboats... repeat no lifeboats in the sea... but there are five life rafts deployed on the starboard side of the stern half of the ship with people trying to swim to them. The oil fire is raging around them and preventing most of these people from reaching the life rafts. The SEALs are reporting that most of the passengers in the sea are either dead or will soon be from exposure... The ship itself is on fire with hundreds of passengers still on board... The two halves will sink beneath the waves within five to ten minutes... There is little that we can do to help. God... I don't think that I have ever seen anything like this..."

"Roger Search One... Continue to stay on station. There are two other HC-130s and five Ospreys about to arrive with other SEALs. The Coast Guard and Navy are deploying every aircraft they have available and should be there within twenty minutes. They will deploy life rafts and other rescue personnel. Instruct your SEALs to assist in aiding any and all passengers and crew of the Titanic into these available life rafts. Two Coast Guard cutters and one Canadian cutter will arrive on station within three hours... Do the best you can... over and out."

Colonel Allan looked at Potter and said, "What are the odds that the Prime Minister can get to a raft?"

Potter removed his glasses and rubbed his eyes. His voice was distant as his mind searched for an answer, "About million to one... maybe more. Not very good odds I'm afraid. The sea temperature is 31 degrees Fahrenheit. If the Prime Minister is in the sea and doesn't get to a raft... he will die in about fifteen to twenty minutes of hypothermia. It's not a bad way to go since the bodies core temperature drops to a point where the person just goes to sleep and never wakes up. Eventually the heart stops and its all over. Then again there is the oil fire that would possibly raise the sea temperature a bit in the vicinity of the Titanic extending his overall endurance to the cold for a brief period longer... but there is a strong possibility that the oil fire would be far more deadly than the sea temperature. If he is still on the Titanic and if he is still alive... I doubt that there is anything anyone can do to save him. The explosions, the fire... the smoke... the suction when the ship sinks..."

"Isn't there anything we can do?"

"I am afraid that the only thing left is to pray that God in His mercy somehow spares his life."

Colonel Allan's face was drawn and his eyes were blood shot. He was very tired and for the first time since the ordeal had begun, he had momentarily lost his eternal optimism in the belief that good would always conquer evil. He had lost the fight and stood silent, looking at Admiral Potter. His eyes went blank and seemed to stare through Admiral Potter as if watching something far, far away. Slowly he leaned on the console and said, "When I was a kid, my mother always grabbed me by the ear and took me to church on Sunday. Oh how I hated those hot … steamy summer mornings. The church windows would be open and everyone would be fanning themselves as the preacher tried to scare us all to death… warning of eternal hell fire and damnation if we did not follow the teachings of the Good Book. I would always jump when the preacher yelled and pounded his fist into the Good Book… I remember one Sunday in particular when Sally Jones, a fifteen year old girl in our town was raped and beaten half to death by two drifters as she walked home from morning services. The drifters were eventually apprehended, sent to jail and hung two years later. Sally got pregnant. A couple of months later… Sally… quietly walked into her parent's bedroom, closed the door behind her, found her fathers 38 revolver and blew her brains out all over the ceiling and wall. The following Sunday, the preacher talked about Sally Jones… how she had always been full of life, had always been eager to help others and would always be remembered as a good Christian soul who was now in heaven with Him. The preacher was in tears when he finished talking about Sally that morning. We all were crying… especially me… Sally gave me my first kiss… She was my first love. That Sunday morning I remember Sally's mother screamed from the back of the church asking the preacher why this had happened to her baby. The preacher could only say that God worked in strange ways and that things, no matter how horrible, always happened for a reason… I sure wish that I could figure out what the reason is for all of this death and destruction tonight… One hundred and thirty-three men are dead on the Tiger Shark, twelve men on the Orion, God knows how many men on the Kilo sub and most of the 2,223 passengers and crew of the Titanic will also die tonight… and for what? You know, I don't think that Sally's mom ever figured out what the reason was for her daughter suicide, but we had better find out what the reason is for this. Things do happen for a reason and whatever the reason is for this… it really scares the hell out of me… even more than the Preacher scared me when I was a kid."

Colonel Allan stared at the console, slowly picked up the red phone and said in a somber tone, "Get me the President."

TITANIC, 2350 HOURS

The two halves of the Titanic sat motionless in the sea like gigantic fishing bobbers 150 yards apart from each other. The bow and stern were pointing up at an angle of almost 90 degrees. Orange light from the burning oil in the sea and from the interior fires of the ship illuminated the two towering structures. Without warning, the two halves began their death slide into the sea. The screams of the passengers and crew on the Titanic and of those in the sea filled the air with a unified roar that resembled the sound of a Super Bowl game when a touchdown was made. However, the cries and screams of the passengers and crew of the mighty ship were quickly muted by the gushing, hissing and gurgling sounds of the ship in its final death throes as towering columns of steam exploded skyward, mixing with billowing black smoke and glowing cinders. Some of the passengers onboard tried to jump into the sea, while others hung onto the doomed ship, disappearing with it beneath the burning sea. As the downward momentum of the Titanic increased, large bubbles of air rose to the surface creating several small tsunamis that rippled outward in a large circle. Finally, with one loud sickening slurping sound, the Titanic was gone.

Jacky and Joshua had jumped into the sea five minutes earlier. They were both stunned when they hit the water. Jacky had entered almost feet first, but Joshua had turned to one side, entering the water butt first, favoring his right side. The water felt like a sheet of concrete and it knocked the air from their lungs and water had immediately filled their nostrils, making their sinus cavities burn as if filled with acid. Their bodies had been driven deep into the cold Atlantic by the force of their fall. They had separated as the buoyancy of their life vests propelled them toward the surface, shooting them out of the water into two different directions and into the raging flames. Joshua splashed the water away from his face as Captain Smith had instructed. Looking around 360 degrees he cried, "Jacky… Jacky… Where are you?"

Nothing was heard except the deafening cries of the other passengers, muffling any reply that could have been heard from Jacky. He could see a life raft twenty yards away. Did she make it to the raft? How could she? They were together only a few seconds earlier. Where was she? Joshua's suddenly felt a sharp pain in his right side. He had fractured two ribs. As he tried to do the breaststroke, the pain increased. Winching in pain he cried out, "Jacky… Jacky… Do you hear me… Where are you…"

There was a faint reply from Jacky, "Joshua… over here… over here…"

Joshua turned toward the direction of the voice. He could see nothing but a wall of burning oil. Swimming through the intense pain in his right side, Joshua splashed forward through the wall of fire. The oil had now covered his face, hands and life vest. Swimming toward the sound of Jacky's voice, his hands and face ignited several times, forcing Joshua to hold his hands and head under the water to extinguish the flames. As a result, both of his hands and his face began to smart from first and second degree burns. He could smell the burning odor of his own eyebrows and hair being incinerated by the flames. The only thing keeping him going was the sound of Jacky's voice. As he passed through the wall of burning oil, he saw Jacky frantically splashing and screaming, "Joshua… Joshua… Over here!"

For what seemed like an eternity, Joshua struggled to reach her. As he approached, he could see that she was badly burned. For the most part, her beautiful red hair had been burned off and her hands, arms and face were badly burned and blistered. Joshua finally reached out for her trembling body. When she felt his touch, she spun around in his direction and grabbed him, "Joshua... Joshua... Is that you?"

Joshua looked at her face and realized that the fire damaged her eyes, she could not see. His heart almost stopped as he realized that she was in very bad shape and would most certainly die from the combined cold and burns unless he got her out of the sea immediately. In a firm, but loving voice he said, "Jacky... Jacky... Listen to me... you are badly burned and I need you to do exactly what I say... Do you understand?"

Jacky's voice trembled from the cold as she replied, "Yeees..."

"Good... there is a life raft about twenty yards away from us... we can make it. Do you remember what Captain Smith said about doing the breaststroke?"

"Yes..."

"Good... I want you to swim with me..."

"...But I can't... I can't see... Oh Joshua... I can't see..."

"Don't worry darling... I will be your eyes. As long as we take it slow... one stroke at a time and stay together, we can reach the life raft over there. The oil fire is not so bad over there and when we are inside we will be safe and warm. Now when I tell you, I want you to lean forward into your life vest and start doing the breaststroke like Captain Smith said. Can you do that?"

Splashing around in the water, following Joshua's voice, Jacky said, "I think so..."

"Good... I want you to tell me if you get tired. We can stop and rest."

Jacky seemed to nod off mumbling, "Joshua... I'm so cold... I'm soooo cooold. I just want to sleep."

Realizing that Jacky was going into shock, Joshua screamed, "*NO JACKY... DON'T SLEEP! YOU CAN SLEEP IN THE RAFT!*"

Jacky opened her eyes and said weakly, "OK…"

Joshua looked at Jacky and continued, "The sooner we get to the raft the better. There are provisions on the raft to keep you warm… are you ready?"

"Yes… Yes, I am ready…"

"OK… here we go…"

Together, Joshua and Jacky began to swim toward the life raft. Behind them, the Titanic disappeared and one of the tsunami waves took them by surprise, pushing them toward the raft. Jacky screamed as the water and burning oil rushed up quickly from behind. It was like a hot hand pushing, shoving and burning at the same time. Joshua used his hands to keep the flames from igniting on Jacky's neck and back as they rode the wave.

Jacky screamed, "Oh Joshua… Help me… I'm burning… Help me…"

Joshua put his arms around Jacky's vest and said, "You're OK… You're OK… There was a wave from the Titanic… Its over now and the raft is much closer. Keep swimming… Please keep swimming"

As the two continued to struggle toward the raft, Joshua thought that he heard a voice call his name, "Joshua… Joshua… Over here… Over here!"

There was a brief moment when Joshua thought that he was delusional. He looked in the direction of the voice and saw Moosavi standing in the raft with his hand out stretched toward him. Was this a dream? Was he going out of his mind? How did Moosavi get to the raft? Wasn't he still on the Titanic? That's right, the Titanic sank… didn't it? Dr. Moosavi yelled, "Get to the raft quickly… I'll pull you both in… Come on… don't stop now… you can make it!"

Joshua told Jacky, "Swim hard darling, we are almost there…"

Jacky suddenly stopped swimming. Looking back, Joshua could see a look of terror on her face. She was motionless in the sea doing nothing but staring in the direction of Moosavi's voice. It was as if she had seen a ghost. She did not move. It was as if she had entered a catatonic state.

Moosavi saw Jacky seemingly staring at him and yelled, "*AUHSOJ!!*"

Suddenly, Jacky seemed to panic and tried to swim away from the raft. Joshua yelled, "Jacky... Jacky..." She did not respond and suddenly went limp, passing out from exposure and exhaustion. Her head bobbed back and forth with the motion of the sea as Joshua yelled to Moosavi, "Have you got a rope... She has passed out."

Moosavi disappeared into the covered life raft and returned with a rope. Kneeling over the lip of the raft, he threw the rope toward Joshua. It landed four feet short. Joshua grabbed Jacky's life vest pulling her along as he began to swim toward the raft yelling, "Try again..."

The rope was thrown again and landed a foot from Joshua's hand, "AGAIN..."

Finally, Joshua grabbed the rope and quickly tied it around Jacky's waist yelling, "Pull her in!"

Moosavi began to pull in the rope. Joshua swam toward the raft following Jacky.

Ten strokes later, Joshua was beside Jacky at the edge of the life raft. Moosavi reached for Jacky first and pulled her into the raft. Joshua waited for Moosavi to return to the opening. After what seemed like an eternity, Moosavi finally returned. He seemed to hesitate for several seconds as he stood silently looking down at Joshua and then reached down to offer his hand. Joshua grabbed at his arm and pulled himself in. As he entered the interior of the raft, Joshua could see Jacky sitting quietly. Her body was trembling from the cold. Her eyes were open and fixed. She seemed to be staring at Joshua, but Joshua knew that she could not see him. He fell to his knees beside her and said, "Jacky... Jacky darling, are you OK?"

Jacky made no reply as Joshua began to look around the raft, finding a small zipper storage compartment. Quickly, he removed the contents. In frustration, he yelled out the contents, "Bottled water, food, whistles, chemical cold lights, a flare gun, extra flares... Where are the blankets?" Joshua threw the contents about the raft in frustration and finally said, "Damn… You would think that they would have thought about blankets."

As he turned toward Moosavi, he saw the ASP 9mm in Moosavi's hand, the cold steel barrel reflecting dimly in the orange glow of the oil fire. Moosavi looked at Joshua and said, "I was going to shoot you in the sea, but then I wasn't sure that I could be certain that you were dead."

Joshua quickly reached for a bottle of water to throw at Moosavi. Moosavi saw the bottle. Using the gun as a wand he pointed to the floor of the raft and said, "Drop it…"

Dropping the water bottle, Joshua stood on his knees, "What is the meaning of this… I demand an answer."

Moosavi smiled as he squeezed the trigger sending a hot slug into Joshua's thigh, "I didn't give you permission to speak."

As Joshua cried out in pain, Moosavi continued, "The Jihad Mr. Prime Minister… as described in Islam is the holy war against infidels… Jews, Christians, Zoroastrians and Mandeans. Jihad is a duty that must be done by every Muslim like myself. There is no meaning of the word Jihad that you, a Jew, could possibly understand or appreciate, other than the simple fact that you are about to die."

"Kill me and you will be tracked down like a mad dog and killed."

"As I said earlier, you cannot understand the meaning of Jihad. If I am killed in a battle against infidels, I will become a martyr … a shahid and will be guaranteed a place in Paradise. Death does not frighten me as it does you."

Jacky remained silent as she listened to Moosavi's voice. Quietly, she felt around the floor of the raft. Her hand found the discarded water bottle. Making no outward sign, she continued to search.

"You Mr. Prime Minister are the sacrificial lamb that will be slain so that a new order… a new era can be born and allow for the peace of Islam to replace the slime and filth created by your infidel society. Your death will naturally summon the leaders of the free world to attend your memorial service in Israel as the death of King Hussein summoned the leaders of the world to Jordan. When that glorious day comes, your people and the other leaders of the so called free world who have trampled Muslims under their feet for centuries and who have not followed the teachings of Allah will join you in hell in a massive nuclear explosion delivered by Allah himself."

The pain in Joshua's leg altered his voice as he spat, "What are you talking about Moosavi… have you lost your mind?"

Moosavi stood, his legs wide apart. Slowly he raised the ASP 9mm. Jacky's hand reached behind her and felt the cold barrel of the flair gun. She quietly turned the gun around in her hand to find the grip. Her trembling finger encircled the trigger as she listened intently, using her ears to locate the direction of Moosavi's voice.

Moosavi continued, "This glorious night, the sinking of the Titanic, has been in the making for over ten years. Each part of the plan was carefully thought out and executed brilliantly by hundreds, if not thousands of Muslims like myself. All of the plans were made to get you to this very moment… here on your knees before me and about to die. Your bride was brainwashed and trained by me to be your assassin. Did you know that? She sent you your stupid ring because I told her to send it to you. She brought you to the Titanic so that you would walk into my hands. She married you and made love to you because I instructed her do so. She does not love you… She doesn't know the meaning of love… She can't because she is nothing more than a psychological robot… a mental zombie. She was going to kill you tonight in your wedding bed, but as you can see, there was a change in plans. You have no wedding bed… do you… HA… HAA… HAAA. I have decided that I will have the honor of killing you myself… and then Jacky will follow you. The raft will sink and both of you will… how do you say… will sleep with the fishes. When I am rescued, I will know nothing of your whereabouts and your people will believe that you went down with the ship… how tragic… how romantic… end of story."

In a quick swinging motion, Jacky brought the flare gun from behind her back. She aimed for the voice and squeezed the trigger. The flare gun made a large bang and the shell exited the barrel and flew directly into Moosavi's mouth. The ASP 9mm fired blindly into the side of the raft, puncturing the main flotation pontoon. The oil on Moosavi's face immediately ignited and quickly spread over his body. Dropping the ASP 9mm, Moosavi began to thrash about, beating the flames with his hands. Two seconds later, the magnesium charge in the flare exploded sending brilliant white flames exiting from his eyes, nose, mouth and ears. The impact of the flare entering his mouth and the subsequent explosion of the shell inside his head, knocked Moosavi backward out of the raft and into the sea. His life vest kept him upright in the water as his arms waved frantically about his head and face. Moments later, his arms went limp and hung quietly in the sea. The magnesium flare continued to burn inside of his skull, cooking his flesh and rendering his facial body fat as large sections of Moosavi's facial tissue slid off of the charred skull and into the sea. Inside the raft, Jacky sat motionless holding the smoking gun in her hand, her arms outstretched. Lowering the gun, she began to scream, "Is he dead? Is the bastard dead?"

Joshua remained silent for several seconds watching Jacky break down and cry. He removed the gun from her hand, placed his arms around her and said, "Yes... the bastard is dead..."

Suddenly from above, the pulsating drone of a V-22 Osprey filled the small confines of the raft. Towering above the tiny raft, the Osprey's twin 38-foot diameter props driven by the two Allison T406-AD-400 engines were tilted vertically and provided the lift to keep the aircraft stationary in the air. The craft hovered in the air like a prehistoric bird and then slowly descended toward the raft as two SEALs jumped from the aft tailgate into the sea. They swam to the raft yelling, "Is there anyone in the raft... Ahoy... Is there anyone in the raft?"

Joshua yelled back, "In here... Yes... In here..."

One of the SEALs reached the raft and pulled himself into the opening. Joshua extended his hand as the SEAL crawled over the rubber lip of the raft and fell inside. Quickly, he looked around and radioed to the Osprey pilot above, "There are two people in the raft..."

The second SEAL remained outside and watched as the crewmen of the Osprey lowered a rescue collar on a tether. Being blown by the wash of the 38-foot diameter props, the yellow collar swayed back and forth wildly as it descended to the sea. After two failed attempts, the SEAL finally grabbed the collar and yelled inside, "I have it... who goes first?"

Joshua said, "Send her up first... She is badly burned and cannot see."

The SEAL removed his Ka-Bar® and began to cut through the roof of the raft, "This has got to go." Moments later, the roof was cut to shreds and discarded into the sea. The force of the prop wash was now pounding the occupants of the raft like a blast of air from a hurricane. The noise from the Osprey was deafening as the props chopped mightily through the air sending tiny droplets of seawater through the air like grains of sand in a sandblaster. The water hit the Joshua in the face as he tried to shield Jacky's face with his body. Jacky screamed as the water hit her blistered eyes and face. Quickly, the collar was secured under her arms and a secondary safety strap was fastened around her waist. Joshua gently placed his hands on each side of Jacky's face and held her gently, "Jacky... listen to me. You are going to be hoisted to the aircraft above. It is about fifty feet above us. Hold on and don't let go. In a few minutes, you will be safe and warm."

Jacky said nothing as the slack in the line was taken up. Slowly, she began to ascend toward the Osprey. Joshua stood silently and watched as the SEALS in the Osprey pulled her into the aircraft. Moments later, they sent the collar down for Joshua.

Sitting quietly in his raft fifty yards away, Boris watched the Osprey rescue mission. Raising his binoculars, he watched the SEALs pull Jacky into the aircraft. Slowly, he returned his attention and scrutiny to the occupants in the raft below. As he looked at Joshua staring upwards, he suddenly leaned forward, pressing the eyepieces closely to his face. There was a quickening in his breathing as he held the glasses steady and looked at the face of the man he thought he recognized, but could not believe was alive. The Captain had posted pictures of the Prime Minister in the sub galley. He didn't have the picture with him now, but he was sure that the man was Joshua Cane. He held the glasses to his chest as he closed his eyes trying to see Joshua's picture in his mind. How could he still be alive? Slowly, he looked through the glasses, studying the face again. Yes… there was no doubt about it. The man standing in the raft was the Prime Minister of Israel, the man he and his crew were sworn to kill.

Resting on his back on the raft, Boris replayed the mental images of the final moments of his comrade's lives. He remembered the wake of his sub's torpedoes racing towards the Titanic. He saw the P-3C Orion drop two torpedoes that went after his sub and relived the moment when his sub surfaced and fired a ground to air missile at the P-3C Orion. He closed his eyes as he remembered the resulting simultaneous explosions of the Titanic, sub and Orion. In an instant, his sub and his comrades were gone. Anger and hatred filled his mind as he opened his eyes. They were now steely gray and were fixed on the image of Joshua Cane still standing in the raft. His sub and crew were lost and for what? Anger filled his mind as he reached for his AK-47.

Joshua reached for the collar and placed it over his head and arms. The SEAL secured the safety strap around his waist. He radioed, "Send him up."

At the same time, Boris raised the AK-47 and lined up his shot, but suddenly, there was a lurching force that violently pushed the raft forward, knocking Boris into the sea. He dropped the AK-47 and fought his way to the surface. As his head broke through the waves, something grabbed him like a vice. In an instant, he was lifted out of the water like a periscope mast and was carried through the sea in a zigzag motion. Boris began to scream as the teeth of a great white bit into his flesh.

Joshua was looking up toward the Osprey as the frantic high-pitched screams from Boris were being drowned out by the Allison engines. Momentarily, he looked down and saw the horrible sight of Boris being eaten alive. Suddenly, Boris vanished beneath the sea as the great white bit through his thighs and waist. Twenty feet away, Boris surfaced again briefly as he gurgled blood from his mouth, his screams were high pitched and his arms were thrashing frantically about. The shark took another large bite and Boris vanished beneath the waves for the last time. Only his black knit hat remained behind floating silently in the sea.

Joshua watched in horror and finally turned his head back to the Osprey. Two SEALs quickly grabbed him and pulled him into the aircraft. One of the SEALS radioed down to the SEALs below, "We are sending the collar down for you guys, better get the hell out of there before you guys become the main course."

One of the SEALs replied, "Roger that… Things are getting very nasty down here."

CHAPTER ELEVEN

Colonel Allan sat motionless as he listened to the voice traffic of the rescue teams. His eyes were red and his face was drawn from the events of the night. He looked defeated. In his hand was a cup of tea. The cup rested between his open palms as he rolled the cup back and forth between them. In one night, he had lost the lives of a Los Angeles class sub, a P-3C Orion and the Titanic. Thousands of people had died because he had failed to solve the puzzle. Deep in his heart, he knew that the Prime Minister of Israel was dead. He could not fathom the consequences of his death on international politics. Who was responsible? Why did it happen? What did they have in mind next? Allan leaned forward as he listened to one of the reports of the rescue team. Quietly he sipped from the cup of tea, "We have two people rescued from a raft... male and female. The female is badly burned from the fuel oil fire. We have tentative identification of both parties as being a Mr. and Mrs. Joshua Cane..." The cup of tea fell from Colonel Allan's hand and shattered as it hit the floor. Allan looked at Admiral Potter. Potter stood and said, "Praise God..."

Reaching for the microphone, Allan yelled, "This is Colonel Allan... Say again... who did you rescue?"

"A male Joshua Cane and a female Jacky McGuire... Over."

"The man Joshua Cane is the Prime Minister of Israel... Is he OK?"

"Roger... He has a leg wound from a gun shot, fractured ribs and is suffering from exposure, but he will be OK as soon as we can get him back to the base and in a hospital... Over."

"Do not take him back to the base... I want him taken to Andrews Air Force base immediately... Do you copy..."

"Roger... but we will need refueling to make the trip... over..."

"You just fly that aircraft son... I'll see to it that you get refueled... over and out."

The remaining SEALs were plucked from the sea as the Osprey began to change the position of the rotor assembly to a horizontal flying position. Minutes later, the aircraft soared westerly into the darkness leaving behind the flaming wreckage of the Titanic.

Joshua held Jacky's head tenderly on his lap as the three SEALs kept the rear door open and began to toss out unnecessary gear. Rafts, guns and anything that could go was discarded out of the rear of the craft. Two of the SEALs made a makeshift bed using a partially inflated one-man raft as an air mattress. Together, Joshua and the two SEALs placed Jacky into the raft; she was shivering from the cold and moaning softly. Her arms lay limp across her breast as one of the SEALs covered her with a blanket that had been stowed away in a compartment of the craft marked Survival Gear. Another SEAL removed the first aid kit. He opened it and quickly removed the packages of bandages and a tube of hydro gel and sat next to Joshua.

"Her eyes... She cannot see..." Jacky lay motionless as the SEAL removed a syringe from the First Aid kit and broke the seal. Looking for a safe point of entry, he jabbed the syringe into Jacky's arm.

"This is morphine... it will kill the pain for a while." The SEAL looked at Jacky's burnt hair and blisters that covered her arms, chest, neck and head. "She is badly burned from the fuel oil fire. Did you say that she could not see?"

"Yes... the fire hurt her eyes... She told me several times that she could not see." Tears began to roll down Joshua's cheek, "Is she going to make it..."

The SEAL took a small flashlight from his utility belt and shined it directly into Jacky's eyes. She was lying on her back face up. Her pupils responded slowly as the SEAL placed the light directly in her eyes and removed it quickly several times. Saying nothing, he reached for a tube of hydro gel and began to spread the gel over her forehead, cheeks and chin. Joshua looked at him and said, "Are her eyes OK...?"

"She is badly burned around her face. I am not a doctor and only know a few things... her pupils responded to the light and that is good. Beyond that... I don't know. Help me put this gel on her burns and stay away from her eyes."

The Seal stood up and searched around the cabin several times and then returned to Jacky's side with a tennis ball, "I use this for hand exercising to pass the time." Using his Ka-Bar®, he sliced the ball into two equal halves. He next placed two gauze squares over Jacky's eyes and then placed the tennis ball halves over the gauze.

"Hold her head so I can bandage her face." Gently, the SEAL applied more hydro gel cream to Jacky's burns and then started wrapping Jacky's head in the gauze strips, being careful to leave a space for her nose and mouth. He then turned his attention to her arms and hands. In less than ten minutes, Jacky resembled an Egyptian mummy with her head and arms wrapped in gauze and her arms folded across her chest.

"That's about all I can do I'm afraid. We will keep her warm and sedated until we get to Andrews and they will take it from there."

"How long will it take to get there... she is so badly burned..."

The SEAL stood and approached the cockpit. Leaning over between the pilot and co-pilot he said, "How long before we get to Andrews..."

"About four hours plus a refueling rendezvous... barring any problems there... between four and five hours."

"Any way to make it any faster...?"

"Yea... dump anything we don't need out the back. Everything helps. Say, by the way... you do know who that guy is don't you... The Prime Minister of Israel and his wife!!"

The SEAL said nothing as he returned to Joshua and his men. "Listen up... lets get everything that is not nailed down and throw it out the back… I mean everything. We have to get these people to Andrews ASAP. The lighter we make this crate, the faster she will fly." Looking down at Joshua, the SEAL said, "Don't worry Mr. Prime Minister… She will be fine. You have my word as a SEAL on that. Now let me look at that leg of yours." The SEAL ripped the trousers exposing the gunshot wound. It was a blood-encrusted hole in Joshua's leg. The bleeding had stopped, but the area around the wound was angry and swollen. "Can you stand up or bend your knee? I want to see the other side of your leg."

Joshua stood and the seal ripped off the rest of the trousers. "Good… there is an exit wound. The slug passed through your leg, missing the leg bone or you wouldn't be standing right now."

The SEAL placed two gauze squares on each side of the leg covering the bullet wounds and gently bandaged the leg, "This should hold you until we get to Andrews… You are a very lucky man Mr. Prime Minister… That slug could have hit an artery and you could have bled to death or it could have hit and shattered your leg bone, leaving you a cripple for the rest of your life. Now… lets have a look at those ribs."

Opening another package, the SEAL removed an Ace® bandage and proceeded to wrap Joshua's chest tightly to give his ribs support and then helped Joshua as he sat next to Jacky.

"Thank you for your help…"

"Think nothing of it Mr. Prime Minister… It's all in a days work…"

Joshua looked for a name or something to identify the SEAL by and said, "Call me Joshua please… uh… uh…"

"Call me Ben, Mr. Prime Minister… Now you cover up and get some sleep, I'll let you know when we get close to Andrews."

ANDREWS AIR FORCE BASE, 0700 HOURS

Andrews Air Force Base lies ten miles southeast of Washington, D.C., in Prince George's County Maryland. It is the home of Air

Force One, the Presidents aircraft and is also the home of the 89th Airlift Wing that provides for safe and reliable worldwide airlift and logistical support for the President of the United States, the vice president, cabinet members and other high-ranking civilian and foreign government officials. The base also is host to more than 60 separate organizations that include operating units from the Army, Navy, Marine Corps and the Air Force Reserve. In all, more than 26,000 people live and work at Andrews.

Colonel Allan and Admiral Potter arrived at the base through a remote entrance along with a host of other military brass and secret service agents. The procession of black Lincolns proceeded slowly to a remote tarmac on the air base and parked next to three helicopters, two medical choppers and one military. Teams of doctors and nurses huddled together in small groups and orderlies leaned forward against two gurneys.

Allan and Potter waited inside their car talking quietly. The tension in their voices of a few hours earlier was now replaced by the tone of exhaustion and the need for sleep. The sky was gray and overcast with visibility of five miles. The tarmac was wet from rain and small puddles that reflected the fleet of cars like pieces of a broken mirror scattered across the ground. It had just stopped raining twenty minutes earlier. A host of armed military police dressed in full battle gear approached in double time, splashing through the puddles of water and quickly formed a large circle on the tarmac. The secret service men exited their cars and joined the military police forming a second, but larger circle around the military police. They too carried their weapons in their hands, their eyes looking forward, looking for anything unusual. Colonel Allan rubbed his bloodshot eyes and worn face with his hands as he squinted into the cloudy morning sky and said, "How many souls were lost last night?"

Admiral Potter replied sadly, "The final reports are not yet in, but it looks very bad… I think perhaps only fifteen to twenty people… perhaps fifty at most were rescued from 2,214 souls aboard the Titanic… and some of them will probably die before they get to hospital. The

Titanic sank in roughly ten minutes after the torpedoes hit her and split her in half. The poor bastards never had a chance. The passengers and crew of the Titanic perished either in the oil fire that engulfed the two sections of the Titanic, died from hypothermia or sharks in the sea or simply never made it off the ship before she sank. It all happened so fast that the lifeboats could not be launched. Only the automatically inflatable rafts provided sanctuary for those lucky enough to make it to them. Added to the list of the dead is the crew of the Tiger Shark and the P-3C Orion both lost in action, as well as the crew of the Kilo sub that started this fucking mess. Who were they and why did this happen?"

Allan looked toward the sky and replied, "Whoever they are and whatever their purpose for doing this will be ascertained and appropriate actions will be taken… that I can assure you Admiral. How about the press? Do they know about this?"

"Not all of it… they know that the Titanic issued an SOS, but they have not found out about the Prime Minister or the sinking. All they know it something has happened, but they will probably find out soon enough."

"I want the Prime Minister's presence here in Washington and his survival kept under wraps for the time being. I don't even want the Israeli government notified until I have a chance to debrief the Prime Minister and speak with the President. Something is eating at my gut and it tells me that it, as Yogi Berra would say, ain't over till it's over… and it ain't over. I want a lid put on this thing until we have had a chance to digest everything we will hear from the Prime Minister and his wife."

The Osprey suddenly descended through the cloudbank and made a wide starboard turn toward the tarmac. The drone of the Allison engines filled the air. As it descended, the blades of the rotor system cut a 38-foot diameter circle through the air sending ribbons of mist trailing off the wing tips. Allan and Potter watched as the Osprey approached and began to turn the rotor assembly from a horizontal forward position to a vertical lift position. The craft's forward motion slowed as the rotors turned. With her nose up, the craft seemed to drift upward slightly as the forward motion of the craft stopped. The Osprey now resembled a gigantic double bladed eggbeater, hovering two hundred feet above the tarmac. The army guards and secret service men widened the diameter of their protective circle, standing stoically like the stone statues on Easter Island, their firearms in their hands, their backs to the tarmac and their eyes searching for anything unusual.

The Osprey rotated its position in the air like a second hand on a clock and faced its nose in the direction of a man holding a flashlight in each hand. The man stood with his arms stretched outward, pointing one flashlight at nine o'clock with his right hand and three o'clock with his left. The roar of the Allison engines became increasingly louder as the Osprey increased the pitch of the rotor blades, beginning its descent. The wash from the props shot downward creating a swirling mist from the puddles on the tarmac. In an instant the army guards, secret service men, Allan and Potter were drenched. As the Osprey descended lower, the man with the flashlights began to raise his arms toward the imaginary twelve o'clock position and then, he formed a cross with the flashlights. Instantly, the pilot of the Osprey cut the Allison engines. Two secret service men ran under the craft with wheel blocks placing them fore and aft of the tires. The Osprey rocked gently on its suspension as the blades came to a stop. The tailgate began to open and in an instant, the two secret service men took positions on each side of the ramp as the teams of medical doctors, nurses and orderlies entered the tail section of the Osprey. Moments later, Jacky was placed on a gurney and carried off of the Osprey to an awaiting helicopter that would take her to Bethesda Medical Center. Seconds later, the Prime Minister was removed from the Osprey and placed in a second helicopter. Allan did not want both of them on the same craft fearing that if one somehow crashed, he would never know what had happened aboard the Titanic. Watching silently, he waited until both helicopters were in the air and then approached a third chopper that would take him and Potter to Bethesda.

The airlift to Bethesda took less than twenty minutes. The hospital had been notified of their impending arrival and the entire landing pad, hospital grounds and hospital had been cordoned off by the secret service. A cover story was released explaining that a disaster drill involving the supposed injury of the President and the First Lady would be taking place and to expect helicopters. The three helicopters approached Bethesda in typical military formation. First the helicopter carrying Jacky landed, then the Prime Minister's chopper touched down and finally Allan's and Potter's. Within minutes, Jacky and the Prime Minister were rolled into the medical units on the third deck. Allan and Potter waited outside the operating suites in the waiting room. The secret police took their positions in the halls.

In less than an hour, the Prime Minister was rolled out of surgery and placed in the President's suite. The doctor approached Colonel Allan and said, "He will be fine. He suffered a bullet wound in his right thigh that passed through the muscle tissue without hitting any vital arteries or shattering any bones and he received two fractured ribs as he jumped from the Titanic into the sea. He is also suffering from exposure and has first and second degree burns on his chest, arms, hands and face. You should be able to speak with him in about three hours. He will experience some pain, but we will get him out of bed and up and around tomorrow."

Allan looked relieved and then asked, "… and his wife?"

"Dr. Greene is still in surgery with her. She suffered second and third degree burns to her chest, arms, hands, face and eyes. She too is suffering from exposure but she is in good hands with Dr. Greene. Nevia is an excellent optical surgeon… the best we have. I am sure that she will be fine."

Allan looked at the doctor's and said, "Optical surgeon??"

"The Prime Minister's wife has severe burns to her face. She told us that she could not see and Dr. Greene was brought in to assess her condition."

Allan looked at Potter and said, "Thank you doctor for your report."

"Dr. Greene will fill you in on Mrs. Cane I am sure."

The doctor left the waiting room leaving Allan and Potter alone to themselves. Minutes passed without a word between the two men. Allan sat back in a padded chair, placed his feet on a coffee table and rubbed his eyes and said, "When is the President going to arrive?"

Potter looked at his watch and replied, "I would guess that he has been informed about the Prime Minister's condition… I would dare say in about an hour or less. I am sure that he will want to speak with us before he visits the Prime Minister."

"I am not sure what we can tell him at this point, all we have is a lot of ideas that are fairly well founded, but nothing you could hang your hat on. What we need is to speak with the Prime Minister and find out what really happened out there."

"The President is no fool. I am sure that he will listen to us and make a decision to let us debrief the Prime Minister as soon as possible."

Allan used his arms to lift himself out of the chair and leaned forward to turn on the television set that sat in the corner of the room. The tube suddenly became alive and the stern face of a ZNN news anchorman glared back at Allan. Reaching for the remote, Allan turned up the volume, "Repeating our breaking news, the Titanic sank in the Atlantic approximately 1200 miles from its final destination, New York City. Initial reports are that there are very few survivors." The tube suddenly changed and the image of a massive oil fire flickered into view.

"This live footage is being broadcast from the scene by one of our news camera crews. As you can see there is no sign of the Titanic. If you look closely, you can see a few rubber rafts in the area."

The image of an Osprey darted through the view as the voice of the anchorman continued, "Hello Keith, can you describe what you are seeing?"

"Yes I can… the sea is ablaze with a massive oil fire, presumably from the fuel tanks of the Titanic. The military is flying rescue missions using the Osprey to send down divers. The divers are searching the area for survivors."

The camera operator zoomed into the flames and the image of burning bodies littered the television tube, "As you can see, there are a lot of bodies floating in their life vests, on fire and presumed dead."

"Have you seen anyone rescued?"

"Not really… no let me take that back. About ten minutes ago, we saw three people being hoisted up to the hovering Osprey aircraft." The camera again zoomed into the fire and the image of a burning body suddenly shot through the water and then disappeared beneath the sea. The voice continues, "Things are really getting bad down there. From the looks of it, sharks are feeding on the dead bodies… God… this is a really awful…"

The tense face of the anchorman suddenly reappeared as he continued, "The Titanic sent out a distress call earlier this evening. All communications with the Titanic ceased at that time. Our news organization responded with an inquiry to the Coast Guard and received no information regarding the status of the Titanic. Our news team arrived at the scene approximately fifteen minutes ago and began transmitting the pictures that you just saw. As incredible as it sounds, the Titanic apparently sank at the exact location of the original Titanic disaster. It is also reported that the Prime Minister of Israel, Joshua Cane and his new bride were also on board the Titanic. It is not known if the Prime Minister or his wife survived this tragic event."

Allan hit the mute button and said, "Shit!"

Potter looked at Allan and finally said, "We have very little time. The Israeli government will be contacting the White House and demanding information about the Prime Minister. We must move fast."

There was a bell sound in the hallway as the elevator door opened and several secret service men turned the corner approaching Allan and Potter. The President followed behind the secret service men as two more secret service men followed him. Both Allan and Potter stood at attention and saluted the President. The President returned the salute and said, "Colonel Allan... Admiral Potter..."

They both replied, "Mr. President."

"How is the Prime Minister doing?"

"He should be able to see you Mr. President in about an hour..."

"The God damn press have the story now and are plastering it all over the airways."

Allan replied, "Yes Mr. President... we just saw it for the first time a few minutes ago." and pointed to the muted television set.

The President continued, "Would you believe that those bastards flew a private jet with a camera crew to the area... The Israeli government is now demanding to know what happened to the Prime Minister and you... are requesting that his rescue be kept a secret... Why Colonel Allan?"

"Mr. President, there is strong evidence that suggests that there is a massive plan unfolding before our eyes. If someone or some government wanted to simply kill the Prime Minister, why hide a sub under an iceberg? Why not just put a bomb on the ship or simply place their sub at the spot where the Titanic would be and sink her? Why all of the James Bond bullshit? There was a firefight on the Titanic between several terrorists and the Prime Minister's bodyguards. Last night, we lost the Titanic, Tiger Shark and her crew, a P-3C Orion and her crew and the Kilo sub went down fighting like a son-of-a-bitch! Admiral Potter and I do not think that whatever is going on is over. We must talk with the Prime Minister and find out what he knows. It is very possible that he or his wife may hold the key to unlocking this mystery."

The President stood silently for several seconds weighing the magnitude of the disaster and probability that Allan and Potter were on to something. Finally he replied, "You really think that there is something going on and I can respect that. As soon as the Prime Minister is awake, debrief him and report to me immediately with your findings. However, remember this, keeping the Prime Minister here against his will and not telling the Israeli government is tantamount to kidnapping their head of state. If we do that... we had better have a very good fucking reason."

Allan saluted the President and said, "Thank you Mr. President."

The President smiled and returned the salute, "Tell the Prime Minister that I will visit with him and his wife as soon as the doctors give their permission." The President entered the elevator and paused, "Better make sure he doesn't have a damn TV in that suite. Let me get back to the White House and put up a smoke screen. It won't last forever, so work fast gentlemen." The elevator doors closed as Allan and Potter looked at each other silently and then returned to the waiting room and turned up the volume as they watched the continuing coverage of the disaster.

Thirty minutes later, the White House press secretary, Chuck Balling, made an official announcement regarding the sinking of the Titanic and the Prime Minister, "The President has extended his deepest sympathy to the families of the passengers and crew of the Titanic. Every effort is being made to rescue any and all survivors. The survivors are being airlifted to Andrews Air Force Base. At the present time, there is no information regarding the whereabouts of the Prime Minister of Israel. It is hoped that he and his wife are among the survivors."

Potter looked at Allan and said, "That gives us about four hours."

The door to the OR opened and Jacky was rolled down the hall and placed in another suite adjacent to the Presidential suite. Moments later, Dr. Nevia Greene pushed open the door, removed her surgical mask from around her neck. Dr. Greene was a native of Columbia, born in the small town of Bahia, about 750 miles north of Rio. She had arrived in America at the age of seven and worked hard in school receiving scholarships from the Harvard medical school. She joined the Navy and was described by her superiors as a career Navy woman. Placing the mask in the trashcan, she looked up and flashed her beautiful smile. Her white teeth and beautiful smile flashed across her light brown face. She saluted and then extending her hand to

Colonel Allan and Admiral Potter she said, "I am Dr. Greene. It is a pleasure to meet you."

Allan led Dr. Greene to the waiting area and offered her a chair. Both Allan and Potter placed their chairs in front of hers and sat down. Allan spoke first, "Tell me about the Prime Minister's wife…"

"She is badly burned about the face. Most of her hair was burned off and her eyes were severely damaged by the fire. Her right eye will require a cornea transplant, but she should regain most of her sight in her left eye in a few days. She will require some plastic surgery to her face and other parts of her arms and chest."

"When can I speak with her Dr. Greene?"

"Not until tomorrow I am afraid. She is heavily sedated and her eyes and face are bandaged which will make speaking difficult."

"This is a matter of national security Dr. Greene, we must speak with her as soon as possible."

Dr. Greene stood and said, "Like I said, sometime tomorrow she should be awake. I will remove some of the facial bandages so she can speak to you, but I must warn you both, she will be in a great deal of pain for the next few days. I cannot allow you to jeopardize her health or recovery."

"Thank you Dr. Greene…"

Dr. Greene left the waiting room as a nurse approached Colonel Allan, "The Prime Minister is awake and wants to speak with you."

Allan and Potter walked swiftly to the door of the Presidential suite knocked softly and quietly entered the room. The Prime Minister's bed was cranked up so that he was sitting up in bed. His arms and hands were bandaged, but he looked fully awake. His voice was raspy but friendly, "Please come in." Allan and Potter approached the bed.

"Mr. Prime Minister, I am Colonel Allan and this is Admiral Potter. There are some questions that we need to ask you about last night."

The Prime Minister winced in pain as he adjusted his position in bed and replied, "…and there are things that I need to tell the President that are of the utmost urgency."

"The President asked me to tell you that he will see you as soon as the doctors feel that you are up to it. He also asked me to speak with you at this time on his behalf. Before we begin however, let me say that your wife is well and recovering from her injuries in the next suite."

"How are her eyes?"

"She will see again Mr. Prime Minister. I spoke briefly with her doctor a few moments ago and she assures me that she will be fine. Today however, they are keeping her sedated, but you should be able to see her tomorrow."

"Thank you for your thoughtfulness…"

"What is it that you need to tell the President?"

"The sinking of the Titanic was designed to be a cover for my assassination. The plan was carried out by Iraqi extremists who are using the Jihad as an excuse to wage war against my country, the US and anyone else that does not agree with them."

"How do you know this?"

"Dr. Moosavi, who was my wife's doctor and psychiatrist, was an Iraqi operative. He was in charge of my assassination. When the Titanic exploded, Captain Smith escorted Jacky and I to the boat deck…. Did he make it?"

"I am afraid not," replied Potter.

"Captain Smith was a very brave and honorable man." The Prime Minister paused and then continued, "Captain Smith realized that the life boats could not be launched and took us to the boat deck section that had rubber rafts. He deployed them and then instructed that Jacky and I jump into the sea and swim to them for safety. The oil fire was everywhere and Jacky was badly burned. Somehow Moosavi got to a raft and then helped rescue the both of us. Once inside the raft however, he turned into a mad man, shot me in the leg and began to rave about the final Jihad."

Potter leaned forward in his chair and said, "Take your time Mr. Prime Minister. It is very important that you try to remember exactly what he said."

The Prime Minister closed his eyes and placed his head back on the pillow. "I will never forget his voice and that look in his eyes until the day I die. I think that I can quote him… Yes… He said…"This glorious night, the sinking of the Titanic, has been in the making for over ten years. Each part of the plan was carefully thought out and executed brilliantly by hundreds, if not thousands of Muslims like myself. All of the plans were made to get you to this very moment… here on your knees and about to die. Your bride was brainwashed and trained by me to be your assassin. Did you know that? She sent you your stupid ring because I told her to send it to you. She brought you to the Titanic so that you would walk into my hands. She married you and made love to you because I instructed her do so. She does not love you… She doesn't know the meaning of love… She can't because she is nothing more than a psychological robot… a mental zombie. She was going to kill you tonight in your wedding bed, but as you can see, there was a change in plans. You have no wedding bed… do you… HA… HAA… HAAA. I have decided that I will have the honor of killing you myself… and then Jacky will follow you. The raft will sink and both of you will… how do you say… will sleep with the fishes. When I am rescued, I will know nothing of your whereabouts and your people will believe that you went down with the ship… how tragic… how romantic… end of story!"

Potter spoke softly, "Did he say anything else that might suggest what this was all about Mr. Prime Minister?"

The Prime Minister wiped a tear from his eye and took a slow deep breath and replied, "Yes… You Mr. Prime Minister are the sacrificial lamb that will be slain so that a new order… a new era can be born and allow for the peace of Islam to replace the slime and filth created by your infidel society. Your death will naturally summons the leaders of the free world to attend your memorial service in Israel as the death of King Hussein summonsed the leaders of the world to Jordan. When that glorious day comes, your people and the other leaders of the so called free world who have trampled Muslims under their feet for centuries and who have not followed the teachings of

Allah will join you in hell in a massive nuclear explosion delivered by Allah himself."

Allan looked at Potter and replied, "My God..."

Potter sat back in his chair and said, "It fits like a glove. The missing sub, the one that was supposed to have sunk while it was being delivered to Iran, was used to hide under the iceberg and get into firing position to sink the Titanic. Our SOSUS system prevented them from just driving to the spot and wait in ambush... they knew that we would hear them and get curious if we heard them tooling around in the Atlantic. It would seem that they had two plans, the sub and Mrs. Cane. If one failed, the other would be a backup plan and the Prime Minister would be dead regardless. Moosavi was right, if the Prime Minister were killed, there would be a state funeral and every nation friendly to Israel would send their head of state. At that moment, they would launch a nuclear strike and kill them all... brilliant... absolutely brilliant."

Allan looked at Potter and said, "Who is behind all of this?"

"Iraq of course with a little help from their friends, the Muslim extremist... Bin Laden and the like. The use of the word Jihad by Moosavi is most telling. During the Six Day War, you never heard mention of the word. During the last ten years however, the Muslim extremist have been lashing out against the United States and have been funding terrorism all over the world blowing up our embassies, the World Trade Center in New York in '93 and again last year. These people believe that it is their duty to Allah to kill Jews and others that do not believe and practice Islamic religion. This plan of theirs would wipe out all heads of state of the countries that they hate, create a state of political instability, and... would probably be the beginning of an all out war with Israel and the United States. In their religion, they believe that the end of the world will come only if Israel is destroyed. They also believe that if they die in this Jihad, they will go to paradise. If they start World War III, so be it. To them, nothing matters but their belief that they are doing Allah's work. This is a very serious matter. We must speak with the President as soon as possible."

THE WHITE HOUSE, 1300 HOURS

The President had requested an emergency meeting with his National Security Council. In 1947, the National Security Act created the National Security Council (NSC) to consider national security issues that would require a command decision by the President of the United States. The NSC consisted of the President, the Vice President, the Secretary of State and the Secretary of Defense. Also in line to assist the President and the NSC was the Chairman of the Joint Chiefs of Staff and the Director of Central Intelligence (CIA). One by one, the black limos drove leisurely through the streets of Washington, the cherry blossoms reflecting their soft pink presence off of the black polished hoods of the cars. Approaching the gate of the White House, the drivers rolled down their windows and the MP checked their credentials and that of the passengers they were carrying.

The first to arrive was the Chairman of the Joint Chiefs of Staff, Admiral Lewis Daniel Sheppard. Admiral Sheppard had joined the Navy in 1965 and was assigned to sea duty during the Viet Nam conflict. Sheppard had quickly moved up the ranks from Lieutenant Commander, to Commander and finally Captain before serving as Assistant Secretary of the Navy and Executive Assistant to the Chief of Naval Operations. Prior to his assuming the position of Chairman of the Joint Chiefs of Staff, Sheppard served as the Director for Operations (J-3), Joint Staff and briefly as Director of the Joint Staff. Sheppard was known for having the Wisdom of Solomon, the elocution of Patrick Henry and the balls of John Paul Jones. At 54 years of age, he was at his prime and greatly respected by the President.

Twenty minutes later, the second limo arrived carrying the Director of Central Intelligence, Mark B. Crowley. Crowley was newly appointed by the President and had been confirmed by the Senate Select Committee on Intelligence and the full Senate. Crowley had previously served as Special Assistant to President Reagan. Hand picked by the President, Crowley spoke softly, but was well known to carry a big stick and use it freely if needed. The CIA had been established in 1947 with the creation of the National Security Act and signed into law by President Harry S. Truman. The charter of the CIA was to coordinate the country's intelligence activities at home and abroad regarding matters that would affect the national security. Crowley loved his job and being unmarried, lived at Langley forever reading intelligence reports from around the world. His special interest and passion was the Middle East.

Pulling in next was Secretary of State, Nick Scrivanich, the first Croatian descendent Secretary of State. Scrivanich was a 28-year military veteran, who had reached the rank of four-star General in the Air Force. During the Gulf War, he served as Director of the Joint Chiefs of Staff and was very concerned with the recent 18-month build up of military weapons by Iraq. He rarely smiled and had earned the nickname once given to General McArthur "Blood and Guts" by his comrades in arms. Scrivanich loved only three things in life, his country, his job and in particular, serving the President of the United States as Secretary of State.

The limo carrying the Secretary of Defense was last to arrive, the Honorable Douglas Q. Cali. Cali had served in Viet Nam in the Army and retired from the Army with the rank of three-star General. Cali entered private business, running a large aerospace company and serving on the board of directors for several large defense contractors before being called to Washington to serve in an advisory capacity for two Republican administrations. He was no stranger to the Washington scene and knew not only where the ropes were, but also how to pull them to get the job done. His passion was technology. Cali had been behind the scenes during the development of the Stealth Bomber and followed each sortie that flew missions in Desert Storm like a kid watching a war movie at a Saturday afternoon matinee. He had been chosen for Secretary of Defense because of his innate ability to understand the military, the military industrial complex and to make the tough decisions quickly and correctly in time of need.

Once inside the White House, the men were escorted to the Oval office. The four men arrived one at a time and took their seats quietly; the President sat with his back to the room looking out of the Oval office window, lost in thought. When Secretary of Defense Cali arrived, they all looked to the President saying nothing. As Cali took his seat, the President swiveled around in his chair and looked up for the first time. Quietly he stood and addressed the gathering, "I have called this emergency meeting of the National Security Council regarding a matter of grave importance to the security of Israel and the United States. I am sure that you all know about the Titanic... sinking in the Atlantic, the loss of the Tiger Shark and one of our P-3C Orions. What you don't know is that the Prime Minister of Israel and his wife are alive and safe in the Bethesda Naval Hospital."

There was a quiet shuffling noise that filled the room as each of the men leaned forward in unison hanging on every word spoken by the President. "The Prime Minister and his wife were rescued by one of our Osprey aircraft and flown directly to Andrews Air Force base this morning. Both have received medical treatment, the Prime Minister was shot in the leg and his wife suffers from second-degree burns to her upper body and face. She cannot see at the moment, but is expected to recover completely in a few months. My purpose for calling this meeting is to discuss the Prime Minister and his wife's rescue by our military and to possibly withhold information of their rescue by us... In short gentlemen, kidnapping them for a while."

Scrivanich spoke softly, "Mr. President... by what right do we kidnap anyone?"

"That is just the point, we have no right..."

Cali spoke next, "I would guess that there is something that we do not know at the present time that has made this act a definite possibility in your mind Mr. President?"

"Yes there is. This situation has been followed almost from the start by Colonel Allan and Admiral Potter of our intelligence department."

Crowley replied, "Yes, both of them are good men. What have they told you?"

"They are currently on their way here to fill us in on their debriefing of the Prime Minister, but they believe that there is a bigger plot unfolding..."

Allan and Potter were suddenly ushered into the Oval Office by two security guards.

The President sat in his seat and waited until the two men approached the table and sat down.

The President looked at the two men and said, "What did you find out?"

Admiral Potter placed his glasses on the end of his nose, looked at Colonel Allan and said, "Mr. President... it is very apparent that the sinking of the Titanic was a direct act of terrorism that was designed as a cover to kill the Prime Minister and to unleash a plot to kill the heads of state of the free world by launching a nuclear holocaust during the state funeral for the Prime Minister."

Everyone in the room remained silent as they listened intently to Admiral Potter, "This plan has been in the making for about ten years... since the Gulf War. I believe that it is being orchestrated by Iraq and Muslim extremists who are working together in unison. Despite our best efforts since 9/11, Muslim extremist cells are in hiding in Afghanistan and Pakistan. Pakistan has nuclear capability and would probably sell a few bombs to the extremists if the price were right. Our satellite surveillance of Iraq and Afghanistan did show a recent truck convoy heading into Iraq from Afghanistan. We believe that the origin of the convoy was Pakistan. We have not had any UN investigators inside of Iraq for almost 42 months... God knows what they have been up to and have had time to build."

The President asked, "Where did the convoy go once it was inside Iraq?"

"All three of the trucks split up. Their final destination was three mosques spread across Iraq to Baghdad, Al Basra and Irbil. As you know, the UN inspection forces were never allowed access due to the Iraqi claim that the mosques were religious sanctuaries. The mosques in question are new and large enough to hold a short to medium range missile that could hit Israel and God knows where else with a nuclear bomb."

The President turned to the Cali and said, "I didn't think that the SCUDS were that reliable."

"The SCUD is not the weapon of choice Mr. President. China and others are selling missiles."

"What about our embargo?"

"China has violated the embargo for quite some time as you know. They or some other country could have sold them directly to Iraq or the extremists could purchase and arrange for the delivery of the missiles to Iraq and we could not stop them. The embargo is only good as long as other countries respect it."

The President stood and walked slowly around the table. "Sounds fucking serious."

Cali replied, "Our boys could go in there and knock out the mosques in question without any problem Mr. President."

"What if your boys don't get them all? What if they don't have them in the mosques, but have them somewhere else? If we were wrong and if they do have weapons of mass destruction… and if we don't get them, all they would have to do is hide them and blame us for blowing up their mosques… the United States would be crucified by the rest of the world! Then, they could create another plan designed to use the bombs somewhere else like Washington D.C., New York or God knows where. We must know where they are before we send your boys in."

The Secretary of State spoke up and said, "Smoke them out Mr. President."

"How?"

"Colonel Allan and Admiral Potter are right about withholding information that the Prime Minister is alive. If they think that they were successful in killing the Prime Minister and if Allan and Potter are correct in their assessment of this situation, they would immediately put their final plans in motion."

The President looked at Allan and Potter and said, "That means that the Prime Minister must agree to play dead until this is over. Do you think that he will play ball?"

Allan looked at the President and said, "Yes I do. He was very anxious to speak with you and tell you what he knew. I am sure that when he knows that we could take them out once and for all and would agree to the plan to smoke out the terrorists."

The Secretary of State looked at the President and said, "You realize Mr. President that this plan also puts you in harms way."

"How so??"

"You will be one of their prime targets and they will want you in Israel when they launch the strike. What if we send the Vice President?"

The President stood silently for several seconds and said, "Hell I am not going to let a bunch of fucking camel jockeys blackmail me, the United States or anyone else for that matter. If I have to be the bait, then I will be the bait. Gentlemen, we dropped the ball at the one yard line during the Gulf War and failed to take that bastard out... we will not make that mistake again!! Besides, if we send the Vice President, they might not complete their plan." The room was silent as the President continued, "What the hell... our boys are good and I am positive that we can pull this thing off without any problems. I want a plan of action on my desk by ASAP. You have my authorization to position our forces wherever necessary to get things started. Get them in place ASAP because if the Prime Minister does agree with our plan and we announce his death to the rest of the world, the Israeli government will hold the memorial service within days. That timing we cannot control. Colonel Allan and Admiral Potter, lets get back to Bethesda and talk with the Prime Minister."

BETHESDA NAVAL HOSPITAL, 1620 HOURS

The President, Allan, Potter and a swarm of secret service men exited the elevator on the third deck of Bethesda Naval Hospital and walked briskly toward the Presidential suite. The President's ETA had been transmitted to the hospital security department by the secret service team, initiating the removal of non-essential personnel from the area. The nurses saluted as the President walked past their station. With a quick jerk of his arm, he returned their salute. Silently, the secret service men took their positions in the hall, backing up the team that was already in place. A Navy doctor approached the President, stood at attention and saluted. The President returned the salute and said, "Is he awake?"

"Yes Mr. President... he is expecting you."

The President knocked softly on the door and then entered the suite. Allan and Potter followed behind. As the door opened, the Prime Minister pressed a button and his bed elevated his head to a raised position. As the President entered he said, "Mr. President."

"It is good to see you again Mr. Prime Minister. I only wish the circumstances were different."

"As do I..."

"I have been briefed by Colonel Allan and Admiral Potter regarding the assassination plot... and from what I can understand from my staff, your concerns are valid."

"Unbelievable isn't it Mr. President... to think that their plans of world domination almost came to fruition. If I were dead right now, God knows what might have happened. You and the other leaders of the free world would probably have been consumed in a nuclear holocaust during my funeral."

"It could still happen somewhere else in the world if we allow this nightmare to continue." The President moved closer to the bed and looked the Prime Minister dead in the eyes and said, "I need to ask a very big favor of you and your countrymen."

"You only have to ask Mr. President… what can I and my people do for you."

"The cost of freedom comes at a very high price. There are times when the people of the free world have to make very tough decisions and make great sacrifices to keep the forces of evil in check. This is one of those times Mr. Prime Minister. I must ask you to allow my government to keep the news of your rescue and that of your wife quiet for a while. It is of the utmost importance that the rest of the world, including the people of Israel, believe that you and your wife perished last night."

The Prime Minister looked stunned as he pondered the President's words. "Why do you ask this of me and my country?"

"Our intelligence believes that Iraq, with the assistance of Muslim evil doers, have secured several nuclear weapons and plan to use them at your state funeral. This much you have confirmed with the statements made by Dr. Moosavi. It is our intention to allow this state funeral to take place giving us the opportunity to locate and knock out these weapons of mass destruction before they can be used. In effect, Mr. Prime Minister, we will smoke them out with their own plan."

"What if you fail to knock them out in time and they launch their missiles? Millions of my people will die."

"If that happens, I will die too Mr. Prime Minister because I will attend your funeral. As I said earlier, the price of freedom is high and tough decisions must be made to preserve it. Your funeral must go off as they have planned to set in motion the final part of their plan. When they do, our forces will detect the missile positions and destroy them. I, along with the other heads of state will be the bait, but only you and I will know the price that will be paid if we fail. We cannot tell anyone, neither the heads of state of the countries that would attend your funeral… or even your own people. If Iraq were to have the slightest inkling that we knew their plan, they would stop and create another plan to use their weapons of mass destruction somewhere else. We must stop them now."

"Where do you believe that they have these weapons?"

"We believe that the missiles are located in three newly built mosques spread across Iraq. We have them under surveillance by satellites and our armed forces are moving into position to knock them out as we speak. I need your permission to allow my government to announce your untimely death. Will you cooperate with us Mr. Prime Minister?"

The Prime Minister lowered his eyes for several long minutes, his silence was deafening. Raising his eyes to the President he said, "I would agree with you that if we do not strike now, they will do this again at some other place and at some future time. This is a decision that requires the Wisdom of Solomon. I am afraid... like David must have been... standing before Goliath, and yet it is not I that will be standing alone in the field of battle, it will be you. My people face the horrible possibility of being sacrificed in a terrible holocaust if you fail in your mission to destroy these weapons. If I say no, the same threat will surely exist sometime in the future... and at that moment in time; we may not be so fortunate in knowing how and when they will plan their future attack. On the one hand, there is the possibility of death and a good chance that we can stop them... while on the other hand, there is only the possibility of death." Again the Prime Minister lowered his eyes and sat silent for several long seconds. Raising his eyes again he continued, "You are either a very brave man Mr. President or a fool. I do not believe that you are a fool, but rather a man who is willing to make the tough decisions and pay the high price for freedom if it is required of you... Yes... I will allow you to announce my death to the world and cooperate with you in any way possible to put an end to this madness Mr. President."

The President stood silent as he listened to the Prime Minister's reply, "Thank you Mr. Prime Minister... we will not fail I assure you. Colonel Allan, please contact the White House and tell the press secretary to make the announcement."

Colonel Allan quickly left the room as the President looked around the room. Looking at Admiral Potter he said, "Please have someone get a television set brought to the room. I am sure that the Prime Minister and I would like to watch this announcement together."

Admiral Potter left the room and returned quickly with two men carrying the television set from the waiting room. Minutes later, the face of the ZNN anchorman announced, "We are switching now to the White House where Press Secretary Balling is approaching the podium."

Press Secretary Balling cleared his voice, "The President has asked me to announce that the Prime Minister of Israel... Joshua Cane and his wife are presumed dead and lost at sea. All of the survivors of the Titanic have been airlifted to Andrews Air Force Base and the Prime Minister and his wife are not among them. The President has notified the Israeli government of the presumed death of the Prime Minister and extends to them his deepest condolences."

The White House press core immediately began shouting questions to Balling.

"Is the search for the Prime Minister being called off?"

"Not at this time."

"How did the Titanic sink... did she hit an iceberg?"

"We have little to go on at this time but there were icebergs in the area."

"There were reports of some type of sea engagement in the area... Can you comment on that?"

"No comment."

"How has the Israeli government responded?"

"Shock and concern..."

Press Secretary Balling suddenly raised his hands indicating that he would no longer take questions and left the podium. The face of the ZNN anchorman returned, "The White House has just made an announcement that the Prime Minister of Israel, Joshua Cane and his wife are missing and presumed dead in the sinking of the Titanic. Please stay tuned as our continuing coverage of the death of the Prime Minister continues in two minutes."

ZNN went into a commercial break as they scurried to get several correspondents onto the set to discuss the announcement. The President turned off the television and turned to the Prime Minister, "The die is now cast. I must return to the White House Mr. Prime Minister."

The Prime Minister raised himself up in the bed and said, "God be with you Mr. President."

The President, Allan and Potter left the Presidential suite and talked briefly in the hall. Allan spoke first saying, "Mr. President... I think that we have done our job. You have the football. I think that it would be beneficial however, if Admiral Potter and myself remain here to debrief Mrs. Cane. There are still a lot of questions that we need answered that could aid you in your plans."

The President looked at Allan and replied, "Both of you have done a fine job... Yes by all means stay here and report back to me after you speak with Mrs. Cane. Anything that you can find out will be of the greatest importance."

The President saluted Allan and Potter and entered the elevator to head back to the White House.

ISRAELI KNESSET, 0200 HOURS

The Israeli government's electoral system operates on a principal of proportional representation. Unlike the United States whose President is elected using the electoral college system, meaning that the popular votes in a state directs the electoral college representative to cast their votes for the President, the Israeli Knesset members are elected by the popular vote of the people of Israel.

The Israeli voter does not however, vote for a particular individual, but rather a particular party that produces a list of candidates that includes the Prime Minister. In 1992, the election laws were changed thus limiting the number of parties that could run candidates for seats in the Knesset. The 1992 change limited the seats in the Knesset to be held by legally registered parties or an alignment of two or more registered parties. The proportion of the popular votes received by any one party or coalition during the election would determine the total number of Knesset seats, of which there are 120 that any party could occupy. Any party or coalition of parties with ten or more seats in the Knesset could produce a candidate for Prime Minister.

The Prime Minister would have to be an Israeli citizen, at least 30 years of age and be the head of his or her party's list of Knesset candidates. The Prime Minister would be prevented from running for office if he or she were Prime Minister for seven consecutive years. During an election, the winning party must receive more than 50 % of the vote. Failure to do so would result in a runoff election between the top two parties. As in the case of the United States, elections are scheduled to be every four years. However, the Knesset could extend the four-year period as it did during the Yom Kippur war or call for a vote of "no-confidence" of the Prime Minister at any time and force a new election. Once elected, the Prime Minister would have 45 days to form a government (a list of ministers to run the government) and receive Knesset approval of his ministers. If the Prime Minister were unable to continue in office due to resignation, impeachment, vote of no confidence or death, the Knesset would appoint one of its members as acting Prime Minister until a new Prime Minister is elected and takes office.

With the announcement of the presumed death of the Prime Minister by the United States, an emergency meeting of the Knesset was called. The 120 Knesset members sat silently as the President of the Knesset, Raymond Hochberg spoke, "I have been in touch with the President of the United States and I am sorry to say that it does appear that the Prime Minister, Joshua Cane is presumed lost at sea and dead. It is therefore my duty to call for a vote that will elect an acting Prime Minister until such time that a new Prime Minister can be elected."

There was a hush in the assembly as one of the Knesset members spoke, "Mr. President… giving the abruptness in which this loss has descended upon us and in the spirit of unity that I feel that we must show to avoid a political crisis in Israel, I propose to the Knesset that you Mr. President, act as Prime Minister until after the people of Israel pay their respects to Prime Minister Cane and a new election can be held."

The assembly broke out into a buzz of conversations among the different parties that occupied the 120-seat Knesset. Raymond Hochberg was 59 years old, a "hawk" who, along with Prime Minister Cane, had been swept into power after a no-confidence vote. At that time the Palestinian issue had consumed the Knesset with anger as the negotiations had evolved into possibly giving up most of the West Bank and control over parts of the east Jerusalem to the Palestinians. In the minds of the majority of the Knesset, there was no room for any "peace at any price" policy. There was no tolerance for any form of liberalism to take seed in the Knesset. If there was to be another war, the popular sentiment was to have it now and get on with their lives. Far too many Jews had died defending the soil of Israel and they were not about to give it away. In an unprecedented act of unity each of the 120 members of the Knesset spontaneously stood up and began to applaud. Moments later there were shouts and cheers.

Hochberg stood silent watching the members of the Knesset honor him. Raising his arms in the air, he pleaded for silence, but the applauds and cheers continued for several minutes longer. Finally, the members of the Knesset took their seats and as the new acting Prime Minister began to speak, "I am honored by your outpouring of support for me to continue forward with the policy that was created by Prime Minister Joshua Cane. It will be difficult to fill those shoes, for Prime Minister Cane was a dedicated man who often times said he would do anything to keep Israel in one piece and make it a country that would bow to no one. I echo his words to you … Israel will never again allow itself to become a pawn in world politics. Israel will never again allow itself to be forced to even consider for one second… giving up one centimeter of its sacred soil to any Palestinian. This land was given to us by God and paid for with the blood of the people of Israel who have died to preserve it. I thank you for your vote of confidence and gladly accept the position of acting Prime Minister."

WHITE HOUSE, 19:45 HOURS

The President had returned to the White House two hours earlier and had dinner in the Oval Office by himself. His agenda for the evening and the foreseeable future had been cleared. The First Lady was traveling on the West coast, supporting his educational program that had been a major plank in his election platform. He leaned back in his chair looking at the Oval Office ceiling, his fingertips touching lightly. He closed his eyes and was lost in thought. How many Presidents had faced problems of this magnitude? There was Washington, Lincoln, Wilson, Roosevelt, Truman, Kennedy, Johnson, Reagan, Bush and now he faced the problem of making the tough decisions to use the military might of the United States against the forces of evil that would stifle world freedom.

The world was spinning out of control. Since the fall of the USSR, the United States had become the only major superpower in the world that had the guts and military might to fight the dark side. The small and often time's defenseless free world countries looked to the United States to defend them against these forces of aggression. After the cold war, it seemed like hundreds of religious fundamentalist organizations, political extremists, dictators and countless terrorist organizations suddenly surfaced, filling the vacuum created by the death of the USSR. As the Soviet navy lay rusting in her ports and her ICBMs became more and more obsolete with each passing day, these forces of evil created conflicts across the globe that exploded with the random regularity of popcorn kernels popping on a hot skillet. Like it or not, the United States had become the world's police force and the President had become the chief of police. Why was it that everyone in the world couldn't realize that the planet earth was all we had and we somehow had to learn to coexist in peace? Suddenly, the phone rang. Opening his eyes, he reached for the phone.

The soft voice of a secretary said, "Forgive me for disturbing you Mr. President."

"That's quite all right…"

"Acting Prime Minister, Raymond Hochberg is on line one."

"Thank you…"

Adjusting his position in his chair, he reached for a pad of paper and pen. He cleared his throat and pressed the blinking button on the phone, "Mr. Prime Minister…"

"Mr. President, thank you for taking my call…"

"No problem… Congratulations Mr. Hochberg… I was briefed earlier about your unanimous vote by the Knesset to be acting Prime Minister."

"Thank you Mr. President for your kind words. It is a sad time for Israel. Prime Minister Cane was a gifted leader and respected by the people of Israel. It will be difficult to fine someone who will be able to fill his shoes."

"I am sure that the people of Israel will choose wisely in the next election and find that man. I think that it is important for you to know Mr. Prime Minister that you and the people of Israel will continue to receive the full cooperation and support of the United States throughout this transitional period. It is critical that the United States continues to show solidarity with your people so that a lasting peace can be forged between Israel and the Palestinians.

"Thank you Mr. President… Your words and commitment to the people of Israel are most reassuring."

"What are your plans for the memorial service for Prime Minister Cane?"

"This is in the planning stage as we speak… I will be making an official announcement to the people of Israel as soon as the plans are complete. Jewish law would have required an immediate burial, but since the body of Prime Minister Cane is lost at sea, we have time to plan a fitting tribute to Prime Minister Cane for his tireless service to the people of Israel. I would say that the service should be held within seven days and the elections would follow shortly thereafter."

"The First Lady and I will attend the memorial service."

"Thank you Mr. President... we are receiving requests for information regarding the memorial service from the leaders of other countries... Great Britain, France, Spain, Jordan... the list goes on and on. We even have a request to attend the memorial service from the Palestinians... that one will be a sticky issue indeed... Tell me Mr. President... our people are telling me that there was some type of military action that involved the Titanic... can you confirm this to me?"

The President leaned forward as his mind raced to find the suitable reply, "There was no overt military action on our part if that is what you are asking."

"My security staff is telling me that one of your subs is missing, as well as an aircraft that was apparently trying to destroy a mystery sub in the vicinity. There is also the fire on the Titanic and its rapid sinking... one would almost suspect that the ship herself was torpedoed..."

"Well if that is what they are telling you... then their intelligence is better than mine... I cannot affirm anything that you have asked so far. The best thing that we can arrive at is that there was a bomb on board the Titanic that led to the fire and sinking. My intelligence reports that there were several terrorists on board and a firefight between the Prime Minister's security men and these terrorists. I would imagine that you have more information on this event than I. Can you elaborate on these events?"

"From what I am told, there was a firefight... I would imagine that these men could also have planted some explosive device on the Titanic with the intention of sinking her and killing the Prime Minister..."

"That is what we think occurred. Our activities in the North Atlantic were strictly search and rescue... it is unfortunate that more people were not saved."

"I agree with you Mr. President."

"If you like, I will instruct our CIA to contact your Mosad... let's compare notes and see what comes up."

"Excellent thought Mr. President. We will await their call. I will notify our staff. Have a good night Mr. President."

"Thank you Mr. Prime Minister."

Both the President and the Prime Minister hung up their phones. They both sat silent, looking at the receiver knowing full well that they both knew more than they were willing to tell the other. The President quickly picked up the phone, "Get me Mark Crowley... Yes now!"

The President leaned back in his chair looking at the ceiling of the Oval Office once again. He touched the fingertips of each hand and played a silent drumbeat with his fingers. Replaying the conversation with the Prime Minister in his mind he yelled our one word that summed up his feelings, "FUCK". Turning in his chair slowly, he looked out of the Oval Office window and said under his breath, "Somewhere out there is a fucking spy..."

BETHESDA NAVAL HOSPITAL, 2100 HOURS

Prime Minister Cane lay in bed watching ZNN. The news of the Titanic had dominated the news station, along with news from Israel that the Knesset had named President Raymond Hochberg to be the acting Prime Minister until a new election could be held. He thought that Hochberg was a good choice... that is... until he returned. One interesting point was that he was still Prime Minister, until there was a new election; he was still the Prime Minister... even if the world thought he was dead.

He watched, with a feeling of embarrassment, as ZNN did a fifteen-minute broadcast on his life and accomplishments. He watched silently as his life passed before his eyes, ending with his picture and the dates of his birth and death printed across the bottom. Reaching for the remote control, he switched off the television set, looking trancelike at the black tube. His mind was filled with anger and helplessness, both for himself and his country. Why was he doing this? Why didn't he just get out of bed and get on with his life? He knew the answer all too well. Playing dead could possibly put an end to the terrorist activity, maybe not forever, but at least for a long while. He reached down and touched the bandage on his leg. Wincing, he moved his leg and sat on the edge of the bed. Slowly, he placed his weight on the leg and slowly stood. With a shuffling motion, he walked toward the door. He reached for his robe and turned the doorknob. The guard outside his suite immediately turned to face the Prime Minister. The Prime Minister cleared his throat and said, "Forgive me for startling you… I cannot sleep and need to walk a bit."

Two security guards immediately awakened Allan and Potter, they were sleeping in two suites further down the hall. As they approached the Prime Minister, Potter spoke, "Are you OK Mr. Prime Minister?"

"Yes… I am fine. I just need to move about a bit."

Together Allan, Potter and the Prime Minister walked slowly down the hallway towards the nurses' station. The Prime Minister looked at the nurse and said, "How is my wife doing?"

"She is sleeping Mr. Prime Minister…"

"Can I see her?"

"Dr. Greene left specific instructions that she was not to be disturbed…"

"Yes I understand… but if I could only sit quietly in her room to be with her…"

The nurse picked up a phone and dialed a number from a list on a clipboard that hung on the wall. The Prime Minister listened as the nurse spoke to Dr. Greene. Looking at the Prime Minister, the nurse replied, "Dr. Greene will allow you to sit with her Mr. Prime Minister, but please do not disturb her sleep… she needs all the rest she can get… I am afraid that Dr. Greene will not allow you gentlemen to see Mrs. Cane until sometime tomorrow."

Allan and Potter gave approving nods of their heads and then followed the Prime Minister and the nurse towards Jacky's suite. The nurse opened the door for the Prime Minister. With the exception of a small light near the door and the blue glow and occasional beep from the monitors that traced Jacky's heartbeat, respiration, body temperature and other vital signs, the room was dark and silent. The nurse quietly moved a chair near the bed and helped the Prime Minister sit.

"I will be at my station. If you need me, press this button." The nurse pointed to an alarm switch and left the room.

Joshua leaned forward and looked at Jacky. He had not seen her since they had arrived at Bethesda. Her arms and hands were bandaged. There was a strong smell of medication about her. Her face resembled that of a mummified alien with large black bug eyes protruded through the facial bandages. These bug eyes were protective eyecups that gave her the look of a woman not of this earth. She looked like she was dead, stiff and not moving. Her left arm was connected to an IV drip of Parkland formula, which would replace the fluids lost by her body that resulted from the fire. Because of the IV and the severity of her burns, Jacky was also catheterized to monitor her urine output, which had to be stabilized at a rate of 50 ml/hr. Two fingers of her left hand were attached to a blood pressure device. The monitor traces raced across the screen showing her BP at 100 mmHg and her CVP of 8 mmH2O. Her heart rate jumped on the monitor screen like a trace of a continuous earthquake. With each heartbeat, the monitor made a soft beep. Joshua rubbed the tears from his eyes as he sat silently looking at her. Slowly, he placed his trembling hand on hers. The bandages prevented him from feeling her warm soft skin that he loved so much. There was no response. Placing his forehead on the bed, he muttered a prayer and began to sob for several minutes. Looking up at Jacky again, he dried his eyes and sat motionless. He would stay with her until she awoke.

CHAPTER 12

APRIL 16TH

WHITE HOUSE BUNKER, 0600 HOURS

Four hundred feet below the White House foundation was a complex affectionately called the "bunker". The bunker had been built during the late 50's and early 60's during the height of the "cold war" as a bomb shelter designed to protect the President from a direct hit from a preemptive nuclear strike. However, with the increased accuracy and mega tonnage of the nuclear arsenal of the former Soviet Union, the bunker was deemed obsolete and now served as a secure meeting place where sensitive information could be discussed without fear of counter intelligence forces overhearing the conversations. Due to the fact that the very existence of the bunker was classified "TOP SECRET"; underground tunnels connecting the bunker with other branches of the government were constructed over the years to allow unobserved access. These tunnels were secretly dug and connected the White House to the Pentagon, CIA, FBI and the Capital building. Tunnel digging had become a science as well as an unspoken art form for the US government. Tunnels seemed to be everywhere beneath Washington, D.C. as evidenced by the tunnel that was secretly dug beneath the Russian embassy in the '80s and later discovered by the Russians in March of 2001. In times of extreme national crisis or otherwise, the required staff of any branch of the United States government could be summonsed and assembled at a variety of meeting places unnoticed by the press or other prying eyes.

Inside the bunker were several main rooms. The first was a conference room. The conference room itself was rectangular in design, 250 foot by 150 foot by 80 foot high and sported a large stainless steel table in the center of the room. The table was fitted with a

294 – Dick Sheppard

variety of recessed control and communication buttons, keyboards, microphones and recessed flat screen monitors. Around the table were fifty black leather chairs that were pulled up to the table, their high backs looking like silent unmarked tombstones. At the head of the table was the Presidential Seal, proudly engraved into the shiny stainless steel surface and filled with gold. Eight giant 30 feet by 50 feet flat screen monitors, complete with a sound system were positioned on the walls of the bunker that surrounded the conference table. These screens would be the eyes and ears of the President and his staff during a national crisis. In an adjacent room to the left of the conference room was the control center for the bunker. The control center housed all of the necessary hardware to communicate to the spy satellites, other information databases and communications networks that could be displayed on the monitors. Adjacent to the conference room on the right were toilets, vending machines, a small eating area, storage closets and sleeping units.

The President had called for an emergency meeting and an army of military and security personnel from the Joint Chiefs of Staff, NSC, CIA and other branches of the government had assembled, sitting around the stainless steel table addressing their computer keyboards that protruded from the smooth surface of the table. Flat screen monitors exited the table from thin slots and stood silently, their monolithic screens displaying a variety of pictures and graphs. In the control center sat a multitude of technicians that were speaking softly into headsets and pressing an array of buttons that controlled the images that would be viewed by the President and his staff. The big screens inside the conference room were now ablaze with activity. On one screen, the magnificent view of the earth, with its blue oceans and puffy clouds could be seen as satellite images from the "big bird" spy satellites were displaying real time images of the Arabian Sea and Persian Gulf. Another screen zoomed into downtown Baghdad. The images on the screens continuously changed as the technicians in the control room issued commands that increased or decreased the resolution of the satellites. A comprehensive videotape record of the suspected mosques was also being recorded for the review of the President, the NSC and Joint Chiefs of Staff. Historic photographic archives of the areas in question were also being pulled from the thousands of previous images of the region. Careful attention would be paid to the mosques that had been the final destination of the truck convoy. The glass eyes of the "big birds" stared coldly at the earth from their perch in outer space, looking at the mosques and searching for anything that would indicate that something was new or different about the structure.

There was a swishing sound as the elevator door opened and the President approached his position at the head of the table. Everyone in the room stood silently as the President approached his chair. Looking up, the President saluted and said, "Gentlemen… be seated… we have a long morning ahead of us." The gathering returned to their seats as the President placed his palms on the table and leaned forward, "As you all undoubtedly know by now, the Titanic was sunk by a renegade Kilo sub. We lost the USS Tiger Shark, a C-130 aircraft and all but a handful of passengers aboard the Titanic died. Fortunately, the Prime Minister and his wife were rescued and are currently in safe keeping at the Bethesda Naval Hospital. There is considerable evidence before us that indicates that Iraq is behind all of this and our old friend Sadaam is once again up to his old tricks. This time, he seems to have formed an alliance with Muslim extremists and is about to carry out an attack with nuclear tipped missiles aimed at Israel… and will launch this attack during the proposed memorial service for the late Prime Minister Cane that will be held in Jerusalem. We need to take him out and destroy the missiles before they reach their target." The President sat in his chair and said, "Let's hear it gentlemen…"

The Chairman of the Joint Chiefs of Staff, Admiral Sheppard spoke first, "Mr. President… As you know, the UN inspectors that were put in place after the Gulf War were kicked out of Iraq in October of '98. Since that time, we have maintained heavy satellite surveillance of Iraq. In view of the recent information regarding the truck convoy, we have reviewed the satellite image archives of the three mosques that have been built recently and have determined that they have significant differences in their structure as compared to the older mosques architecture... in particular, their domes."

Pressing a key on his keyboard, all eight giant screens suddenly produced the image of three mosques as Admiral Sheppard continued, "The first mosque is in Baghdad. The second is located in the town of Irbil and the third is located in Al Basrah. All three mosques have two things in common. First, they were all visited by a military truck convoy that was part of a convoy of trucks that had its origin in Afghanistan. It is strongly believed that their cargo was three nuclear bombs from Pakistan. The second common element is that these three mosques have extensive design changes to their domes. Each dome has been built with what seems to be a sliding rail system that would expose the interior of the mosque."

The images on the screens began to show time lapsed images of construction around the domes. Many of the images were obscured by a large canvas tarp that had been placed above the mosques during much of the construction process. Toward the end of the time lapsed images, the tarp was removed, revealing the traditional golden dome, but with one major feature that was different from any other mosque, a steel structure that resembled a scaffolding of some type. The structure resembled two rails that protruded beneath the rim of the dome. The rails were wide enough to support the dome and long enough for the dome to slide horizontally and expose the interior of the mosque. The image of the mosque vanished and was replaced by a three-dimensional wire drawing of a mosque. The image of the mosque rotated exposing all sides of the structure. Suddenly, the wire frame image of the mosque paused as an animated sequence began showing the top view of the mosque. The dome slid to the right and a missile exited the mosque through the opening. The image rotated once again showing the building from the front. Again, the dome slid to the right. The interior of the mosque was shown to contain a missile that ignited and flew into the sky through the circular opening.

"As you can see, this form of structural modification would allow for the dome to be removed and provide for a suitable launch pad for a medium range ballistic missiles that could reach the intended target."

The President responded, "What type of missile?"

"I do not believe that Sadaam will use the SCUD missile this time around because they are very unreliable and are not accurate enough for a mission of this magnitude and importance. We believe that the missile of choice would be of Chinese origin."

"Chinese…"

"Yes Mr. President… I would like to allow the CIA to continue at this point Mr. President."

Mark Crowley rose and said, "Mr. President… The Chinese have been developing short, medium and ICBM range missiles for quite some time and have sold some of them to Pakistan and Syria… and they have repeatedly broken the trade embargo with Iraq." Pressing a key on his keypad, he continued as the screens began to show high-resolution images of a multitude of missiles, "The Dong Feng/Julang series missiles are quite impressive. Starting at the top, there is the Dong Feng 5 ICBM missile. It has a range of 7,500 miles, carries a single 3-megaton thermonuclear device, has two stages, uses liquid propellant and is accurate to within 300 meters. We believe that China has 20 of these deployed across China. Next is the Dong Feng 31 ICBM. It has a range of 7,500 miles, carries a single 2.5 Megaton thermonuclear or three 90-kiloton nuclear devices. This missile is a three-stage solid propellant missile with internal/fiber optic guidance systems and is accurate to within 300 meters. China has just completed development of this missile and is starting to deploy the missile across China. Next is the Dong Feng 25 IRBM. This missile has a range of 1,500 miles, carries three 250-kiloton nuclear devices in a MIRV missile nose-cone bus, uses internal fiber optic guidance and is accurate to within ten meters. China currently has ten deployed across China. The Julang 1 Great Wave 1 SLBM missile has a range of 1,200 miles, carries a single 1-megaton thermonuclear warhead, is a two-stage solid propellant missile using internal/fiber optic/GPS guidance systems and has an accuracy of less than 200 meters. China has deployed 16 of these missiles. Next is the Dong Feng 21 IRBM. This missile has a range of 1,200 miles, carries a single 1 megaton thermonuclear device or the new "X" version carries a 250 kiloton nuclear device, uses internal/fiber optic/GPS guidance systems and is accurate to within 10 meters. China currently has deployed 90 of these missiles. The Dong Feng 15 Tactical Missile is designed to carry a 1,100 lb. chemical, nuclear or conventional warhead, a 10 KT. neutron weapon or a 20 KT. tactical nuclear warhead. The missile has a range of 370 miles, is 3.3 feet in diameter and 30 feet long, weighs 13,700 pounds, uses solid propellant and is accurate to within 100 meters. China has deployed 300 missiles and has sold 20 to Syria. Finally, the Dong Feng 11 Tactical Missile has a range of 186 miles, carries a 10-kiloton tactical nuclear warhead, uses solid propellant and is accurate to within 200 meters. China has deployed 100 and sold 20 to Pakistan."

"Which missile do you believe may be in the possession of Sadaam?"

Crowley pressed another key on his keypad as the high-resolution satellite image of a Dong Feng 21 missile appeared on the screens. "The Dong Feng 21 missile Mr. President. The missile is mobile and could be easily transported to Iraq and has the range required to strike any target inside Israel if fired from any of the three mosques in question. Whereas the Chinese have not reportedly sold this missile in the past, it is about the only missile that could do the job that would have the range, be reliable and accurate enough to do the job and come from a country that would be willing to let Sadaam have it to create global instability. The Chinese would not be against selling a weapon system if it would fit into their long-range plans for global domination. Creating a crisis of this magnitude would surely benefit them in the long run."

The President replied, "Nick... do you agree with that assessment?"

Secretary of State, Nick Scrivanich answered, "I am afraid so Mr. President. China is continuing to build her ICBM capability as well as an impressive blue water navy. They have eyes on Taiwan and will surely put up a fight in the not too distant future to take possession of that country... Unfortunately, it's just a matter of time. Allowing the US to get into a war with Iraq would please them I am sure and fit into their long-range plans. They are on a path for global domination and destined to fill the vacuum created by the fall of the USSR and become the next "Evil Empire", to quote President Reagan... If they throw sticks under our feet to trip us up every so often... it would fit into their long-range plans... They are not our friends, Mr. President. Look what happened last year with our EP-3E intelligence aircraft. Our aircraft was in international airspace and yet their F-8 fighter aircraft flew to within 20 feet of our aircraft, created air turbulence that caused the our aircraft's wing to dip and hit their F-8. The Chinese pilot was killed in the process as the second F-8 fighter shot at our EP-3E aircraft and forced it to land on Hainan Island... To add insult to injury, they detained our personnel, stripped the EP-3E of its intelligence hardware and blamed us for violating their sovereignty by landing without their permission. They are calculating bastards Mr. President. In my opinion, they would sell missiles to Iraq in a New York second."

"I am afraid that I must agree with you Nick." Looking at everyone the President continued, "Our missile defense system will not be operational until 2004. It would be nice if we had it now, but we don't. How do you propose that we take them out?"

Admiral Sheppard replied, "With a surgical air strike Mr. President. If they are allowed to launch their missiles, we could not possibly stop the attack... one or all of the missiles could reach their targets. Since these missiles will be armed with nuclear weapons, we cannot count on knocking them out of the sky over Israel with the Patriots... As you know, they were not that reliable during the Gulf War. If the Patriot did strike the missile, God knows what would happen to the nuclear device... it could explode or rain down radioactive contamination over a large area. We also have major concerns regarding using our "fire-and-forget" weapons. In 2001, our attack on Baghdad was less than 80% effective. This job will require that we use our newest F-22 fighter and a well trained pilot to blast them to hell."

The President looked at the Chief of Naval Operations, Admiral McCort and said, "Mike... I would guess that the Navy will deliver the strike force..." Admiral McCort replied, "Correct Mr. President... The Seventh Fleet under the command of Vice Admiral Kreen has been placed on full combat status. He is currently awaiting our instructions." As he continued, he pressed a key on his keypad and the images of the Seventh Fleet were shown on the screens, "The Seventh fleet has two aircraft carriers, the USS Nimitz and USS George Washington. Each carrier has one air wing for a total of 160 aircraft. Each carrier has received twenty of the new F-22 fighters. The F-22 is a stealth craft, can go 1.5 Mach without afterburners and 1.9 Mach with afterburners. If we have to, we could possibly chase down one of the missiles if it got off the ground. The F-22 carries air-to-air and air-to-ground missiles as well as a payload of 450-pound GBU-32 JDAM bombs... more than enough to do the job. The attack mission will be during the day... the F-22 will be able to avoid the increased number of radar guided antiaircraft batteries that Sadaam has installed around these locations. The speed of the aircraft, its stealth design and weapons payload should assure a successful mission. All in all Mr. President, we have more than enough fire power to do the job."

The President leaned forward and said, "... and if we fail to take them out... what then?"

Admiral Sheppard replied, "Then it's all out war Mr. President. If we fail to take out the missiles, we will have no other recourse other than turning the entire country into a parking lot. If they launch a nuclear attack against Israel and are successful, we would have no other choice but to retaliate using our nuclear capabilities. We have in position two boomers that can take them out and..."

The President immediately slammed his fist on the table and said, "Are you proposing that we start WWIII? If we attack Iraq, then most certainly their allies, known and unknown would step in. The Chinese and Russians will do something. If we attack Iraq and if China did sell them these fucking missiles, the Chinese would probably launch some type of attack against Taiwan. Maybe not right away, but they would do something to turn up the heat. Do you remember when they told Clinton that we could not send our fleet through the Formosa Strait and the incident last year regarding our intelligence aircraft? They do have big balls Admiral... the size of church bells. One thing would lead to another and we would find ourselves fighting them sooner than you think. The Russians... what about them? They are heating up the "cold war". The communist movement in Russia would have a field day with this one. Whereas they are not the military threat that they once were, they can cause a lot of trouble... and need I remind you that they still have ICBMs and a nuclear arsenal. Missing the missiles and fucking up is not an option..."

Scrivanich added, "You are forgetting Israel Mr. President."

"In what regard?"

"Israel is rumored to have nuclear devices. If Sadaam were to successfully complete his mission, we may not have to worry about turning Iraq into a parking lot because they would do it first."

"I have read those reports Nick... but are we sure that Israel has nuclear capabilities?"

"As sure as anyone can be without seeing them first hand. They certainly are not going to show anyone their stash of nuclear bombs. Having rumors of their existence is enough for them to keep the world guessing and maybe enough to keep the Arabs under control for a little while longer. I know one thing... if Sadaam drops his nuclear bombs on Israel, the world will find out if they have them in short order..."

Crowley added, "I agree with the Secretary of State Mr. President. Our sources confirm the fact that they have had them for quite some time... and if I may add one other thought. If Israel retaliates and blows up Iraq, the Jihad would really get the boost it needs and the total destruction of Iraq, her men, women and children could possibly unite the entire Muslim world community into a holy war against Israel. This would certainly mean that we would be drawn into a war that would possibly never end. If you thought that Viet Nam was bad, wait until you see this. It would be at this time Mr. President that China would probably take some form of action against Taiwan. With our hands filled with a Jihad holy war on one front in the Middle East, China would probably make her move. I wouldn't be at all surprised if North Korea jumped in to the act as well and attacked South Korea... with the aid and support of the Chinese. It's a big global chess game Mr. President. The missiles that China may have sold to Sadaam and Sadaam himself are nothing but pawns on the global chess board and China wants to place us in checkmate."

McCort interrupted and said, "Why don't we just do it now before the memorial service... why risk allowing this situation to get out of hand."

The President replied, "The die is cast... the memorial service will take place within seven days. If we are wrong and they have moved the missiles to another place we could tip our hand, blow up the wrong targets and they would simply use these weapons somewhere else... I am afraid that we are committed to seeing this thing through."

There was a deafening silence in the room as everyone considered the ramifications of the decision they had to make. Finally, the President spoke, "There is only one way that we can find out where the missiles and bombs are located and that is by taking these missiles out at the last minute... when they roll back the domes on these mosques and launch their attack. I will be in Israel and will be the only person at the memorial service that will know what will happen if you fail in your mission."

Scrivanich replied, "I must protest Mr. President... you cannot allow yourself to be a sitting duck waiting for a nuclear bomb to be dropped on your head."

"I appreciate your concern Nick, but my mind is made up... I am going!"

"... And if we fail, the leader of the free world is eviscerated..."

"Yes... along with the heads of state of almost every other free world country. Quite frankly, being consumed in a nuclear blast would be a blessing on one respect. The world as we know it will not exist if Sadaam is successful. This mad dog has got to be stopped and if I have to put myself in harms way to stop him... I will. I am going to the memorial service with or without your approval. The Vice President will be in charge if you fail in your mission. For my sake, the people of the free world and the people of Israel... God willing... you will not fail."

The Secretary of State squirmed in his seat as he asked, "How long do we have once we have a visual from the birds that the domes are in a launch position... until the missiles can be launched?"

Sheppard replied, "Not very long... one to two minutes... maybe three if they launch as soon as the domes are in position. Then again, they could roll the domes back ahead of time long before they intend to launch."

The President replied, "How long will it take us to get the F-22s in position?"

"From our carriers and with afterburners... about fifteen minutes Mr. President."

"Then you are telling me that we have to have our F-22s over Iraq before they launch."

"Correct Mr. President."

"And how do you propose doing this without tipping our hand?"

Sheppard pressed another key on his keyboard and continued as the screens displayed a map of Iraq. The 33rd and 36th parallels were shown as two yellow lines that cut Iraq into three pieces. The north and south no-fly zones were shown in orange and the fly zone was in white, "The no-fly zones Mr. President. We have enforced the no-fly zones in Iraq since the Gulf War in '91 to prevent Sadaam from attacking the Kurdish rebels in the north and the Shiite Muslims in the south. We, and our allies, patrol Iraq on a regular basis. Since the no-fly zone is north of the 36th parallel and south of the 33rd parallel, all we have to do is swap the usual patrol aircraft with the F-22. The southern no-fly zone places Al Basrah directly in our patrol area and Irbil is in the north no-fly zone, with Baghdad within striking distance within the allotted time of two minutes."

The President replied, "Sounds like you have thought it through… but how quickly can they react once they have been given the attack order?"

Crowley replied, "We can view the mosques in real time Mr. President. We will be observing for signs of activity outside of the mosques as well as the dome itself." Pressing a button, the screens suddenly began to view the mosque in Baghdad. "This is the mosque in Baghdad, as you can see, we can watch the mosque and the surrounding area around the mosque in real time."

The President watched as the traffic drove by the mosque. Suddenly, the image focused on the dome and the superstructure that had been erected next to the dome. The image zoomed in closer and the rails and the bolts holding them in place became clear and distinct. Crowley continued, "As soon as they start to move the dome back, we will issue the attack order."

McCort also added, "At that moment, Mr. President, the battle group from the Seventh Fleet in the Mediterranean will launch cruise missiles that will pulverize the area after the F-22 attack."

General Robert Kent, Chief of Staff, USAF commented, "Mr. President, we will deploy the stealth bombers and attack fighters to continue the attack after the cruise missiles have completed their mission. The air attack will continue to eliminate any other odds and ends that Sadaam may have. We are planning for a 72-hour blitz around Iraq. There are military defenses that Sadaam has rebuilt in recent months. These defenses have become an ever-increasing threat to our aircraft as they patrol the no-fly zone. As long as we are there, we might as well knock out those too. At the moment the attack begins, we will bring all of our military bases worldwide to a Threatcon Delta alert status."

The President sat back in his chair and commented, "Sounds like a plan... I like it."

Nick leaned forward and asked, "Are you sure that you want to do this... set yourself up as a sitting duck?"

"Positive Nick... I wouldn't have it any other way."

"Are you taking the First Lady with you?"

"Yes..."

"Does she know?"

"No... The only person that will know what could happen will be me and me alone... We cannot have it any other way."

"Why is that Mr. President?'

"Mark... fill in everyone on the conversation you and I had last night."

Crowley replied, "The acting Prime Minister of Israel somehow found out about the engagement in the Atlantic between the Tiger Shark, our C-130 and the Titanic. We may have a deep seated mole somewhere."

The room came alive with the sounds of movement as Crowley continued, "The military action that took place was classified. I am confident that the military personnel that took part in the rescue and care of the Prime Minister are cleared of any espionage. The other air rescue teams are currently being detained at their bases and are not being allowed any outside contact with anyone... even their families. The medical staff at Bethesda is remaining at the facility and they too are not allowed any outside contact. The Coast Guard and Navy rescue teams are still at sea and will remain so until this operation is over. That leaves the CIA, NSA and other supporting agencies that were involved with certain messages and other intelligence that was received. As you know, the Russians had a mole in the FBI for quite some time... approximately 15 years. That spy was apprehended in March of 2001. Since then, all branches of the intelligence community have increased security within their own organizations. We are currently looking at this situation very carefully."

The President replied, "Any clues as to the identity of this individual or individuals?"

"Not yet Mr. President… As you can see, we have a security problem and we must keep the fact that the Prime Minister is alive and well a closely guarded secret… even if it means sending the First Lady into harms way. If anything looks unusual, if any information regarding our plans or the fact that the Prime Minister is alive leaks back to Sadaam, the entire mission to stop him will be compromised."

The President stood and looked at the assembly and said, "Thank you gentlemen…"

The Joint Chiefs of Staff, members of the NSC and all of the others stood in silence. There was a look of respect in their eyes for the President that had not been there before the meeting as they saluted their Commander and Chief. The President returned the salute and looked back at them silently. As the President walked toward the elevator, the sound of applause came from one pair of hands and quickly was followed by the applause from every person in the room. The President paused, turned and gave them a "thumbs-up" sign and left the bunker.

ALEXANDERIA, VA: 0630 HOURS

The early morning dawn dimly lit the kitchen of a modest townhouse as Ronald Phillip Henderson read the morning Washington Post and sipped his coffee. Henderson, 57, was married with two children, a son 23 and a daughter 25, both married and his daughter was about to make him a grandfather. He graduated at the top of his class at MIT and for the last twenty-five years, had been employed by the CIA and worked in the S&T (Scientific, Technical, and Weapons Intelligence) branch of the Directorate of Intelligence or DI. Over the years, he had been promoted to a manager in his section and was regarded as a good worker, outstanding family man and had been given top-secret clearance for sensitive information that often times went directly to the President.

On the outside, Henderson was viewed as the ideal American, but on the inside, he was a tormented man. Looking at the paper, he turned to the classified section and placed his glasses on the end of his nose. Leaning forward, he scanned the ads closely. His eyes darted around the page several time before he turned the page and continued the process. His hand reached for the coffee cup and stopped as his eyes focused on a small ad, "Single male 19, seeking an older man for a lasting relationship..." He sipped the coffee and closed his eyes thinking back to the day that he answered his first ad after he had secretly acquired a PO box across town. Each morning, he would jog to the box and anxiously look for a reply to ads that he had answered. Over the years, he had arranged for several one-night stands with young men. They had excited something in him that he did not understand. All he knew was that he felt a rush when he read the ads, answered the ads and enjoyed the few hours he could spend with these men. These hours were indescribably erotic to him. Reaching down, he pulled at his manhood with his left hand as he placed the paper on the table.

Over the years, his morning jogs had led him to a variety of men. He had started out timidly at first and yet, as the years rolled by, he became more and more bold. He now realized that his boldness had led him into a trap from which he could never escape. Ten years ago, he had answered a simple ad from a young man seeking an older man. He answered the ad and corresponded for several months with the young man that called himself Michael. First, Mike had sent him nude photos of himself from the neck down and had asked Henderson if he liked what he saw. Henderson had always replied "yes" and grew more and more anxious to meet, but Mike would always play with him by suggesting places to meet and then either changing the meeting place or simply never showing up. Finally the two met and went to Mike's place and had a steamy love relationship for several hours. One week later, Henderson jogged to his PO box and found a CD wrapped in brown paper and addressed to him. He jogged back home and went straight to his den. His wife was always asleep at this time in the morning. He placed the CD in the CD drive and put on his headset. What he saw next made his heart stop. There he was in bed with Michael. The sounds of their lovemaking made him excited and scared at the same time. His face froze as the image changed to the face of Mike. He did not move as Mike spoke to him, "Hello Ron... I guess that you have seen the fun we had the other day... I want you to know that I know who you are and how to get to the CIA and your wife. I am sure that you do not want me to do that so I would like for you to listen to me very carefully. You are to immediately stop going to the PO box on your morning jogs. Instead, I want you to jog in the park that is one mile east of your house. There is a bridge that crosses over a small brook. As you approach the bridge, there is a sign that says "CAUTION NARROW BRIDGE AHEAD". If you go under the bridge, you will find a black plastic garbage bag. This will be your drop point. When you make your drop, I want you to place a piece of black electrical tape over the letter "D" on the sign. I will take the drop bag and leave another empty bag. What do I want... I want any information that you may have on the affairs of Israel, Iraq, Iran and Syria, Russia, China, the President... everybody... got it!!! I want to know what the CIA is sending the President. You can put this information of computer 3.5" disks or CD. Remember, I want anything and everything that you know. If you refuse... well... this CD can be sent to the CIA and to your wife. Now pay attention... when I want to send you a message, there will be a piece of tape on the letter "D" and a red plastic bag under the bridge. Be alert for my signal... I will change the drop point every so often. Now tomorrow morning, I want you to place a single piece of paper in the black drop bag with the following message..."I UNDERSTAND." Ron... this is not a joke... be there tomorrow morning. Oh by the way... this CD is about to self dist..." There was a hissing sound and the computer disk drive erupted into flames. Henderson watched as the monitor went blank. Several seconds later, the smoke alarm in the den went off and seconds after that, Henderson's wife ran into the room screaming at him to put out the fire.

That was how it had all started ten years earlier. Over the years, the drop site was changed on a regular basis so no one could recognize a pattern in his jogging activities. Drop sites included phone booths, a waste container in the parks and hotels, trees in the park, a playground, a dugout in a ball field, and countless other random locations. Today, he was back to where it all began, the bridge. Henderson came back to reality and looked at a disk on the table. He reached over to the disk and placed it into his jogging pants pocket. Sipping the last swig of his coffee, he exited the house and jogged toward the park. Inside of his pocket was information about the missile capability of China. As usual, he looked at the sign for a signal from Mike. Seeing none, he placed the tape on the letter "D" on the sign and jogged under the bridge. Seconds later, he reappeared and turned toward his house.

Five minutes later, Mike jogged toward the bridge from the opposite direction and darted under the bridge. Reaching down, he picked up the trash bag and removed the disk, placed it into his pants pocket and approached the sign. Pretending to adjust his shoe, he placed his left hand on the sign and removed the tape and then jogged away.

Mike's real name was Victor Thieme. He was now 35 years old, six foot five inches, good looking with blond hair, blue eyes and a drop out from Georgetown University where he had tried to get a degree in political science. For all practical purposes he was a failure in everything he had tried to accomplish in the real world and therefore completed his education on the streets of Washington D.C. He had become very streetwise and had turned to crime to support himself. Living in the shadows of Washington, D.C. he had learned the art of mugging people, stealing cars and male prostitution to survive. He quickly learned how to blackmail his prostitution victims for money, cars and whatever else he thought he could get. Ron was his biggest fish yet. When Ron had answered Mike's ad, Mike delayed making contact with Ron until he could find out who Ron was, where he lived and where he worked. He watched the PO box and waited for Ron to make the initial pick up and then followed him home. After that, he waited until Ron went to work and quickly discovered that Ron worked for the CIA. After learning all of this, Mike sat back and began to create a plan in his mind that would quickly put him on easy street.

Ever since Mike had been a child, James Bond, the FBI and the CIA had fascinated him. He had followed the exploits of the FBI and CIA as they tracked and captured the people they wanted. His secret hero was the Jackal. At home, he would watch the Discovery® channel, the History® channel and The Learning Channel® when there were specials on crimes that people had committed. He watched these stories to learn what mistakes they had made that had led to their capture so he would not make the same mistake twice. He loved the web sites that would allow him to pull down the law cases of the spies and other people who had been captured by the FBI and CIA. He would spend hours in the public librar-ies using their web-enabled computers to dial up the FBI and CIA websites to read the arrest warrants and indictments of actual spies. He found it hard to believe that the FBI and CIA would actually publish entire histories of spies, how they worked, who they con-tacted, how they made their drops and how much they were paid for their information. To Mike, Ron was ripe for the plucking and he was just the guy to do it.

Mike didn't know what information he would receive from Ron. His first request from Ron was to learn what he actually did at the CIA and what type of information he had access to. Over the years, Ron had moved internally inside the CIA and Mike quickly learned that he had access to almost anything. This offered to Mike the pos-sibility of setting up a supermarket of intelligence information that could be sold to almost any government. With that in mind, he col-lected information from Ron as he set about making contact with the embassies in Washington that he thought would buy his infor-mation. Mike would tell Ron to give him the names of known agents and support personnel for the various governments he needed. After receiving this information, he would send a letter to the support person's residence in Washington D.C. He wore rubber gloves and used a mail service to insure that the letter would always be postmarked from Philadelphia, Baltimore, or New York City to maintain his anonymity. Inside of his letter was always a second letter that was sealed. On the outside of this letter, he would say "DO NOT OPEN. TAKE THIS ENVELOPE UNOPENED To _____" Inside the sealed letter, he would write:

Dear Mr. _____

I will be sending you a disk that contains sensitive information from the highest level of the United States intelligence community. Please use this information wisely since the information itself can lead to my discovery. I am sending you this information free of charge as a sign of my sincerity. Thereafter, there will be a charge of $100K for future information. As a sign of the validity of the information that you will receive about the United States, I will now describe some of the information that the United States has regarding your government.

At this point, Mike would select certain pieces of information that he held that outlined specific details regarding the governments secrets that he knew was impossible for anyone to know unless it came from the CIA. After that, he would finish up his letter by saying:

Future payment instructions and future contact procedures will be sent directly to you. If you want this relationship to continue, place a message in a plain envelope that says "I ACCEPT" and place the envelope in the waste basket in the front lobby of the Embassy Suites Hotel®, downtown Washington D.C. on the _____, of _____, no later than 12:00 noon. Hereafter, I will add 7 and you will subtract 7 from months, dates and time for future communications.

—Q

Using this procedure, Mike contacted almost every embassy in Washington that held opposing views toward the policies of the United States. Over the years, he was amazed at the ease in which he sent the information to these governments and the amounts of money they were willing to pay. After a short time, he decided to open a Swiss bank account to hide his money and purchased a new wardrobe, moved out of his apartment and started using different names as he checked into a variety of hotels. After a while, each hotel would recognize him, but each hotel would know him by a different name. His cover was an executive for a variety of fictitious companies. He always paid cash for his hotel stays and would stay in each hotel for no more than a week at a time. It had been ten years ago that he had started his intelligence operation and he had saved a modest fortune of over $10 million in his Swiss bank account. Ten years was a long time and he was growing tired of the game. He wanted to retire and spend the rest of his life in Europe, but to do that, he calculated he that needed a little more cash, about $15 million to live the life style of his dreams. All he needed was one really big hit. Mike checked into another hotel and as he did, he received a complementary copy of USA TODAY® and read the headlines regarding the sinking of the Titanic and the death of the Prime Minister. He smiled as he thought about the $100K he had received from Israel about the sub information. Placing the paper under his arm he approached the elevator and wondered what would be the piece of information that would allow him to retire.

BETHESDA NAVAL HOSPITAL: 0800 HOURS

Joshua was asleep in the chair next to Jacky. The nurses had let him stay with her throughout the night, checking on both of them on a regular basis. Daylight seeped into the rooms around the edges of the heavy drawn curtains as Joshua stirred and opened his eyes. For a second, he was lost and could not remember where he was, but the beeping sounds from the monitors connected to Jacky quickly returned him to reality. He reached for her hand and lovingly stroked it as he had done onboard the Titanic.

Jacky reached for the familiar touch and said, "Joshua... is that you?"

Joshua quickly started to stand, but pain shot through his leg forcing him back into the chair. Wincing in pain, but speaking softly he replied, "Yes my beloved... how are you feeling?"

Jacky's raspy voice replied, "I... feel like a rag doll... that has been used for a dust mop... I ache all over..."

"I know... you had quite a time of it out there. You are in the Bethesda Naval Hospital. You have had surgery last night and your face is bandaged."

"I feel funny Joshua... woozy and I can't see..."

Reaching for the alarm button to call the nurse, Joshua pressed it and replied, "You will be fine my love."

The door to the suite opened as a nurse entered the room. Joshua smiled and said, "She is awake."

The nurse looked at the IV drip and reached for Jacky's wrist and looked at her watch. She wrote down a few notes on Jacky's chart and turned to Joshua saying in a cheerful voice, "I am afraid that I must get you back to your room. Dr. Greene will be arriving shortly and she will need to examine your wife. Your doctor will be looking for you as well. Let me help you to your feet."

Reaching for Joshua, the nurse helped Joshua stand as Joshua leaned over Jacky and kissed her softly over the gauze that covered her lips. "I'll see you in a bit."

Jacky tried to reach for Joshua to return his kiss, but the bandages on her arms and IV drips held her back. She whispered softly, "I love you Joshua."

Joshua replied, "I love you too."

Colonel Allan and Admiral Potter had spent the night in the waiting area. They stood as the Prime Minister was returned to his suite and corralled the nurse as she returned to her station.

"Is she awake?"

The nurse looked at Admiral Potter and replied with a frown, "Yes... Dr. Greene will be arriving in a few minutes and I am sure that she will answer your questions."

Allan and Potter returned to the waiting room. Another television set had been placed in the room. Allan turned the set on and sat down. The face of the ZNN anchorperson filled the screen, "Israel is in a state of mourning for the late Prime Minister Joshua Cane." The image changed to show images of downtown Tel-Aviv. The flags were at half-staff and pictures of the Prime Minister were everywhere draped in black. The commentary continued, "It is reported by the Israeli government that a memorial service will be held in six days and the heads of state of almost every country in the world will be attending. ZNN has learned that the President and First Lady will be attending the memorial service to represent the United States. After the memorial service, the President and acting Prime Minister of Israel, Raymond Hochberg will meet privately to discuss Israeli/ United States relations during the transitional period until a new Prime Minister of Israel can be elected."

The face of the anchorperson returned, "The families of the passengers of the Titanic swarmed the offices of the newly formed White Star Corporation today, to learn the fate of their loved ones. It is reported that only 47 passengers survived the disaster at sea." Once again, the image changed showing a videotape of the flaming wreckage of the Titanic taken the night before, "A Congressional hearing is being demanded by the grief stricken family members to learn the cause of the sinking. Many questions are being raised as to how this ship could explode in flames and sink so quickly. Of the 47 survivors, there are no crewmembers or officers of the Titanic to explain what might have happened moments before the tragedy. Looking at other news, the stock..."

Allan switched the set off and looked at Potter, "The President is really going to go over there and smoke out Sadaam... You know, if you tried to put this in a book... no one would believe it."

Dr. Greene stuck her head into the room and smiled, "Good morning gentlemen... I'll see you after I visit Mrs. Cane."

Potter smiled and nodded his head. Looking at Allan, he said, "Want some coffee?"

Allan grumbled, "Yea... why not..."

Dr. Greene and the nurse entered Jacky's darkened suite. Jacky was laying quietly and did not move as the nurse rolled up a stainless steal table that held sterile gloves and other sterile items that would be needed by Dr. Greene.

"How are you feeling Jacky?"

"I ache all over... can I have some water?"

"Certainly you may..."

The nurse poured a glass of water into a glass and guided Jacky's mouth to the end of the straw that was placed between the gauze that covered her face as Dr. Greene put on her sterile gloves and mask.

"Thank you..."

"Jacky, I am going to remove some of the bandages from your face so that you can speak freely and feel a little bit more human. Last night, I operated on your face removing some dead tissue and hair. I will want you to be still as we position your bed to a sitting position. We will place a pillow behind your back so that you can hold your head away from the bed. Do you feel up to this?"

"Yes... I think so."

The nurse pressed a button on the control module for the bed. The head of the bed slowly rose until Jacky was almost sitting as though she were in a chair. A pillow was placed behind her back and Dr. Greene reached for a pair of bandage scissors, "Now I want you to be very still. I am going to cut through the first layer of bandages..."

There was a faint snip and then the clatter of the bandage scissors being placed back on the table. Dr. Greene slowly began to unwrap Jacky's head. Layer after layer of gauze was unwrapped and placed on the table. Finally, the last remains of the first gauze wrap was removed, revealing a second layer that covered from the bridge of Jacky's nose to her forehead. Jacky's hair was missing in the top areas of her scalp. The fire had burned much of her hair off, leaving ugly patches of burned skin. During the surgical procedure the night before, Dr. Green had cut away the long strands of hair that remained, leaving only a red fur covering in the good area located on the back of her head. Fortunately, the oil fire did not burn the back of her neck and scalp because of the position of her life jacket that fit snug and high about her neck. The second wrap of gauze was therefore wrapped over the fur area in the back, reducing the risk of infection to the top of her head that had suffered the brunt of the fire.

"How does that feel Jacky?"

"Much better…"

"Jacky, I am going to remove some of the bandages covering your eyes… There are pads that cover each eye and are held in place by the gauze. As I remove the gauze, I want you to tell me if you see anything. Once the gauze is removed, I will lower you back slightly and remove the pillow. I want you to then lay back and again be very still. Do you understand?"

"Yes…"

Again, there was a snip of the bandage scissors and the rattle of the scissors being returned to the table. Slowly, Dr. Greene began to unwrap the bandages. Finally, the pillow was removed and the bed lowered. Jacky lay back and held her head still. Dr. Greene removed a small flashlight from her lab coat and began to trace a line from one eye patch to the other.

"Can you see anything Jacky?"

"I… I think so… It's like looking at the sun with your eyes closed… there is like a red hue…"

"Good. Now I am going to remove the eye patch from your left eye. When I do, keep your eye lid closed until I tell you to open your eye… OK?"

"Yes…"

Dr. Greene turned off the room light over Jacky's bed and then removed the eye patch and said, "Now open your eye for me…"

Jacky opened her left eye. The room was dark. There was a back-lit image of someone next to her. She found it hard to focus on the image.

"Tell me what you see?"

"I think... I think that I see you but it is very dark in here..."

"Turn your head to the left... towards me... I will slowly turn up the light above your head. Tell me if the light hurts your eye..."

Dr. Greene slowly turned the rheostat that controlled the light intensity. Jacky watched as the room brightened ever so slightly. The face of Dr. Greene was visible now. Dr. Greene continued to increase the light intensity and finally said, "Tell me what you see?'

"I... I see you... I see you..."

"Good... How well do you see me?'

"I... I see your face... your white coat... there is something written on your coat... I can't read what it says..."

"Very good Jacky... Now I am going to lower the light and follow the same procedure for your right eye... OK?"

"Yes..."

Dr. Greene removed the patch from her right eye and said, "Open your eyes... both of them..."

Jacky opened her eyes and watched as the light in the room began to brighten. She could see from her left eye, but the image from her right eye was cloudy... she could not see very much except that brightness in the room."

In a panic Jacky said, "My right eye... I can't see..."

"Tell me what you see Jacky..."

"Everything is a blur... I cannot make out anything except the light in the room."

Dr. Green said, "Jacky... I am going to place the patch back on your left eye and then I want to examine your right eye... OK?"

"Yes..."

Dr. Greene placed the patch on the left eye and then removed an ophthalmoscope from the table and looked into Jacky's right eye. She adjusted the aperture to a plain white circle and moved back to a distance of approximately two feet from Jacky's eye and looked for a "red reflex" and then moved to within two inches of her eye. Dr. Greene adjusted the diopter dial to bring the retina into focus and looked for a blood vessel that would lead her to the optical disc. Using this as a point of reference, she looked for abnormalities. After several seconds, Dr. Greene said, "Jacky... I am going to place the patch on your right eye and bandage your eyes..."

Several minutes later, Dr. Greene finished and stood silently for several seconds to collect her thoughts. Clearing her throat, she said, "Jacky... Your left eye is fine and will heal nicely. Your right eye has a damaged cornea. That can be replaced with surgery and after that, you will be as right as rain. There are burns on your face and arms that we need to address, but all in all, you are a very lucky woman, you will recover fully. I will keep your eyes bandaged for a few more days and we will also keep your IV drip in place for another 24 hours. Do you have any questions?"

Jacky turned toward the direction of Dr. Greene's voice and asked, "Will I be disfigured..."

"Your hair will need to grow back and there may be a need for plastic surgery in a few areas, but I think that you will return to your former radiance in a few months. I need to ask you a question... Are you up to receiving visitors?"

"Uh... yes... I guess so."

"There are two men that need to speak with you. If you like, I can hold them off until this afternoon."

"Who are they?"

"They represent the President, Mrs. Cane. They need to speak to you as soon as possible."

"Yes... I can see them... I mean I can talk with them."

"Normally, I would not allow this type of visit so soon after surgery, but if you are sure that you are up to it, I will allow them fifteen minutes. After that, I want you to rest."

"Can I see Joshua?"

"I think that I can arrange for that. Now remember, in fifteen minutes, I want you to rest."

Dr. Green and the nurse left the suite as Allan and Potter approached the doctor. Folding her arms across her chest she said, "You have fifteen minutes now and another fifteen minutes this evening. As she improves, I will extend the time limit."

Allan replied, "Fifteen minutes will be fine for the time being. Thank you doctor."

Allan knocked softly on the door and then entered the suite with Admiral Potter. They approached the bed quietly and arranged two chairs near the bed. Allan spoke first, "How are you feeling Mrs. Cane."

"I... am feeling as good as could be expected... I am sorry, I didn't mean to sound rude... I am OK."

"Mrs. Cane, my name is Colonel Allan... Admiral Potter is also with me."

Potter replied, "It's a pleasure to meet you Mrs. Cane?"

Allan continued, "Mrs. Cane, the President has asked that we speak with you regarding the circumstances that led up to the sinking of the Titanic... We understand that you were under the care of Dr. Moosavi... Is that correct?"

"Yes..."

"What can you tell us about this man?"

"I thought he was my friend, but he was a monster..."

"In what regard Mrs. Cane?"

"It's a long story Colonel Allan... He was my psychiatrist and doctor for many years... it started with the death of my son... that was when I had a nervous breakdown and Dr. Moosavi began seeing me."

"When you say seeing me, you mean he started treating you as a patient... correct?"

"Yes... that is correct. He took me to Oslo, Norway where he tried to brainwash me."

Admiral Potter spoke up, "Brainwash?"

"Yes… he placed me in a tank of some kind. I could not see, hear, smell, feel or taste anything. It was like I was in a void… it drove me crazy… then they gave me a lot of drugs."

Potter looked at Allan and replied, "Sensory deprivation… it is used to quickly break a person. The brain is deprived of all senses. The tank is usually a water tank kept at body temperature. The eyes, ears, and nose are plugged with an odorless material. The mouth is sealed with a breathing tube that feeds the body filtered air. After a while the brain is starved for sensory input and the mind begins to hallucinate and eventually goes mad. The drugs used after that, control the patient and continue to allow the person to be brainwashed. It is a very quick and effective form of mind control."

Allan asked, "What happened after that?"

"I really don't know how to explain what happened… It was like there were two of me… One part of me wanted to kill Joshua and the other part… loved him… it was horrible… and standing between us was Dr. Moosavi. He controlled me and trained me to kill Joshua. He wanted me to kill him on our wedding night…"

Again Potter explained, "The treatment bifurcated her personality."

Allan raised his eyebrows and said, "What?"

"Split in two… like Dr. Jekyll and Hyde… one person with two personalities."

Allan looked at Jacky and said, "Did he ever say anything about a sub… or anything else that would lead you to believe that there were others involved with a plan to blow up the Titanic?"

"No… I really cannot remember him referring to anything like that…"

"There was an armed confrontation on board the Titanic prior to the sinking… did he say anything about the terrorists?"

"No… he was with me when that happened… I don't remember him saying anything about the men that were killed."

Admiral Potter replied, "He was playing his cards very close to his chest…"

Allan asked, "Other than the time that you were in the lifeboat, did he mention anything about the Jihad?"

Jacky remained silent for several seconds and replied, "Yes… there was a mention of the word Jihad when I was in Oslo… there were men who were talking to him. They did not believe that I would kill Joshua and demanded that he make me kill someone."

"What did they look like?"

"They were Arabic I think… like Dr. Moosavi and one looked Chinese."

"What did Moosavi do?"

"When I was returned to the US, they took me to some warehouse in Jersey City and told me to kill a woman with a knife. She was a pregnant woman… and I cut and butchered her like a cow in a slaughter house."

"Were these men, that Dr. Moosavi talked to, at the warehouse?"

"Yes… they watched me kill that poor woman." Jacky began to sob and turn her head from side to side as Dr. Greene entered the suite. Hearing Jacky, she rushed across the room toward Allan and Potter, "What are you doing to my patient? Please leave this suite immediately."

Allan and Potter immediately rose from their chairs and left the room as Dr. Greene leaned over Jacky trying to calm her down.

Allan and Potter huddled outside the suite. Potter said, "I think that we have enough evidence to assume that Dr. Moosavi was working with Sadaam and Sadaam was working with the Muslim extremists. That was an interesting comment about the Chinese fellow."

Allan replied, "I'll notify the President…"

Potter said, "I am going home for a while. I'll be back this evening."

Allan looked at his watch as he walked to the elevator and said, "Let say 1800 hours…"

Potter replied, "Good… see you then."

CHAPTER 13

APRIL 20TH

ARABIAN SEA: 1000 HOURS

The chairman of the Joint Chiefs of Staff issued instructions to alert the two forward deployed carrier battle groups (CVBGs) of the Seventh Fleet to stand ready for immediate orders that would initiate preparations for an attack against Iraq. Since the Gulf War in '91, the United States had kept two CVBGs forward deployed and ready for action in case the Iraq situation once again exploded into a crisis situation. The need for forward deployed CVBGs was further demonstrated by the refusal of some of the Persian Gulf allies to allow the use of air bases on their territory. These bases were required by American forces to enforce the Southern no-fly zone over Iraq. Consequently, every six months, the two CVBGs on station would be rotated out of the area and replaced by two other CVBGs. At the present time, the USS Nimitz (CV-68) and USS George Washington (CV-73) were on station.

The Seventh Fleet in its entirety, consists of the Seventh fleet command ship, two aircraft carriers, four guided missile cruisers, nine destroyers and guided missile destroyers, three guided missile frigates, five fast attack submarines, one multipurpose amphibious assault ship, one amphibious transport dock, two dock landing ships, two mine countermeasure ships, one submarine tender, one auxiliary ship, three survey ships, three fleet oiler ships, four combat stores ships, one command and coordination ship and two anti-submarine ships. Based in Yokosuka, Japan, the Seventh Fleet consisted of approximately 45 ships, 180 aircraft and approximately 26,000 Sailors and Marines that kept a strong American presence in the Pacific, Indian Ocean and Arabian Gulf and is the largest of the Navy's forward-deployed fleets.

The Seventh fleet, with the support of the Task Force Commanders, directly enforced the three principal elements of the U.S. national security meaning deterrence, forward defense and alliance solidarity.

The USS Nimitz (CV-68) was commissioned on 3 May 1975. Nimitz had been stationed in the Arabian Gulf since 1997 and had pulled several tours of duty to enforce the Southern no-fly zone over Iraq. She was the first of the "Nimitz" class of aircraft carrier and was 1,092 feet in overall length, 252 feet in overall width, had a flight deck area of approximately 4.5 acres, had two nuclear power plants that powered four main engines that drove four 5 bladed propellers and could propel the ship through the sea at speeds in excess of 30 knots. Fully loaded, she has a displacement of approximately 95,000 tons and serves approximately 20,000 meals each day to a crew of approximately 6,000 officers and men.

After receiving the orders from the Joint Chiefs of Staff, the Commander of the Seventh Fleet had called an emergency briefing on board the USS Nimitz. He had arrived on board earlier and was waiting for the arrival of the Captain from the USS George Washington. The ship was abuzz with the crew talking about what might be going on. The flight deck of CV-68 suddenly came alive as they prepared to receive the arrival of a single aircraft, a two man fighter jet F-14 Tomcat. The passenger was the Captain of the USS George Washington. The F-14 Tomcat broke from its holding pattern and began its downwind approach. The LSO (Landing Signal Officer) using the "pickle", a hand held remote control device, operated the signals on the "Lens", a series of signal lights that would tell the arriving pilot if his approach was proper and OK. The LSO called to the pilot, "Call the ball!" Hearing the response, "Roger ball!" the LSO watched as the Tomcat completed its final 10 seconds of flight, falling toward the flight deck at a speed of 130 knots. The aircraft arrived screaming toward the flight deck as the tires scorched the deck and the arresting wires snagged the Tomcat's tail hook, bringing it to a sudden stop. The flight deck crew, "greenies", disengaged the tail hook from the aircraft as the "blue shirt" plane handlers directed the aircraft out of the landing area. Once the aircraft was secured, the pilot and passenger disembarked. Within ten minutes, the Captain of the USS Nimitz, Captain Robert Victor and Captain Vincent Kopacka of the USS George Washington were seated before the Commander of the Seventh Fleet, Rear Admiral Thomas.

There was an air of extreme seriousness about the Admiral's face as he stood and addressed the Captains, "Gentlemen, we have gathered aboard the USS Nimitz for reasons of extreme national security. The information that you are about to receive is classified "TOP SECRET". As you know, the Prime Minister of Israel was killed during the sinking of the Titanic. The Joint Chiefs of Staff have reliable information that Iraq will attempt to launch a preemptive nuclear strike against Israel on 23 April while the President and the heads of state of the free world are attending the memorial service for the Prime Minister. Our job is to take out the missile sites with a surgical air strike, followed by a bombardment of the general area by our BGM-109 Tomahawk Land Attack Missiles and concluded with a seventy-two hour bombing blitz of other targets that need to be taken out. The code name for this action will be called "OPERATION THUNDERBALL."

Captain Victor let out a low whistle and said, "My God…"

Admiral Thomas pressed a hand held remote control button and the images of three mosques appeared on a large screen. Thomas continued, "The government of Iraq has installed what is believed to be three Chinese Dong Feng 21 missiles in each of these mosques. These missiles have a range of 1,200 miles and carry a single nuclear device… each capable of eviscerating Jerusalem. It is not known at this time if Sadaam intends to use all three missiles simultaneously or fire them independently. What is known is that he will use them on 23 April… three days from today. Our mission is to destroy these missiles before they can be used."

Captain Victor replied, "Sounds like an easy job… we have gone in before with impunity and taken out what we want… we can do it again. I would assume that we take them out before 23 April."

"I wish it were that simple Bob. We cannot take them out until they commit to the launch... then and only then are we authorized to strike."

Captain Kopacka replied, "Let me get this straight Admiral... Iraq has three Chinese missiles tipped with nuclear bombs, we know where they are and yet we have to wait until they launch to take them out... Who's idea was that?"

"We are to wait until they commit to a launch before we strike... this directive has come down the highest level... the President himself. The President will be the only head of state attending the memorial service that knows of the planed attack by Iraq. He will be present during the memorial service in Israel, along with the other heads of state, to act as bait to smoke out Sadaam..."

Captain Victor replied, "No disrespect Sir... but has he lost his mind?"

"I doubt that Bob... the situation is like this... Sadaam has the missiles and the bombs. If we strike too soon and we are wrong in our assumption that the missiles are in the mosques, we could attack the wrong targets. The international consequences of an unprovoked attack against Iraq are serious. Sadaam is already convincing many of our allies to lift the embargo against Iraq. An unprovoked attack would allow him to have the embargo removed. God help the world and us if he manages to get away with the nuclear devices and hides them... he will dream up another plan and use them somewhere else. If Sadaam launches these missiles and we are right in our assumption that they are inside these mosques, he will have to roll back the domes to fire the missiles. If you look at the images of these mosques, you will see a rail track system. We believe that this track will allow them to move the dome aside so the missile can be fired. We have in position our "birds" and we are monitoring these mosques in real time. We will have our air squadrons in the no-fly zone on the 23rd and will immediately attack when they start to move the dome."

Kopacka asked, "How much time will we have when the domes start to move?"

"Approximately two minutes... maybe three."

"Cutting it close don't you think?"

"Yes... but we've done it before..."

Victor replied, "Many times, but never with the Commander and Chief's life hanging in the balance."

"Each of your CVBGs will be receiving a total of 10 F-22 fighters. Currently, they are in route and they should fly-on in approximately 20 minutes from now. USACOM headquarters has issued instructions for the use of the F-22 because of its speed and stealth capability. This will be a day mission and Sadaam has increased anti-aircraft batteries around these targets. We cannot knock out the SAMs before the attack... the F-22 should have a distinct advantage over the F-14s in this regard. USACOM has trained these F-22 pilots well. Your regular fighter groups will participate in the third phase of the event... the 72-hour blitz of Iraq."

Admiral Thomas reached for two CDs and handed one to each Captain, "These are the battle plans, and they are for your eyes only. Each of your ships will coordinate the attack on the mosque assigned to your battle group. Bob, of your 10 F-22s, five will attack the mosque in Irbil and five will attack Baghdad. Frank, of your 5 F-22s, five will attack Al Basrah. Your remaining five F-22s will be in reserve if needed and will maintain a holding position in the no-fly zone. The new F-22 should be more than enough to do the job. The ships in each of your CVBGs will launch the BGM-109 Tomahawk attack and your F-14 fighter squadrons will complete the 72 hour blitz and finish the job. At 0800 hours on 22 April, you will distribute the orders to the Captains in each of your battle groups. No one... I repeat no one but the flight crews of the F-22 fighters are to be told of the true nature of their mission regarding the President and they are not to be told until their final briefing prior to the attack. Is that understood?"

Both Captains replied, "Yes Sir..."

"Good… I will be remaining on board Nimitz until the mission is complete. Bob… Frank… I have all of the confidence in both of you, your officers and crew. The United States Navy has been chosen to put an end to this international crisis… I know you will do the Navy proud. Good hunting."

Victor and Kopacka stood and saluted and said, "Thank you Admiral."

Captain Victor returned to the flight deck. The Nimitz had four catapults, affectionately called "Fat Cats." Victor's F-14 Tomcat was positioned on one Fat Cat and was ready for takeoff. Climbing into the rear of the Tomcat, Victor strapped himself in and put on his flight helmet. The canopy began to close as the pilot in the forward seat began to increase the thrust. The landing strut holdback device held the Tomcat in place as it reached full power. The canopy closed and the pilot looked to the "shooter", the catapult officer in the control pod, and gave him a salute. Both Victor and the pilot placed their hands on the console to brace themselves against the sudden thrust of the aircraft engines and catapult. In approximately 300 feet and two seconds later, the F-19 Tomcat reached a speed of 180 miles per hour as the onboard computer flew the aircraft off the end of the flight deck. The pilot quickly assumed control of the Tomcat and banked a hard starboard turn as Victor looked back at the Nimitz. The first F-22 landed on the deck of the Nimitz and was snagged by the arresting wire.

BETHESDA NAVAL HOSPITAL – 1900 HOURS

Jacky was recovering better than expected. Dr. Greene had removed most of the bandages on her head, retaining only the eye patch on her right eye. Her arm and shoulder burns were beginning to heal and Dr. Greene had allowed for Jacky's bed to be placed in the Presidential suite with Joshua. Together, they convalesced watching the news events unfold on ZNN and speaking quietly of their future plans.

Joshua looked at Jacky and said, "I am sorry that I put you through this..."

"Don't be sorry... it isn't your fault."

There was silence once again in the room as Joshua turned off the television set. Returning to Jacky's side, he said, "You know... this is going to be very a confused world when this thing is all over. The world thinks that I am dead. When they stop Saddam and I return from the dead... there are going to be those that will be very upset and try to kill me again... that is what worries me..."

Jacky placed her bandaged hand on Joshua's face and said, "I will be there with you Joshua... Don't be afraid..."

"I am not afraid for myself... I am afraid for you..."

"Whatever comes, I will be at your side Joshua... Don't be afraid for me... I am a fighting Irish wildcat... I have survived this far and I can make it the rest of the way."

"There isn't going to be anymore "way" after this is over. I have been thinking... I am going to resign as soon as this mess is over... this is not the life that I had in mind for you. Here we are on our honeymoon... I have a bullet hole in my leg and you... the most important person in my life has an ocean liner shot out from under her, are badly burned, have almost lost the sight in one eye... and all for what... for what... so that some madman can conquer the world? Let someone else carry the fight. This mess will never end... do you realize that? If we stop them now, they will come at us again and again and again. I don't want you to be part of that. I want to spend the rest of my life with you... loving you... not being afraid that someone will try to kill you to get at me... If that happened... I would die myself... they wouldn't have to kill me."

"And if you resign... you will be even more unhappy. Joshua... the people of Israel and the people of the world need you. You must assume your position as Prime Minister as soon as you can. If you run away and hide, you will soon learn to hate yourself... and me. I did not marry a man that runs away... Remember the holocaust... remember the words "NEVER AGAIN"... You are a fighter Joshua...

You are a modern day King David... You are the leader of Israel... my husband. As your wife... I will go where you go and always be at your side... until death do us part."

Joshua looked at Jacky as she spoke. The fire in her eye, the firmness of her voice and the truth that she spoke offered him little escape. He placed his hands on Jacky's and replied, "Are you sure... I could resign and we run away somewhere far from this mess... far away from the killings, the car bombs..."

"But you cannot run away from yourself Joshua..."

Joshua stood and walked around the room silently. There was little he could say. He knew that Jacky was right. If he removed himself from power, he would never get his mind off of the daily events in Israel. Looking at Jacky he said, "As always... you are right... I will continue the fight as long as you are at my side... God Jacky... I love you so much."

CHAPTER 14

APRIL 21, 2002

ALEXANDERIA, VA: 0530 HOURS

The steel gray sky hung low over Alexandria. It was cold and raining. April had been unusual with warm days, followed by dreary weather, accompanied by unusually cold temperatures. Last night, the temperature had fallen to 38 degrees. Ron liked to have the window cracked at night and now the bedroom was cold. The house thermostat was programmed to kick in at 0600. Ron's wife had covered the bed with a hand made quilt the night before. She would have preferred to have the window closed each night, but after years of being married to her health nut, she had learned to give in and simply cover her head with the quilt on cold nights. Ron looked back at the bed and pulled the covers over the spot where he had slept. Only the hair curlers in his wife's hair were visible as she reached for the quilt and disappeared, mumbling something incomprehensible. Ron slept only in jockey shorts. Entering the bathroom, he tossed the underwear into the hamper and shit, showered and shaved. In twenty minutes, he was dressed in his jogging suit and headed downstairs.

For the past several weeks, Ron had become more depressed with his situation. There was little he could do to stop Mike from tormenting him. It had now been ten years and Ron was at the end of his rope trying to cope with his family life, his job, his desires for other men and dealing with Mike. It was because of Mike that he had stopped answering ads in the papers. He knew that Mike followed him. Once, early on in their relationship, Mike broke into a motel room and beat the living shit out of the lover that Ron had found by answering an ad. Mike then told him that he was not to answer any other ads or the next time, Mike would kill the lover and frame Ron for the murder. Over the years, Ron had become more and more terrified of Mike. Due to his lack of homosexual sex, Ron could only close his eyes and remember the feel of another man and relieve himself in the shower whenever the stress became unbearable.

There had also been an increase in security at the CIA. He could not operate as freely as he had done in the past and on more than one occasion; he had almost been caught with sensitive information. Like a fox being chased by hounds, he knew that they were after him and it would only be a matter of time before he was caught. He could feel the breath of the hounds on the back of his neck. If he were caught, he would be a disgrace to his family and to his country. He would lose all of his pensions, go to jail or could possibly be executed as a spy and for murder. It was because of Ron that several operatives in Russia had been captured and executed. If the information that he had stolen was traced back to him, he knew that he would be brought up on criminal charges and murder one.

The teapot began to whistle and he grabbed the pot and made a cup of tea. Walking quietly into the den, sat down before his computer and turned it on. Placing a disk in the "A" drive, Ron copied a file to the disk. He had typed a complete report the night before. As he watched the green light on the "A" drive, Ron's eyes drifted down to his hands, they were shaking, not from the cold, but from fear. The file that was being copied held a piece of information that even Ron found hard to believe. The previous day, Ron had read a file that was called "OPERATION THUNDERBALL". In the file, he discovered that Iraq had possession of short-range Chinese missiles and nuclear warheads. He understood the implications of the death of the Prime Minister and the memorial service that would follow. In an associated file, he soon discovered that the Prime Minister and his wife were still alive and being held secretly at the Bethesda Naval Hospital until "OPERATION THUNDERBALL" was completed. In short, the Americans had set a trap for Saddam. He knew if he gave this information to Mike, he would be responsible for whatever would happen. His depression grew deeper as he removed the disk and placed it on the desk.

Slowly, he slid open the drawer and the butt of a revolver became visible. Ron had a look of terror on his face as he reached for the gun, his eyes were wide open and unblinking, his breathing was rapid and tears began to roll down his face as the cold steel greeted his wet shaking palm. Grabbing the revolver, he closed his fingers around the grip and placed his thumb on the hammer, cocking the gun. The metallic click reverberated in his ears. For what seemed like an eternity, the gun began to rotate toward his face. He formed an oval with his mouth and closed his eyes as the cold barrel penetrated deeply into his oral cavity. The gun barrel tasted metallic and his saliva joined with the metal creating a solution that made his mouth tingle. He sat there trembling waiting for his hand to do something, but nothing happened, the gun did not go off. His finger did not squeeze the trigger. He bit down on the barrel trying to muster the courage to finish the job, but still he sat shaking like a fool with a gun in his mouth. Quickly he yanked the gun out of his mouth and placed it back into the drawer as he had done thousands of times before. Slamming the drawer shut, he placed his head on his arm and cried as he pounded the desk with his fist. Another failure… another point of depression… and another reason to kill himself, he was a coward. If only he could pull the trigger and end his life. At least that way, he would be free, his wife would get his pension and nobody would know that he was a fag and a spy. It was all so simple.

After several minutes of uncontrollable crying, Ron regained control of himself and reached for the disk. He looked at his watch… it was 0622. He was fifteen minutes behind schedule. The door closed quietly behind him as he began to jog. The rain was cold and pounded against his face as he turned toward the park. The distance was 1.2 miles to the bridge. This was the same bridge that he used to make his first drop. Traffic was building and the sidewalks and streets were slippery as he jogged in place waiting for the light to turn green at a busy intersection. As he started to cross the street a speeding car barely missed his legs. The driver blew his horn, yelling something and as he continued down the street. Like a zombie, Ron continued toward his destination. Eight minutes later, he paused at the sign "CAUTION NARROW BRIDGE AHEAD" and pretended to tie his shoe. He placed the tape on the "D" and jogged under the bridge, placing the disk in the black garbage bag. Moments later, he started home.

The voice of the man who had almost cut him down at the intersection echoed in his brain. His pace increased as his feet splashed faster and faster against the wet pavement. There was conviction in his eyes as he neared the intersection. A large delivery truck was approaching. Ron had the red light. His feet moved faster and faster as he watched the truck. The green light for the truck turned yellow and the driver pressed down hard on the accelerator to beat the red light. Ron's timing was perfect. As the truck shot through the intersection, Ron arrived directly in front of the truck. There was a look of terror in the eyes of the truck driver as the truck's grill slammed into Ron's chest. The driver watched Ron's body arch upwards from the impact and sail through the air, crashing into the box trailer like a bird against the windshield of an oncoming train. There was a sickening crunching thud as Ron's body careened off of the trailer and crashed into the street. The driver had tried to swerve to his left to miss Ron. As a result, when Ron's body hit the street, the back tires of the trailer crushed his head like a melon in a vise. The truck continued skidding forward and hit a fire hydrant; the water shot up like a geyser and a crowd quickly formed around the scene. One person tripped over Ron's jogging shoes that were sitting upright in the middle of the street, looked at the body and turned away in disgust.

The driver opened the door of his cab and yelled, "He ran in front of me… he ran in front of me…" Looking at Ron, he cried out to the onlookers, "Oh my God… Did you see him… he ran in front of me… I tried to miss him…" Trembling and in a state of shock, the driver stood in the rain watching an ever increasing pool of blood form around Ron's body as one of the spectators reached for his cell phone and dialed 911.

Mike approached the bridge on his moped. He looked at the "CAUTION NARROW BRIDGE AHEAD" sign and saw the tape signal. Approaching the bridge, he carefully drove off of the road and parked the bike. Once under the bridge he retrieved the black garbage bag and removed the disk, placing it inside of his jacket to keep it dry. In an instant he was back on his moped. Ahead, he could see a crowd of people forming a circle around a truck. Curiously, he headed toward the scene and saw the geyser of water shooting high into the air. A squad car approached him from behind, the siren echoed in his helmet. Pulling over to his right, the squad car whizzed by, spraying him with water from a puddle. Mike proceeded slowly and approached the accident. The flashing lights of the squad car and sounds of another squad car approaching electrified the milling crowd of people. The driver was talking to one police officer as the second officer began to push back the crowd of onlookers. Mike could now see a body lying partially under the wheels of the truck. The blood, hair and brain tissue had mixed with the water in the street giving the accident scene a surreal appearance. The driver was being placed in the back of the squad car. He was crying and kept repeating, "He ran in front of my truck… It wasn't my fault…"

As the police officer continued to push back the crowd of onlookers, Mike got a better view of the body, it was wearing a gray jogging suit. Looking even closer at the body, there was something familiar about it. Mike looked around the street until he spotted the Nike® Boing® running shoes and he knew, the gray jogging suit, the Boing® shoes. The body was Ron. Under his breath he muttered, "Fuck… that stupid son-of-a-bitch…" Ron had been Mike's money cow and now he was dead. How was he ever going to find another guy like Ron? It was simple, he couldn't. There was a feeling of anger as Mike turned around and drove away. What would he do now? He pressed his arm against his side and felt the disk. This would be the last disk that he would ever get. What was on it? As he turned right, an oncoming ambulance shot past him with its siren screaming and lights flashing. He wanted to retire. Was $10 million enough? Why didn't Ron wait for another couple of years before he got himself killed… stupid asshole? As Mike approached his hotel, he resigned himself to the fact that this would be his last stint as a spy in the world of international espionage. He proceeded up the entrance to his hotel, parked in the valet section and gave the keys to the doorman. Minutes later, he entered his hotel room and took off his wet jacket. He removed the disk from the inside pocket and turned on his laptop. As he dried his hair with a towel, the computer alerted him that it was ready with the familiar musical tone as the Windows® logo appeared on the screen. Tossing the towel on the bed, Ron remarked in a low voice, "Thank you Mr. Gates…" Lighting a cigarette, he placed the disk in the "A" drive and clicked on the "My Computer" icon. After that, he clicked on the "A" drive and saved the disk to his document file. Moments later, the document appeared on the screen.

Hello Mike,

The information that I am about to give you will undoubtedly make you a very wealthy man. I hope that I am correct, because this is the last piece of information that you will ever get from me. By the time that you read this, I pray to God that I will be dead and no longer under your power. You have made my life an absolute hell and I cannot take it any longer. For that, I hope that you burn in hell when your time comes. When it does, I am sure that I will be there to greet you and watch you suffer like you have made me suffer for the last ten years.

As you know from my last bit of news that I gave to you, the Titanic was sunk by a Russian Kilo class sub. It is now apparent that this sinking was an attempt by Sadaam to kill the Prime Minister of Israel so that he would have a shot at nuk-

ing all of the heads of state that would assemble in Jerusalem to pay him homage. The US knows of this plan and will attack the suspected targets in Iraq to destroy the missiles that Sadaam intends to use to do the job. This attack has been Codenamed "OPERATION THUNDERBALL" Attack aircraft will be launched from two carrier groups in the Arabian Sea.

The second bit of news is that the Prime Minister, Joshua Cane is not dead and is being held undercover in Bethesda Naval Hospital along with his wife. After the attack in Iraq, he will surface and resume control of Israel.

Mike, I could have easily decided not to tell you this information, but then I decided why not. I will be dead and you will not have enough time to sell this information before the US attacks Iraq. I hope that this torments you like you tormented me for the last ten years. Fuck you Mike and the horse that you rode in on too... see you in hell!

—Ron

Mike read the message slowly several times. The smoke from his cigarette swirled from his nostrils as he exhaled slowly. Ron was correct in that he could make a great deal of money from this information and correct again in that he could not make contact with the right government in time to alert them about the attack from the US. That was however, if he used his normal procedure. He had to move quickly. He knew that he had to get the message to Iraq, but to do that he had to select a government that would assist him in delivering the message. The Russians were out and the only other government that he could think of was China. China had violated the trade embargo of Iraq for years. It was a long shot, but one that he knew he had to make, but how? He couldn't just walk into the Chinese Embassy and tell them what was going on, or could he?

RON HENDERSON RESIDENCE, ALEXANDERIA, VA – 0930 HOURS

The gray overcast sky seemed to hang even lower as the rain continued to pour from the sky. Quietly, two non-descript vans approached Ron's home. Inside were ten men from the CIA. Ron had carried his wallet in his jogging suit. In his wallet was his identification and a laminated photo identification employee pass that he used to enter his office at the CIA. Within moments of his identification, the Alexandria police investigation team had notified the CIA.

Ron had been one of a list of suspects in the increasing CIA internal investigation. The investigation had begun with those people in the CIA that had access to the information regarding the military activity around and the sinking of the Titanic. Ron was among five people that had access to that particular piece of information and was one of three people had actually accessed that data. The CIA was confident that Ron and the other two had not copied any of the information in question to a disk. Since the theft of computer data in Los Alamos during the Clinton administration, all top-secret information had been secured for viewing only. Files could be appended to by the author of the original document, but never erased, printed or copied without higher levels of security clearance. This would include a bio-signature that included fingerprint, retina print and voice identification. Ron did not have that clearance. The concern of the CIA was that even though the files could not be copied, they could be read, memorized and passed on through other means. Slowly, the vans pulled up to the house and the men quietly approached the front door. One of the men rang the doorbell and waited for Ron's wife to appear. The rain pelted the men relentlessly as the doorbell was pressed again. Finally, Ron's wife opened the door. She looked concerned as one of the men produced his leather bound CIA identification photo and shield. Speaking softly she said, "Yes…"

"Mrs. Henderson, my name is agent Anderson and these are my men… May we come in?"

Opening the door a bit wider, she allowed the men to enter her home. The men stood quietly in the foyer as Anderson said, "Is there somewhere that we can talk Mrs. Henderson. I am afraid that I have some very bad news to tell you."

Ron's wife stood quietly as the words sank in and she said, "Is the kitchen OK... I was about to cook a cake for Ron... today is his birthday..."

"That will be fine..."

Anderson followed Ron's wife into the kitchen. He could tell that she was very nervous as she reached for a dishtowel and twisted it in her hands. Alexander said, "Please Mrs. Henderson... sit down." Mrs. Henderson sat down, looking up at Anderson as he continued, "There was an accident this morning and your husband was struck and killed by a truck..."

The men in the foyer said nothing as they heard, "OH MY GOD... NO... NO..."

Anderson kneeled and said, "I am sorry Mrs. Henderson... I was told that he did not suffer..."

"Where is he? I want to see him..."

"I will take you to him. Please take your time and when you are ready..."

"My God... I must call the children..."

"Certainly Mrs. Henderson..."

"How did it happen?"

"Your husband was jogging and crossed a busy intersection..."

"I told him not to jog..."

"Did he do it a lot Mrs. Henderson?"

"Every morning, rain or shine... like clockwork."

"Do you know where he went Mrs. Henderson?

"He never told me..."

"Mrs. Henderson, I have to show you this." Reaching into his coat pocket, Anderson removed a search warrant. "This is a search warrant Mrs. Henderson. I have been authorized to search this house."

"Why... My husband is dead..."

"Your husband also worked for the CIA Mrs. Henderson and we need to search your home for anything that may pertain to his work and return it to the CIA… government property you know."

"He never brought anything home…"

"Yes, Mrs. Henderson, but we still have to check out your home. Did he have a den where he would work on things… a computer…"

"Yes… let me show you…"

The two walked back to the foyer, through the living room and entered a small den. "This is where he would do things on the computer…"

Taking her by the hand, Anderson walked her back to the foyer. Looking at his men, he said, "Check out the den and the rest of the downstairs and basement. I'll take Mrs. Henderson upstairs and when she is ready, I'll take her to the hospital."

Anderson walked behind Ron's wife as his men quickly searched the home. The computer was immediately removed and placed in the van. Other files and documents were also taken. Several of the men opened their travel cases and removed electronic sweeping devices. They were looking for bugs and wire taps. With the exception of the den, the entire downstairs was cleared. They stood patiently as Anderson walked with Ron's wife down the stairs and out to the street. Moment's later; Anderson drove off with her to the hospital. As soon as the van was out of sight, the men started searching the upstairs bedrooms and bath.

CIA HEADQUARTERS – 1200 HOURS

The computer and files were returned to the CIA headquarters for investigation. The files contained nothing of any significance. There were notices of meetings and parties and menus for the month at the CIA cafeteria. The computer seemed innocent as well. There were personal files that contained household checking balances, letters and a few computer games. It wasn't until the computer team checked the "TRASH" file that they hit pay dirt. In the file was the letter to Mike. Either Ron forgot to empty the "TRASH" or he left the letter on purpose. They would never know, but there it was clear as day, Ron was the spy they were looking for. Now they knew that he was feeding information to another man or was it more than one man? How did Ron get involved with this man called Mike? How did Mike get the information from Ron? Piece by piece, the puzzle fell into place. The morning jogs were the method of contact. It was clear that Ron never copied any files but read them and then recreated the information from memory in his computer at home. It was clear that he got up every morning and jogged to his rendezvous point. It was clear that he ran in front of the truck and killed himself. It was also clear that if the letter was delivered, the man called Mike had the information regarding OPERATION THUNDERBALL and knew that the Prime Minister was alive. Instructions were immediately issued for a sweep of the immediate surroundings around Ron's house. They would sweep a five-mile circle around the house, showing pictures of Ron and looking for anything that they could find that might lead them to Mike. A copy of the letter was made and taken immediately to Director Mark Crowley's office. Crowley read the letter and slammed his fist on his desk and said, "Fuck... get me the President."

Moments later, the secretary said, "The President is on the line..."

Crowley reached for the phone and said, "Mr. President... we have a problem. There has been a leak of highly classified information regarding the Prime Minister and OPERATION THUNDERBALL. I am afraid that our attack on Iraq may have been compromised. Yes sir... I'm halfway there." Crowley hung up the phone, grabbed the letter and made his way to a restricted area that housed the elevator that would take him down to the tunnel shuttle and the Whitehouse bunker.

WHITEHOUSE BUNKER – 1500 HOURS

The President and Chiefs of Staff were waiting for Crowley when he arrived. Crowley approached his seat and opened his briefcase.

Removing the copy of the letter, he placed it into a slot that fed the document into a scanner. Moments later, the letter appeared on all eight big screens. Silently, the President and Joint Chiefs read the letter. The President spoke first and said, "Who the fuck is Mike?"

Crowley leaned forward and said, "We don't know. He could be an American traitor... or a Russian, Chinese, British operative. We simply have very little to go on at this time Mr. President."

"Well whoever he is... he knows Israel... Looking at the reference to the Titanic... that is how they found out. That eliminates the Russians and I doubt that the British would have anything to do with him without telling us."

Admiral Sheppard replied dryly, "I wouldn't be so sure Mr. President. The British and Churchill did a number on us during the WWII. They knew more about us on certain matters than we knew about them."

The President replied, "China would be a logical choice... If Mike knows that they have supplied Iraq with missiles, then they would probably pay to find out that we know about their participation in Sadaam's plan."

Crowley replied, "Whereas I would agree with you Mr. President that China would want to know that we know about their missiles... I find it hard to believe that they would pay anything for that information. China does not normally pay anyone anything for information. It is too messy. They do not use "drops" in the park like that FBI agent used last year, Swiss bank accounts, or cans full of diamonds. They prefer to use more subtle means to get information like getting someone drunk or getting them into a compromising position during a visit to China that makes the person tell them what they want to know. Their form of espionage is rather slow... but very effective... they get a person into a situation that makes the person tell them what they need to know. There is no "smoking gun", audit trail from bank deposits or anything else that leads back to them. If Mike goes to the Chinese... he will be in for a surprise. We have already planted a team to watch their embassy. If there is anything going on, I am sure that we will find out. Remember that tunnel that we dug under the Russian embassy... well you get the idea."

The Secretary of State Scrivanich commented, "Jesus H. Christ... If this guy somehow gets this information to Iraq, that will compromise our planned attack... Perhaps we should attack now before it is too late..."

Crowley replied, "I thought about that on the way over and yet, we still really don't know for sure that the missiles are inside the mosques. If they are... and if they know about our plans... that would now give them the element of surprise. They could launch at any time... or not at all. What a Charlie Foxtrot..." The President looked up with an eyebrow raised as Crowley said, "Cluster Fuck Mr. President."

The Chief of Naval Operations McCort commented, "I couldn't agree with your assessment more Mark. They will have us at a disadvantage. We must regain control over this situation. We must get our F-22s in the air over Iraq immediately... That way, if he gets trigger happy, we can blow him away as planned. If I were Sadaam and if I knew our plans, I would probably attack when it was least expected."

Crowley asked, "Meaning..."

"Look... Sadaam wants to kill every head of state in the free world. Maybe he was going to wait until they all gathered at the service sitting around like a bunch of ducks in a pond like we originally thought and be assured that they would all die with only one or two missiles. Now he has a problem. He knows that we know. If I were Sadaam, I would target the city with all three missiles and immediately attack as soon as the last arriving head of state's aircraft's tires scorch the landing strip. Hell, with three of those damn things, he could target one at the airport... one at the memorial site... and the last at the hotels that the dignitaries would be staying..."

The room was silent for several seconds. Finally, Admiral Sheppard commented, "That would give us the advantage... Mr. President, if you arrive at the last moment before the memorial service, Sadaam would not attack until he knew he could get you. After all, you are the guy he really wants. Our F-22 aircraft would be in position as before and we could get the job done. Admiral McCort, you are correct in your assessment. We need those F-22s in the air from now on until the countdown reaches zero... and that will probably be when Air Force 1 touches down at Tel Aviv."

Crowley replied, "I like it... we can say that the President was detained because of the flu... or something and get him there when we are ready."

The President looked around the table with a gleam in his eye and said, "Sounds like a plan... but make it some other excuse rather than the flu... I don't want the would to think that I am a pussy or something... how about Air Force one having a mechanical problem somewhere along the way to Israel? What are we going to do about this Mike guy?"

Crowley replied, "We have one hundred CIA and FBI agents all over the Alexandria Mr. President. Something will turn up I assure you. Be that as it may, I think we have a plan that will work even if Sadaam does find out. That guy Ron was right you know. Mike is going to have one hell of a time getting this information to Sadaam. The letter says that Mike expects to get a lot of money for the information. After thinking about it more, I would like to adjust my profile regarding this man. I think he is American... I don't think that he is an operative from any other government... This is not your usual operative that spies for love of country... this guy does it for the almighty dollar. This guy will be hard to find. In some respects, he is an outcast in our business... a professional con artist... a slime bucket... someone who will sell his mother for a buck. Nobody likes guys like that and nobody likes to pay through the nose Mr. President. With hot information like this, he will have to break with his usual SOP and that will put him at risk, make him nervous and he will make mistakes. When he does that we will either catch him or they will kill him."

ALEXANDERIA – 1800 HOURS

Mike sat at the desk in his hotel room reviewing the names of the Chinese operatives that had been given to him by Ron over the years. The top guy was Wo Ho Fat, 61 years old, 5'5", 280 pounds, shaved head and traditional Fu Man Chu mustache. He had graduated from Princeton University with honors and had returned to China, working his way up the intelligence ladder. He had become China's leading intelligence operative and soon became the director for intelligence operations in the United States. Over the years he designed a massive intelligence program in the United States that successfully persuaded Chinese Americans as well as Native Americans to deliver top-secret information to the Chinese government. These operations focused on students and professors that were granted permission to study in China. During their stay in China, these unwitting individuals provided information to China that ranged from simple ethnic and cultural habits to secrets that involved the highest level of national defense. Fat believed that all information gathered was important. It didn't matter how insignificant the information seemed at the time, but once archived in the intelligence database, it became a powerful tool that could be used at a later date to force these unsuspecting individuals to provide more important information in the future. There were times when Fat arranged for lavish parties with women, men and drugs. The attendees of these parties were secretly videotaped and the files were archived for future use. If these people became prominent individuals in their field of study, the videotapes, photos, and other evidence of their transgression would be used to gain their cooperation. Extortion and fear were Fat's weapons. It was a rare occasion that he would use money as a tool to get the information he needed.

Fat had been stationed in Washington for the last twelve years. On one occasion, Mike had a piece of information that he tried to sell to Fat. For some unknown reason, his bait was not taken by Fat and the information sat in the park in a waste can to be eventually picked up by the sanitation department and buried in a landfill. Little did Mike realize at the time that Fat never offered money for information. There were easier and more effective methods of gaining information that Fat desired. Methods that would never leave a trail back to him or the government of China.

Mike rubbed his chin as he looked at the name on his lap top monitor. Would he respond this time? Surely he would since this information was really hot. He thought about how he would contact Fat. It had to be tonight. Carefully he started a letter.

Dear Mr. Fat:

I must see you tonight regarding an urgent matter related to Chinese national security. I have important information related to the sale of Chinese missiles to Iraq and plans to destroy those missiles by an air attack by the United States. It will be easy for you to confirm this information with your government.

Meet me at 9 PM at the circular bar at Union Station. Take a table on the main floor and order a double scotch. Be there Mr. Fat. Your country's future security is in your hands.

—Q

Mike read the letter several times and then printed and sealed it in an envelope. He wrote on the envelope, "TO BE OPENED BY WO HO FAT EXTREMELY URGENT". Mike placed the envelope in his jacket pocket and left his room and headed for the cabstand in front of his hotel. The cab pulled up as Mike quickly got in and said, "The Chinese Embassy... 2300 Wisconsin Ave."

The driver turned on the meter and drove quietly to the address. Mike was going through his wallet and removed two one hundred dollar bills. The driver said nothing as he drove through the traffic. As the cab pulled onto Connecticut Ave., Mike said, "How would you like to make two hundred dollars."

The cab driver turned slightly and said, "Say wha'?"

Mike leaned forward and handed the driver the two bills, "I cannot tell you why, but it is very important that this letter gets inside the Chinese embassy. I am being followed and this is a matter of extreme national security. All you have to do is pull up to the embassy and give this to the security guard. Then drive me to Union Station."

"Wha' kinda national security bro... theirs or ours?

"Ours..."

"Why don't you just mail it?"

"There is no time. If this information fails to reach the person that it has to go to... all hell is going to break out."

"Wha' kinda hell?"

"I really cannot tell you, but you will not want to be in D.C. if this letter isn't delivered."

"I could sho' use the money..." The driver looked down at the bills in his hands and rubbed them together before he placed them into his pocket. The Chinese flag hung limp in the Washington rain. The cab pulled up to the gate as the driver took the envelope and opened the door. Down the block sat a non-descript Lincoln town car. Two men watched as the driver approached the security guard and handed him the letter. In an instant, the driver returned to the car and drove toward them. Mike was lying back on the seat below the cab window as it passed the Lincoln.

"Did you see anything?"

"Not really... do you think that we should follow that cab?"

"Yea... let the tunnel guys watch the place. Radio in that we are following the cab." The car made a quick u-turn and sped off after the cab. Mike raised his head and looked out of the back window. He saw the car quickly approaching.

"They are after us... can you lose them?"

"Watch me..."

The cab shot forward and made an abrupt right. The Lincoln followed. The cab driver mumbled under his breath as he increased his speed down the street.

"They will be using their radio calling for assistance..."

"The driver said, "Yea... Tell me about it man..."

The cab driver looked in his rear view mirror and saw the Lincoln. He turned on his right signal indicator, slammed on the brakes and spun the car in a 180-degree turn and headed the opposite direction. As he passed the startled CIA agents in the Lincoln he yelled, "Try that Mutha Fucka..."

"Still want to go to Union Station?"

"Yea..."

"Hold on..." The cab lurched as it went into another wild turn. In an instant, the cab was stuck in a sea of cars. The rain pelted the window so bad that the wipers could not keep the window clean. Mike looked back and did not see the Lincoln.

"I think you lost him..." Reaching into his pocket he said, "Let me give you this... and I will get out here. Thanks for the ride man... you really saved my ass." There were two muffled gunshots that went through the back seat and into the back of the driver. One bullet severed his spine and the other savagely ripped into his heart. The driver slumped forward and his head pressed on the horn. In the traffic, no one paid any attention to the sound of another horn as Mike exited the cab and melted into the rain.

CHINESE EMBASSY – 1830 HOURS

Wo Ho Fat was fighting the bowtie for his tux, as there came a soft knock at his door. Frowning in the mirror as he fought with the tie he yelled, "Come in..."

A Chinese servant opened and bowed, "This came for you a few moments ago Sir. It was delivered to the embassy by a black American cab driver and delivered by one of our security men. The cab driver said it was extremely urgent and that you should read it immediately."

"Place it on the bed…"

The servant placed the envelope on the bed, bowed again and left the room. Fat continued to argue with the tie for a few more seconds and finally gave up. Crossing the room, he picked up the damp envelope. He opened the envelope and read the letter. The look of anger now changed to one of concern. Fat had been involved with the Iraqi plan since its conception. The Chinese government had assisted Iraq since the gulf war for their own reasons. Wo Fat remembered the evening he had spent in the abandoned warehouse watching Moosavi order Jacky to kill a woman to prove that she was capable of committing cold-blooded murder. He quickly left the bedroom and walked to his office and reached for a secure line that would put him in touch with his people in Zhongnanhai. Talking in Chinese, Fat read the letter to the voice on the other end. There were several minutes of silence before the voice returned, Fat's fingers drummed nervously on the desk as he waited. The conversation lasted for three minutes. Fat nodded out of habit and placed the phone back in the cradle and returned to his room. He pressed a button summonsing the house servant. As the servant entered the room he bowed deeply and said, "Yes…"

"Send my regrets to Ambassador Blake and his wife… tell them that I have been called away on important matters… the usual…"

The servant bowed again and left the room. Fat quickly changed into a business suit and gave instructions to have a cab pick him up. Within twenty minutes, Fat took the cab to a subway stop, paid the driver and disappeared below ground. He took the subway to Union Station. Looking at his watch, he had twenty minutes remaining.

The circular bar at Union Station has two decks, the main floor that sports a magnificent mahogany bar and is flanked by tables and a second floor eating area with tables are arranged to give each person a commanding view of the terminal. Mike sat at a table that would allow him to see 360 degrees. Fat would not be hard to miss since he was Chinese, short, fat, no hair and sporting a Fu Man Chu mustache. As he sipped his drink, he spotted Fat entering the main hall from the subway side of the building. Looking at his watch, he smiled. Fat arrived and took a table on the main floor and ordered a double scotch. Mike waited two minutes and slowly walked down the circular staircase and then to his table, "Good evening Mr. Fat... thank you for being early... we have much to talk about."

Fat looked up, stood and smiled as he stretched out his hand, "Have a seat."

"Thank you... did you read my letter."

"Of course... I wouldn't be here if I didn't."

"Did you confirm the missiles?"

"Affirmative... Mr.... uh?"

"Just call me "Q"..."

"Yes I did... what do you want me to do?"

"The rest of the information will cost ten million dollars, deposited in a Swiss bank account." Mike handed Fat a small slip of paper.

"What information is worth ten million dollars?"

"The whereabouts of the Prime Minister of Israel."

Fat laughed and said, "We know where he is... He is in Tele Aviv where he should be." Fat started to get up as he remarked with an angry stare, "Don't waste my time Mr. Q."

"Sit down Fat... I am talking about Prime Minister Cane... he is not dead."

The expression on Fat's face changed dramatically as he sat down. Mike leaned over and said, "Look, Sadaam wants to nuke all of the leaders of the free world. To get them together, Sadaam tried to have the Prime Minister killed so that they would unite in Jerusalem at his memorial service to pay homage to this fallen leader. The US knows about the entire plan. I am sure that Sadaam will want to stop the attack and arrange for the death of the Prime Minister in some other way. When that day comes, then he can nuke the leaders of the free world. If you want to kill Cane, you had better pay me the money so you can arrange for him to die... got it?"

"How did you come by this information?"

"A little birdie told me..."

"I will need to see the documents, do you have them with you?"

"Do you take me for a fool?"

"No… but my people will want to see them."

"Tell you what… there is a park in Alexandria, Jones Point Park. In the park, there is the Jones Point Light, a lighthouse… there is a large metal 55-gallon drum used for trash near the house. Go there tomorrow morning. I will have the documents in a black garbage bag and I will put them the waste container tonight. If you double cross me, I will inform the press about certain matters regarding the theft of nuclear secrets you guys got and how you got them… that would be quite a mess for you wouldn't it seeing as how you are in charge of spying on the US." Fat reached over the table and grabbed Mikes arm and squeezed it like a vice, his eyes were beady and angry, "Don't threaten me or China Mr. Q… not if you want to live to spend your money."

Mike yanked his arm away from Fat and stood, "I'll keep my part of the bargain Fat… you keep yours." In an instant, Mike melted into the crowd. Fat finished his drink, threw a twenty-dollar bill on the table and entered the heart of the Union station. He approached a phone and made a call to the CIA. Speaking slowly he said, "The man you are looking for will be at Jones Point Park tonight. The information about Iraq is in a 55 gallon metal drum by the Jones Point Light that is used for trash disposal by tourist and will be in a black plastic bag." Fat hung up, wiped the phone off with his handkerchief and walked toward the subway station.

ALEXANDRIA – 2330 HOURS

Mike had walked to the front of the Union station and took a cab back to his hotel. He changed into his jogging suit and placed the printed letter from Ron outlining the American plot to set a trap for Sadaam in the bag, along with a profile of Ron telling who he was, his employee number and CIA status. He approached the doorman and ordered his moped. Within thirty minutes he drove through the rain and arrived at Jones Point Park. The park closed at dusk, but he easily skirted around the chain that blocked the entrance and headed toward the Jones Point Light. Jones Point light was constructed in 1856 on the Potomac River, first lit on May 3, 1856 and was now maintained by the National Park Service. The building itself is a simple one and one half story house with a light stuck onto the peak. Vandals had set fire to the lighthouse in 1990. The lighthouse was repaired and the vandals were caught and sent to jail. In actuality, the lighthouse resembled a Hollywood set, it had no interior whatsoever, there was just the outer shell of the building and inside there was a dirt floor.

Mike drove to the lighthouse and parked the moped in the small parking area provided for tourists, leaving the engine running. The rain once again started to pour as he quickly approached the waste can, removed the garbage bag from under his jogging suit and leaned into the can to deposit the bag. As he dropped the bag into the can, he thought he heard movements in the direction of the lighthouse and the noise of a chopper. Looking up, he was blinded by a searchlight of the chopper and heard a voice that said, "CIA... PUT YOUR HANDS ON YOUR HEAD. WE ARE ARMED... PUT YOUR HANDS ON YOUR HEAD." Mike froze like a deer in the lights of an oncoming car. His gun and his left hand were in his jacket pocket. He pulled out the gun as a voice cried, "HE'S GOT A GUN!!!" In an instant, seven CIA agents opened fire as a hail of gunfire and hot lead cut Mike down. His body fell backwards with a jerking motion as the bullets tore through his body. He staggered several steps backwards with his arms outstretched, as the gun in his hand fired wildly into the mud. When the gunfire finally stopped, Mike's body lay in the mud and was riddled with 17 bullet holes. His eyes remained open in death, looking blank and glassy like dolls eyes that stared back at the CIA agents who were forming a tight circle around his body. One of the men found the documents in the can and yelled, "Well at least we got to him before whoever it was he was trying to pass them to got the documents."

Moments later, the single chopper hovering above was joined by a second. They both approached the lighthouse and gently landed as their whining blades beat the rain into a blinding mist. Crowley exited from one of the choppers and approached his men. The documents were handed to Crowley. He gave the documents a cursory glance and then looked at Mike's body. Leaning down, he took a long close look at a man who was selling out his country and then he spat on his face. Standing, he wiped off his mouth with his shirtsleeve and barked, "I want a complete run down on this fucking bastard. Get him out of here and take him to the crime lab... I want fingerprints, ID, rap sheets... the works on my desk in 90 minutes. You got that?"

Mike's body was loaded onto the second chopper as Crowley returned to his. Moments later, both choppers lifted off and disappeared into the night.

CHAPTER 15

APRIL 22, 2001

WHITEHOUSE BUNKER – 0300 HOURS

Crowley arrived at the bunker with a stack of photos and documents. The Joint Chiefs, Secretary of State and President were in attendance. Earlier in the evening, everyone had been notified that the CIA had received the anonymous phone call regarding the whereabouts of Mike. Crowley approached his seat and fed the photos and documents into the scanner. As the material slid into the document feeding slot, Crowley adjusted his glasses and said, "Good morning Mr. President… sorry about the early morning hour… I know you are leaving today for Israel."

"Wouldn't miss this for the world Mark… what have you got?"

The big screens suddenly displayed a mug shot of Mike as Crowley began, "This is Victor Thieme, AKA Mike Lovejoy." The screen changed to police records, "He is a small time drug pusher, was arrested for possession several times and was involved in a car theft ring in Washington. The DA offered him immunity in the car theft ring for his cooperation and he served no time for that offense. He has also been arrested several times for male prostitution. Although never proven, it is believed that he used his services as a male prostitute to entangle his Johns into his web of blackmail." Again the screen changed showing pictures of naked men, "We have searched Ron Henderson's home and came up with a receipt for a mailbox that he kept about ten years ago. We also found a large collection of homosexual magazines in his home. It would seem that Mrs. Henderson had no idea of her husband's second life as a homosexual. Our men have canvassed the bathhouses in the area and a few people identified Ron as a former client. Based on this information, I believe that we can safely assume that Ron Henderson accidentally answered an ad placed by Victor Thieme, AKA Mike Lovejoy. Thieme then used Ron Henderson as a conduit for information for approximately ten years and sold this information to other countries. Based on what we know… Ron told Thieme about the sinking of the Titanic. That would explain the Israeli knowledge of the event. It is a very good assumption that Thieme was about to deliver the information about OPERATION THUNDERBALL and the survival of the Prime Minister to someone."

The President leaned forward and said, "Who?"

"We don't know Mr. President. Currently, we are playing the recorded voice of the informant into our computer database, looking for a possible voiceprint match. We are currently comparing the anonymous voiceprint against the recorded voiceprints of all known operatives in our database. If we are lucky, we may have a match in a few hours."

"Who would want to set up Thieme??"

"I don't know Mr. President. Perhaps it was someone trying to do us a favor?"

Admiral Sheppard grumbled, "I highly doubt that… I believe that everything happens for a reason. Regardless of what Virginia may think, there is no Santa Clause and as the saying goes, you don't get something for nothing in this world… No… I suspect that this Mike or whatever his name is miscalculated and paid dearly for his transgression. I would think that whoever called the CIA had a very good reason to do so… a reason that would benefit them… not us."

Scrivanich asked, "And who do you suspect…"

"You really want my opinion… look at the world today. We are the top banana and a lot of people want to reach up and pull us down. In Iraq, you have this small time hood Sadaam who is attempting to conquer the world by killing off the leaders of the free world. Can he do it… not without help? Who can he turn to? We believe that he has turned to the radical Arab fundamentalists to get these madmen to do his bidding. It would seem that either he or the fundamentalists have solicited the assistance of Pakistan to acquire nuclear weapons and it looks like he turned to China to get the necessary missiles. Which one of those three could Mike have turned to in a short period of time to sell this information?"

The room was silent as Sheppard looked around the room, "Come on gentlemen… it really isn't that hard…"

The President answered, "China…"

"Correct Mr. President… China is not ready to directly confront us at the present time. China would however, like to keep us occupied as she quietly arms herself. Towards that end, China does not want a finger pointed at them in the different arenas of world conflict. They play a very clever game of chess. They fight like Tiger fish. If you place three Tiger Fish in a tank, two will fight to the death. When the victor is tired, the third will attack and kill his weaker adversary. China would be delighted if Sadaam continues with his plans. If he succeeds, we will have our hands filled, because like it or not, Israel would nuke Iraq… and then what… the Jihad would start for real and we would be right in the middle of it. If we blow up the missiles… oh well… we could never prove that they were directly involved… Yes they sold the missiles to Iraq, but then, we sell missiles to our friends and allies don't we? What is good for the goose is good for the gander. I believe that the CIA received a phone call from whoever it was in the Chinese embassy that answered his letter. Did the cab driver say anything about his passenger?"

Crowley responded, "No, he was killed in his cab… ballistics has confirmed that the gun used to kill him was the same gun carried by Thieme."

Sheppard smiled and said, "Well… there you go… all possible witnesses, including the two spies involved in this plan are dead… need I say more? I honestly believe that Sadaam will never know about us. I think it prudent however, that we continue our countdown and anticipate a possible strike when the President arrives in Israel. If I am right, Sadaam will wait until the memorial service in Jerusalem."

The President looked at Sheppard and said, "You make a very compelling argument."

The phone at Crowley's seat blinked silently. He picked up the receiver and said, "Yes... Thank you."

Everyone in the room looked at Crowley, "We have a match... Wo Ho Fat, the director of espionage in the US for China." Crowley pressed a key on his keypad and the face of Wo Ho Fat appeared on all of the screens with his baldhead, narrow eyes, Fu Man Chu mustache and smiling face, it seemed as if he was laughing at them.

The President replied, "Good work Mark... and the same to you Admiral Sheppard..."

Scrivanich replied, "Well... I guess we keep our plans as they are. If Admiral Sheppard is correct, then we will attack at the memorial service. If he is wrong, they will probably attack as soon as you touch down in Israel. Either way, we are ready..."

The President stood and suggested, "Gentlemen... I think we had better get some sleep. Today is going to be a very long day."

ARABIAN SEA – 1200 HOURS

The flight decks of the USS Nimitz and USS George Washington were crawling with men and F-22s. The carriers elevators were bringing up the F-22s as the aircraft handlers wearing blue "float-coats" (life jackets) connected the tractors to the aircraft and placed them in position for fueling and ordnance. The red float-coats handled the ordinance and the purple float-coats, aircraft fuel crewmen who were affectionately called "grapes", fuelled the aircraft. Each color team had a specific duty and attacked each F-22 like an army of ants.

The F-22 was the latest and greatest aircraft that was to replace the aging carrier fighters, the F/A-18 Hornet fighter/bomber. The F-22 was 62 feet 8 inches long, weighed 60,000 pounds, equipped with two Pratt & Whitney F119p-PW-100 engines that could reach speeds of Mach 1.7 with afterburners and equipped with a M61A2 long-barrel 20 mm cannon that holds a 480 round magazine. The

F-22 has four internal weapons bay areas. Two of the bays are at the bottom of the mid-fuselage. The remaining two were located on the air intake sides of the aircraft. The F-22 was equipped with four hardpoints that could carry extra fuel tanks or ordinance. For this mission, there would be no fuel tanks, only ordinance.

The F-22 was originally designed for the Air Force but the Navy had expressed an interest in the aircraft because of its speed, stealth and continuing presence over Iraq enforcing the no-fly zones. This resulted in the F-22 being modified for the Navy carriers. For this mission, each F-22 would be fitted with 12 internal AGM-88C HARM anti-radar air-to-ground missiles and two internal 400 pound GBU-32 JDAM bombs, one AN/ALQ-184 Electronic Attack Pod and eight external AIM 120A AMRAAM air-to-air missiles. The AGM-88C HARM anti-radar missiles were designed to take out ground based SAM launch facilities. These missiles reached speeds greater than MACH-2 and could be automatically set for a "self –protect" mode that would identify a radar threat and automatically fire at the radar site, a "target of opportunity" mode that would recognize a lock-on target and attack a radar emitter or the "pre-briefed" mode that would fire the missile in the general direction of a target and the missile would seek any radar emitter, lock-on to the emitter and destroy it. If there were no radar emitters in the direction of the area, the missile would self-destruct. The AGM-88C HARM also had a 360-degree engagement capability allowing the missile to be launched at targets in back of the aircraft, but in this firing condition, a severe range penalty would be a limiting factor in the successful destruction of the target. The GBU–32 JDAM bombs were the latest in high tech weaponry in that once released, the bomb directs itself to the target using internal GPS and INS guidance technology. For this mission, the bomb was ideal since it could be delivered by the F-22 and launched from either a very low or very high altitude or launched from a dive, toss, loft or straight and level flight using an on-axis or off-axis de-livery. The AN/ALQ-184 Electronic Attack Pod would protect the F-22 against radar threats by directing high power jamming signals against multiple radar emitters. The AIM 120A AMRAAM air-to-air missiles uses on board guidance of the F-22 prior to launch to calculate a launch acceptability zone. Once launched, the missile flies to the anticipated coordinate and then uses on-board active radar to fine-tune its trajectory for the hit. Since this would be a daylight attack against hardened targets with increased antiaircraft defenses, regardless of the position the pilot found himself in over the target, the weapons could be launched successfully against the mosque. One by one, each aircraft was armed, fueled and moved toward the "Fat Cats" that would launch them toward Iraq.

Below decks on both carrier groups, the flight crews were assembling for their final briefing. Aboard the Nimitz, Rear Admiral Thomas and Captain Victor would conduct the briefing. A similar scene was being enacted aboard the USS George Washington with Captain Kopacka and his flight crew. A voice cried, "TENN HUT" as the Admiral and Captain entered the briefing room. The pilots immediately stood and snapped to attention. Captain Victor stood by the Admiral as he addressed the pilots, "Be seated, gentlemen." Walking to the podium, the Admiral continued, "The mission that you are about to undertake is perhaps the most important mission of your careers." The screen behind the Admiral began to show the three suspected mosques, "Your mission will be to take out these three mosques in Iraq. One is located in the city of Irbil, the second is located in Al Basrah and the third is located in Baghdad. You will be divided into three attack groups of five men per squadron. The Red squadron will attack Irbil, the White squadron will attack Al Basrah and the Blue squadron will attack Baghdad. You will remain in the north and south no-fly zones until you receive specific instructions from me to attack. We will be observing these mosques from our satellites in real time. The moment they start to prepare to launch, we will issue the order to attack. The code name for this mission is OPERATION THUNDERBALL. When you receive code name OPERATION THUNDERBALL and the "go" command, you will attack. Until then, it will be business as usual. The purpose of this attack is to eliminate what is believed to be nuclear tipped Chinese missiles that are located in each of the three mosques. It is believed that Sadaam will attempt a preemptive nuclear attack against Israel with the specific intent to eliminate the leaders of the free world that will be gathered to pay homage to the fallen Prime Minister Cane. It is also believed that this attack could come at any moment after the President and Air Force One lands in Tel-Aviv. The USS George Washington will be rotating their squadrons with you. We will fly continuous coverage in the no-fly zones until Sadaam commits to the launch. At that moment, you will attack. The Red and White teams will have the advantage that their targets are located in their specific no-fly zones, the Blue team will have a maximum of two minutes to arrive over Baghdad and attack their mosque. Each of you have been trained and trained well to fly the F-22... it is time to show us your stuff... any questions?"

The room was deathly quiet. Finally, one pilot stood and asked, "Is the President aware of the missiles?"

"Yes... and he has confidence in all of you that you will complete your mission."

The men looked at each other and cracked a few jokes between themselves to relieve the tension as the Admiral stepped back and Captain Victor took the podium, "I don't have to tell you of the importance of this mission. We have the element of surprise on our side and the best men and material in the world. I only wish that I could trade places with one of you and do it myself. Gentlemen, your F-22s are fueled and are waiting... now lets kick some ass."

The room became charged with excitement and the Captain and Admiral shook hands with the flight crew. Moments later, the two were alone in the room. The Captain looked at the Admiral and replied, "What do you think?"

The Admiral answered, "Only time will tell... but if anyone can do it... they can."

ZHONGNANHAI, CHINA –1530 HOURS

The eight-member Central Military Commission (CMC) sat silently reading the report received from Wo Ho Fat. The CMC was an eight-man group that directed the activities of the People's Liberation Army, including the People's Republic of China's army, navy air force and all espionage operations. Their main function was to meet on a regular basis to formulate military policy and strategy. The Fat report outlined the death of the American spy Mike Lovejoy at the hands of the CIA, as well as the capturing of the information that he had been trying to sell. For security reasons, the members referred to themselves by number, one through eight, with no order of priority. One by one, the men read the report and placed the document on the table as they finished, waiting for the rest to complete their reading. Finally the last member, number seven, placed the document on the table and said, "Number three… what do you make of this?"

"It looks like the Americans have successfully figured out what Sadaam is about to do…"

"… And what are your thoughts?"

"I do not believe that we should get involved… this is not our fight and it does not fit well with our long range plans."

Number eight replied, "I agree… if the Americans know about the missiles and the planned attack, let whatever happens, happen. If we intervene and notify Sadaam, he will do something stupid like he always does and possibly bring us into the forefront… we can't afford that. It is better off that he does not know that the Americans know of his plans."

Number one commented, "Still it would be nice if the Americans get stuck in the middle of this trap and the only way that they could get stuck is if they fail to stop the missile attack and Israel is bombed with nuclear weapons. Israel would most likely retaliate with their nuclear weapons against Iraq and that would start the Jihad."

Number five remarked, "Perhaps, we should focus our attention on the eventuality of the Americans stopping the attack, what should we consider doing to keep the American's feet in the fire?"

Number two asked, "What about the radical Arab fundamentalists... there is a lot to be said for them. As the Americans would say, they have balls the size of church bells. Perhaps, we could arrange for them to greet Prime Minister Cane when he returns from the dead and they could put him away for good."

Number two remarked, "We do not know where the Americans are keeping the Prime Minister."

Number four replied, "We do not need to know where the Americans have hidden the Prime Minister. If the Americans do successfully stop the attack, we should demand an immediate emergency session of the United Nations and paint the Americans as the imperialistic whoremongers that they are. I am sure that we could gain the support of our allies, Russia, Pakistan, Afghanistan, Iran and even perhaps a few of the western countries. At that point, the Americans would have no other choice but to make the Prime Minister reappear to save face. When he does, our fundamentalist friends can do with him as they may."

Number five replied, "With a little help from us of course." There was laughter in the room.

Number seven smiled as he looked around the room, "Then we are in agreement?"

Everyone in the room nodded their head. Number seven continued, "Then we will notify the fundamentalists after the attack. If the Americans fail, we have nothing to do but watch the Middle East explode. If they succeed, I am sure that the Arab extremist groups will arrange to have a surprise waiting for the Prime Minister at his resurrection."

BETHESDA NAVAL HOSPITAL – 1900 HOURS

Col. Allan and Admiral Potter were seated in the Presidential suite with Joshua and Jacky. The television was on, but the sound was muted. Col. Allan continued his briefing, "The President has instructed me to bring you up to date. We have determined that there was a spy in the CIA that relayed information to a second man regarding the sinking of the Titanic and the plans for our attack against Iraq. As far as we know, the information made it as far as the Chinese government. There is no way of knowing if the Chinese have relayed this information to Iraq."

Joshua looked tired as he thought about the fact that Iraq could know about the planned attack against the mosques. "I presume that the President is going ahead with his participation in my memorial service?"

"That is correct Mr. Prime Minister. We believe that if Iraq knows about the planned attack, they will do one of three things; they could do nothing, they could attack as soon as Air Force One lands, or they could wait until the service starts and be assured that they could get everyone. It is because of this element of surprise that they possess, that the President delayed his departure so that he will arrive almost at the start of the service. This will keep Sadaam under our control. Currently, we have our F-22s in position in the no-fly zones. The countdown begins when the President lands."

"And when will that be?"

"The President and First Lady are boarding Air Force One as we speak and will arrive in Jerusalem at 11 AM their time tomorrow morning."

Joshua nodded toward the television set as he pressed the remote mute button. The voice of the news correspondent filled the room, "We take you now to the White House where Press Secretary Balling is about to make an announcement."

Balling approached the podium. The Presidential seal hung as a backdrop, "The President and First Lady are currently en route to Israel to attend the memorial service for the late Prime Minister Cane. The President's departure was delayed approximately two hours due to a mechanical problem on Air Force One. That problem has been corrected and the President is due to arrive in Jerusalem at 11 AM tomorrow morning, Jerusalem time. The President will go directly from the airport to the memorial service by motorcade. The memorial service will begin at 12 noon in Jerusalem."

The room was filled with news correspondents yelling questions. Balling nodded as one correspondent asked, "What type of mechanical problem delayed the President's departure?"

"It was a backup navigational computer malfunction. Air Force One has two backup navigational computers, but it was decided to fly with all three in operation."

Balling nodded at another correspondent, "We have reports that there is an increase in military activity in the Arabian Sea and troop build up in the Middle East by Syria, Iraq, Iran and others... Any comment on this heightened activity."

"With the President in the Middle East... our activity is a precautionary measure only I assure you... I have no information regarding the other activity." At that, Balling raised his hands and stepped away from the podium. The television began to display footage of the President and First Lady leaving the White House heading for the helicopter parked on the White House lawn that would take them to Andrews Air Force base. The President and First Lady waved at the reporters as they boarded the chopper. The news anchorperson continued, "The President is expected to have several high level meetings during his brief visit to Israel. ZNN will have complete coverage of the memorial service beginning at 4 AM EST tomorrow morning. In Atlanta..."

Joshua muted the television and said, "God speed Mr. President."

CHAPTER 16

AIR FORCE ONE – 0900 HOURS

Air Force One is a modified Boeing 747 aircraft. The Presidential fleet consists of two Boeing 747-200B aircraft with identification tail numbers of 28000 and 29000. When the President is on board, the Air Force uses the designation of VC-25A and the call sign is "Air Force One".

The VC-25A aircraft has a flight crew of 26, a passenger limit of 70, a traveling ground crew, has four General Electric CF6-80C2B1 engines that have a thrust rating of 56,700 pounds each, fuel capacity of 53,611 gallons that allows for a range of 7,800 statute miles with unlimited range due to in flight refueling capability modifications, a service ceiling of 45,100 feet, is 231 feet 10 inches long with a wing span of 195 feet, eight inches.

The main difference between Air Force One and its commercial counterpart are the physical accommodations, electronic and communications gear modifications. Air Force One is called the flying "Oval Office" which has 4,000 square feet of floor space for the President which includes a conference room or dining room, private quarters for the President and First Lady and office space for the President's senior staff members. Also included in the modifications of Air Force One are work and rest areas for the Presidential staff, media and Air Force One crew members, two galleys with storage capacity of 2,000 meals, self contained air stairs and interior stairways that lead to the main deck. VC-25A has approximately 285 miles of wire, more than twice the mileage of a normal 747 aircraft that is specially shielded to withstand an electromagnetic pulse that would be generated by a thermonuclear blast. Communication equipment allows for worldwide contact with transmission and reception of declassified and secured communications. The communications hardware consists of 85 telephones, multi-frequency radios for air-to-air, air-to-ground and satellite communications. Air Force One is designed to be the functional nerve center for the President when he is on board in either times of peace or war. The communications staff on board was in constant touch with the USS Nimitz and USS George Washington and a direct link had been established with the satellites watching Iraq as well as the Pentagon and Bunker in Washington, D.C.

The President and First Lady had slept for most of the trip. The President had showered and was now dressing as he entered the bedroom to put on his tie. Looking at his wife he said, "How are you feeling?"

"Tired… I can never sleep on an airplane… even if it is Air Force One."

"You had better get up, we are about two hours from touchdown." Finishing his tie, he turned and gave Linda a kiss. "I have a briefing in about five minutes… get dressed and grab something to eat… its going to be a very long day."

Outside the personal quarters sat two military advisors and the President's personal secret service agent. They stood as the President entered the conference room. The President remarked, "Be seated gentlemen… how is everything?"

The military advisors spoke softly, "The Nimitz and Washington have their aircraft in position." The second advisor closed the window blind and turned on a flat screen monitor that displayed the satellite images of the three mosques. "So far… there is no unusual activity at any of the mosques…"

The President replied, "Well they have two hours before we land. If they are smart, they probably have everything all set to go…"

"Perhaps Mr. President… There was an increased level of traffic into and out of the mosques 18 hours ago, but as you can see, everything is quiet for the moment."

The secret service agent said, "Mr. President we have to put a wire on you… could you please remove your shirt?"

"Yea… I forgot about that." The President removed his tie and stripped down to his undershirt. The agent gave the President a look as he remarked, "The T-shirt too huh?" Removing the T-shirt, the President was told to hold his arms out as the agent used an electric shaver to remove his chest hair and then pressed a small transmitter package onto his breastbone in the center of his chest. The transmitter was contained in a bag that had a chemical battery and the microphone was contained in a small circuit that protruded out of the bag. The package itself was coated with an adhesive on the backside. In total, the transmitter package was 1.5 mm thick and looked more like a medical nicotine patch rather than an electronic transmitter package. The agent said, "Please put on your T-shirt Mr. President." In a matter of seconds, the President put on the T-shirt. Next came the white dress shirt and tie. Moments later the agent removed a small three mm diameter receiver from a small box and approached the President, "Please sit down Mr. President with your back to me." The agent then removed a roll of flesh colored tape from his suit pocket and a small pair of scissors. "I am going to tape this to your head behind your ear right … there." The receiver would receive transmissions from the secret service to the President and the transmitter on the President's chest would transmit his voice back to the secret service. Together, the two devices provided two-way communications. This new two-piece design eliminated the telltale earpiece and connecting wire, thus making it almost impossible for anyone to tell that the President was wearing a wire. The agent smiled and said, "Now for a test…" The agent turned his back to the President and walked to the other end of the room. Speaking softly into a small microphone on his tie he said, "If you can hear me Mr. President, please recite the first six words of Lincoln's Gettysburg address."

The President replied, "How fucking loud do I have to talk when I say it?"

The agent turned and replied, "I think we are OK. This will be our communication link with you Mr. President. We will keep you informed as OPERATION THUNDERBALL starts. You can speak to us as well. The system is bi-directional, is a scrambled secure signal and has a range of 50 miles."

The President pressed his hand against his chest and said, "Wow... It's sort of like that GPS unit you guys had installed in my butt... couldn't sit right for a week... this thing isn't going to conflict with that is it?"

The agent smiled again and said, "No Mr. President. As soon as the attack starts, we will be in direct touch with you. If anything goes wrong, we will tell you..."

The door opened to the conference room as Linda replied with a curious expression, "If what goes wrong?"

The President turned and said, "Nothing... just standard operating procedure..."

"Don't give me that look. After 31 years of marriage, I can tell when you are up to something."

The President turned and said, "Gentlemen, would you please give us a few minutes alone."

The military advisors and secret service agent immediately left the conference room and closed the door.

"Sit down Linda... I have something to tell you..."

IRAQ – 1000 HOURS

There was a tense silence inside the underground bunker that housed the command headquarters for the Iraqi missile defense system. A sea of technicians and military personnel watched their display monitors as the generals and Sadaam watched a large screen television set that was showing the latest ZNN news broadcast of the memorial service for Joshua Cane in Jerusalem.

With the hard lessons learned from the Gulf War in 1991, the death of over 100,000 men and the destruction of Iraq, an extensive effort had been made to totally redesign the entire anti-aircraft defense systems throughout Iraq and in particular, around the mosques that housed the missiles targeted for Israel. During the Gulf War, the stealth bombers, Cruise missiles and smart bombs of the United States had simply overwhelmed the obsolete defense technology used by Iraq, thus allowing the United States to bomb Iraq with impunity and destroy any target they desired. The entire defensive air war was frustrating for the Iraqi military. If they attempted to shoot down any of the attacking aircraft with SAMs, the United States aircraft would simply launch a radar-seeking missile that would home in on the radar signal used to track the US aircraft and destroy the SAM site. In a matter of minutes, Iraq was blinded and helpless with no radar defense against the attacking aircraft.

Despite the UN embargo that prevented any sale of military hardware to Iraq, Sadaam had quietly purchased radar systems and other badly needed technology to rebuild his military might and defenses. Iraq had oil and money; other countries needed both and were not going to allow the UN to prevent them from acquiring them from Iraq. Sadaam and his military advisors used their wealth to redesign their entire anti-aircraft defense posture using an array of 100 camouflaged broadband and infrared tracking radar sites around each vital military position and airfield throughout Iraq. Each broadband radar array was connected by a fiber-optic computerized control network that allowed for the simultaneous tracking of any incoming aircraft, cruise missile or smart bomb. Each radar dish in the array would track the hostile incoming target for only a few seconds using different scanning frequencies and then would turn itself off, as the command center computers would turn another not too distant remote radar unit on and continue to track the incoming target. At the same time, the computers that controlled the radar would also direct the anti-aircraft fire against the incoming aircraft. In theory, if radar seeking missiles were fired, the incoming radar-seeking missile would wind up being totally confused as the Iraqi tracking radar units turned on and off, luring it away from the first target it had acquired and make it follow a path that would lead to the next radar unit, thus rendering the radar-seeking capabilities virtually useless.

As the missile changed directions again and again, going first after one radar site and then another, a series of Russian designed Phalanx type rapid-fire 20-mm gun systems could place a wall of steel in front of the missile and launching aircraft causing both to self destruct as they flew through or were directly hit by the hail of armor piercing 20 mm shells. The anti-radar missile either would be destroyed by the crossfire or would run out of fuel before it could successfully lock-on to a target since the missile only had a range of approximately 30 plus miles. The launching aircraft would be dead meat. In the event that the missile was programmed to continue on to the last known target radar emission it had acquired, it would only hit a remote radar dish, not the cannons or the SAMs. The large number of radar dishes would be sufficient to make it impossible for all of the tracking radar units to be destroyed.

A network of 200 rapid-fire 20 mm systems and Russian versions of the Bofors 57 MK3 all target 40 mm cannons were also married to the 100-dish radar array forming a defensive umbrella over each military location. Each 20 mm firing system was capable of firing 4,500 rounds per minute of radar directed hellish gunfire. The Russian version of the Bofors 57 MK3 all target 40 mm cannon was a fully automatic and could fire 220 rounds per minute of super-accurate anti-aircraft ordinance. Finally, backing up the 20 mm and 40 mm cannons were the SAMs. These too were integrated into the radar array, but were mobile, thus avoiding the trap of being a static target for the dreaded cruise missiles and smart bombs attack. As the incoming aircraft pilot defended himself against the 20 mm and 40 mm gunfire, the SAMs would also be launched to knock them out of the skies.

Sadaam looked pleased as he looked out over the sea of monitors and technicians. There would be no repeat of the first night of the Gulf War. The image of ZNN broadcasting the vision of his men firing helplessly up into the night skies was forever burned into his memory. During that first night of the Gulf War, his army had been blinded like a Cyclops, waving its arms in a vain attempt to capture its adversary. His men had fired helplessly into the darkened sky trying to hit the bombers that were buzzing around Baghdad like a swarm of angry bees. This time, he would use this new American technology to his advantage. If the American missiles, smart bombs and other high tech ordinance could follow the signals from his radar defense systems, then let them try to ascertain which radar signal to follow as his anti-aircraft cannons and SAMs blew them out of the skies. He was confident that perhaps he did not have the best technology for his army, but he certainly had a technology that if used properly, could give him the winning hand this time around. His blinded Cyclops would now have the eye to see and to destroy his adversary. Coupled with his newly acquired technology, he also had the element of surprise. He realized that once his missiles were launched, he would face American, UN and Israeli retribution from the skies. He also knew however, that once his missiles left their launch pads, nothing but the hand of Allah could bring them down. When the retribution came, he would be ready. One of the generals looked at Sadaam and replied, "Everything is ready to fire." Sadaam nodded and smiled. Now all he had to do was wait.

AIR FORCE ONE – 1050 HOURS

The President and First Lady had entered the news media section of Air Force One. The correspondents were eagerly taking pictures and asking questions. Linda smiled and looked as charming as ever, even though she was scared to death. The thought of dying in a nuclear explosion was horrible. If she died that way, would there be any pain? If she didn't die right away, would she suffer from radiation sickness and eventually die a slow and horrible death? She had listened to her husband very carefully to the events that were soon to unfold. At first she had been silent as she went over the facts in her mind. Suddenly, her eyes glared at her husband as she lashed out in anger for being treated like a child and then for being used like a worm on a fishhook. Her anger had eventually turned to fear and from fear to a reluctant acceptance of her fate, whatever that would be. Her husband was the President of the United States and she was the First Lady. She couldn't run and hide because there was no place to run. Air Force One was about to touch down at the Ben Gurion Airport and she, with her husband would be on stage with all of the other leaders of the world in Jerusalem. She, along with everyone else would be the bait to lure a madman that would do everything in his power to kill her, her husband and everyone else. She had been told of the military trap that had been set for Sadaam and she believed that the United States could destroy the missiles. A voice in her head kept telling her that everything would be OK and yet she knew that there was always the possibility that things could go wrong. More often that not, they did.

The voice of the captain of Air Force One came on the intercom and announced, "We are in our final approach and will be touching down at TLV, Ben Gurion airport in about ten minutes… Please return to your seats and fasten your seatbelts."

The President and First lady answered a few quick questions and then returned to their conference room and sat on a couch. They both strapped themselves in as the President watched the computer monitors. Looking at the military advisor he asked, "Anything yet?" As the tires of Air Force One scorched the landing strip at the Ben Gurion Airport, the advisor shook his head no. Air Force One's engines roared as the pilot applied the air brakes. The aircraft slowed and gently turned onto a taxi runway to vacate the landing strip and came to a stop. After a few moments, the aircraft's engine noise increased and the aircraft rolled gently in the direction of a distant tarmac where a group of heavily armed American and Israeli troops formed a defensive perimeter around an empty jet way that protruded out of the special VIP arrival terminal. As Air Force One approached, one signalman holding his directional batons motioned the aircraft forward and then signaled for the pilot to turn the aircraft hard to port. Another signalman held his arms in an out stretched position at nine and three o'clock. As the aircraft approached, the signalman began to raise his arms toward twelve o'clock. When the nose gear of Air Force One crossed over two yellow stripes that were painted on the tarmac, the signalman made a cross with the batons and the pilot hit the brakes and shut the engines down. The jet way suddenly lurched forward and in a few moments, black rubber lips of the shroud pressed against the outer skin and door of the aircraft. The President looked at Linda and said, "It's time…" He reached for her hand, giving it a gentle squeeze. Linda smiled and said nothing.

The President and First Lady approached the door of the aircraft as the secret service agents were forming a human wall in front of and in back of the President. Walking quickly through the jet way, they entered the secure VIP terminal where other secret service men and military guards were waiting. The President and First Lady were escorted to an elevator that took them to the ground floor and within minutes, they entered their heavily armored Presidential limo that had been flown to Israel two days before. A motorcade of other limos carrying secret service agents drove in front of and in back of the Presidential limo as a convoy of military trucks carrying Israeli military both preceded and followed the Presidential convoy. Preparations had been made to clear all pedestrian and automobile traffic from the 31-mile route from Tel Aviv to Jerusalem. The normal drive that would take 40 minutes by taxi, sherut, or egged bus, would now be completed in less than twenty minutes. Along the route, the Israeli military blocked all access to the convoy. Both curious Israeli citizens and tourists congregated in crowds along the way trying to get a look at the convoy as it drove by. Overhead, four Israeli helicopter gun ships followed the President, ready to attack anyone that would attempt to attack the convoy.

JERUSALEM – 1130 HOURS

Jerusalem is unlike any other city in the world. With three thousand years of history, it offers a unique mixture of religion, architecture and culture. To the Jews, Jerusalem is not only the capital of Israel, but it is also "The Holy City" and possesses the holiest religious site in Judaism, the Western Wall. To the Christians, it is the place where Jesus Christ was crucified and to the Muslims, it is the site of the Dome of the Rock, the site where Mohamed ascended into heaven.

The Western Wall, often times called the Wailing Wall is all that is left of the Holy Temple that was built by King Solomon and destroyed by the Roman emperor Titus in 68 C.E. When King Solomon built the temple, he had asked God to listen to the prayers of Jews and non-Jews alike calling it the "House of all nations", the point where God-consciousness came down into the world. To the people of Israel, the Western wall represented a permanent reminder of God's presence. The stunning death of Prime Minister Cane had shaken the Israeli people to the core and for the first time, it was decided by the Knesset that the Western Wall would be the only fitting place to hold the memorial service for their fallen leader. The site of the Holy Temple would once again become a house of all nations.

The Israeli military had blocked the entrance to the Western Wall two days prior to the service. As the area was secured, the plaza was cleaned and countless rows of chairs were placed there facing the wall with a special white row of chairs in front. Here, the leaders of the world would sit and wait their turn to approach a small podium to pay homage to the fallen Prime Minister. The Western Wall was soon surrounded by television crews, their trucks packed with electronic gear with large black cables that ascended tall steel scaffolds that supported a multitude of television cameras that would broadcast the memorial service to the world. Overhead, Israeli gun ships flew back and forth keeping a watchful eye on the gathering below.

As the hour approached, the leaders of the world began to take their seats. Starting from the center of the row, they would sit in the order in which they would speak, alternating left and right of the center position. Speaking first and sitting in the center would be the President of Israel. To his right would be the President of the United

States. To his left, would be the President of Egypt. In alternating order, left and right of center, came the Prime Minister of England, Spain, France, Italy and Russia. In all, the leaders of 80 countries would occupy the white chairs. The President and First Lady were the last to arrive. Quietly they entered the plaza and were escorted to their seats. Everyone sat quietly waiting for the Chief Army Rabbi to rise and begin the service.

IRAQ – 1200 HOURS

Sadaam watched the ZNN coverage of the memorial service. His eyes narrowed as the camera zoomed in on the President and First Lady. Crossing his arms across his chest he exhaled slowly and stared at the President. He slowly raised his right arm. The technicians in the room looked at their leader anticipating his command. Sadaam stood rigid, legs parted, knees locked and brought his hand down in a sweeping motion yelling at the top of his lungs, "LAUNCH THE MISSILES NOW!"

The technicians immediately started the procedure to move the domes on each of the mosques by pressing buttons and flipping switches on their consoles. Suddenly, in each of the three mosques, a series of red strobes began to flash as a Klaxon alarm began to sound. The computers in the command center issued launch commands to the missiles that would start their automatic launch sequence countdown. High above in outer space, the American birds continued to send their images to Washington.

WHITEHOUSE BUNKER – 0500 HOURS

The Joint Chiefs of Staff and Secretary of State were watching the live coverage of the memorial service on one of the large screens; the three mosques were shown on three other screens. Suddenly, Admiral Sheppard stood up, pointed to the Baghdad screen and yelled, "*IT'S MOVING…*" Everyone quickly looked at the Baghdad,

Al Basrah and Irbil mosques. The domes on all three were slowly sliding onto the steel scaffolding as expected. Admiral Sheppard had been patched in directly to the Nimitz and Rear Admiral Thomas for the last hour. Leaning forward, he yelled, "*THIS IS ADMIRAL SHEPPARD... COMMENCE OPERATION THUNDERBALL... I SAY AGAIN... COMMENCE OPERATION THUNDERBALL.*"

The President quietly placed his finger behind his ear, pressing the receiver against his head. Looking down, he heard the voice from the secret service agent in Air Force One, "Mr. President... the attack has started." He slowly reached for Linda's hand and gave it a squeeze. Linda looked at her husband. There was a look of terror in her eyes when they made eye contact.

IRAQ – 1200 HOURS

Rear Admiral Thomas and Captain Victor were in the Nimitz command center. Hearing the attack command from Admiral Sheppard, Rear Admiral Thomas picked up a microphone and said, "*COMMENCE OPERATION THUNDERBALL... I SAY AGAIN... COMMENCE OPERATION THUNDERBALL.*"

The command center speakers immediately received acknowledgements from the three squadrons, "Red Leader One... Roger. White Leader One... Roger. Blue Leader One... Roger." There was a brief exchange between the wingmen of the three squadrons as they immediately changed their flight path and proceeded to their targets. One pilot nicknamed "Kingfish" summed up everyone's feelings as his voice boomed over the speakers in the command center, "Let's kick some ass gentlemen."

The images of the attacking F-22s on the command center's display screen immediately fanned out toward their targets. Red Leader and Blue Leader squadrons would be over their targets in 60 seconds. White Leader squadron would reach their target within 120 seconds. Inside each F-22, the pilots watched the HUD display and six liquid crystal display (LCD) panels inside their cockpits. The

Primary Multi-Function Display (PMDF) is located in the middle of the instrument panel, under the ICP (Integrated Control Panel) used by the pilot to enter manually control data and three other Multi-Function Displays (SMDF) were located left and right of the PDMF and designed to give the pilot tactical and non-tactical data. The tactical data LCD would show targets on the screen as colored symbols. The enemy aircraft would be a red triangle, friendly aircraft would be green circles, unknown aircraft would be shown as yellow squares, wingmen are shown as blue F-22s images and SAMs would be represented by pentagons with a data box that would tell the pilot the type of SAM approaching and its lethal range. To keep unnecessary chatter down between the wingmen, the display would also indicate if any of the wingmen had a firing solution on a target as shown by a filled in triangle or no firing solution shown by an open triangle. Also displayed was the fuel and ordinance remaining on all F-22s in the squadron. During the final flight briefing, instructions were issued to go in low on the deck and drop their bombs in a climbing mode as they left the target as each of the five F-22s in each squadron were to approach their targets from different directions.

Inside the Iraq control bunker, the monitor screens suddenly began to flash warnings of approaching aircraft heading toward the mosque in Baghdad as well as the mosques in Irbil and Al Basrah. The Gulf War had taught Sadaam the "stealth" lesson well. The data received from his new radar arrays would be fed to his computers and crunched. The computers would be looking for low radar signatures, infrared radiation, and air turbulence. Using this combined information profile, the computer would weigh the possibility of the target being a bird, cloud, or other natural occurrence. Considering weather and atmospheric conditions and using a variety of other programmed analytical algorithms, the computers would then make the final decision to identify the target as friendly or hostile. In this case, the computers successfully identified the five F-22s approaching each of the mosques and painted red dots on the monitors. Since each aircraft now was given a specific electronic "fingerprint", there could be no escape once their fingerprint was identified. Like a leopard, the F-22s could not change their spots and would be a sitting duck. Sadaam turned his attention to the large screen showing the incoming aircraft and smiled as his defense network automatically sprang into action.

There was no radio traffic between the pilots as they guided their aircraft toward their targets. Suddenly, the quiet of the F-22 cockpits was shattered by the audio warning system on board each aircraft, "WARNING... SAM RADAR LOCK-ON". Each pilot glanced down at the SMDF and saw a barrage of SAMs headed toward them. Three SAMs were targeted at each F-22. Almost simultaneously, an intense pattern of 20 mm and 40 mm fire erupted around them. "Red Leader one... I'm hit..." The 20 mm and 40 mm crossfire had found their first target.

"Jesus Fucking Christ." Looking to his left, Red Leader One saw a distant fireball. The SMDF display was now showing only three wingmen remaining in his squadron, Red 2 was gone.

Instantly, all of the F-22s activated their AN/ALQ-184 electronic attack pods to jam the incoming SAMs radar and fired their AGM-88 HARM anti-radar missiles at the ground radar. The primary defense of the F-22 against a SAM attack was its speed and stealth. The approaching SAM would calculate a position to intercept its intended target. In the case of traditional non-stealth aircraft, the SAM would have enough time to be launched and reach the intended target coordinate and then use active radar to home in on for the kill. The F-22 was built to be almost invisible to radar, thus shortening the time period from launch to the rendezvous coordinate. Since the SAM would be launched later than usual and the F-22 had great speed, the SAM would be forced to perform a low-energy long tail chase and possibly run out of fuel before it could destroy the target. It was clear that something had gone terribly wrong with the F-22 defensive strategy.

The HARMS were armed and launched in the "Pre-Briefed" mode and were looking for any and all radar emitters that might be directing the incoming SAMs. One by one, the HARMS flew towards one target and then another. Watching the SMFD screens, the pilots realized that the HARMS were going ballistic and going nowhere fast. The audible warning continued to echo in their ears as the onboard computer began to launch chaff and flares to combat the incoming SAMs. In an act of desperation, all pilots launched their AIM-120 AMRAAM air-to-air missiles at the SAMs. A few of the AMRAAMs hit their target, but no sooner had a SAM been hit by an AMRAAM, another would be launched to take its place. They were now fighting a battle of numbers and Sadaam had more SAMs than they had AMRAAMs. Reinforcements from the USS George Washington would be too late. It was clear that they were in the middle of a Charlie Foxtrot, a big ass Cluster Fuck. "Blue Leader One... SHIT....". The sky erupted into two balls of fire as Blue Three and Four were cut apart by the crossfire of two 20 mm cannons.

"White Leader One, I'm hit... going down..." The pilot reached between his legs and pulled the ACES II ejection control. In an instant, the F-22 canopy was blown off and the pilot shot out of the aircraft. As the canopy and pilot left the F-22, their images appeared on the monitor screens as "hard targets" and the 20 mm cannons trained their fire on them. The canopy was shattered first and before the pilot knew what hit him, his body was cut in half by the crossfire. The guns continued to fire until there was nothing left of his body and seat to register on the radar. Another second later, a SAM took out his aircraft.

"This is Blue Five... target in sight..." Suddenly, the F-22 was rocked by fire from the 20 mm and 40 mm cannons and exploded as it ran into a wall of 20 mm steel. Over Irbil and Baghdad, SAMs took out Red Leader One and Red Three, as well as White Leader One and Four.

"This is Red Four... have target in site... Bombs away..."

"Red Leader Four... I'm right behind you..." Crossfire from a pair of 20 mm cannons hit Red Five as another SAM found its mark taking him out.

The pilot of Red Four pulled back on his stick and went to after burners as he headed back to the Nimitz. The SAMs gave chase, but the ALQ attack pod and countermeasures confused them enough to allow Red Five to escape. Moments later, the mosque in Irbil exploded. "This is Red Four... Scratch one fucking Iraqi mosque..." A roar of approval came from the men in the command center aboard the Nimitz.

"Blue Leader One... Releasing bombs..."

"Blue Two... Releasing bombs..."

Both pilots went to afterburners and shot into the sky as five SAMs gave chase. The mosque in Al Basrah exploded as four bombs hit their target. Thirty seconds later, Blue Leader One and Blue Two were hit by SAMs and destroyed.

Rear Admiral Thomas looked at Captain Victor and said, "They are being cut to ribbons... just like it was in Nam... we had attack squadrons called Weasels back then. They went in first and were out last. They had to knock out the anti-aircraft batteries so our bombers could get in and out safely. It was a suicide mission... especially when the Soviets gave the North Vietnamese SAMs. Our guys dropped out of the sky like flies." Victor nervously looked at the command screen and saw only two remaining White squadron F-22s heading into Baghdad. The countdown clock on the monitor was three seconds away from the estimated time for the missile to launch. The voice from White Two cried, "Holy shit... the fucking missile is being fired!"

The satellite video of the missile was being relayed simultaneously to the Nimitz and to the Whitehouse bunker. Flames and smoke could be seen shooting out of the top of the mosque. Suddenly, the white missile darted towards the heavens riding a column of orange fire. At the same time, six additional SAMs were launched at the two remaining aircraft. The pilots of White Two and Five looked at their SMDF screens. All they could see were each other and 12 SAMs. The voice of the audible alarm system pounded into their ears, "WARNING SAM LOCK-ON... WARNING... SAM LOCK-ON..."

They both knew their situation was hopeless. Looking at the SMDF, they saw that the only ordnance they had left was the remaining four GBU–32 JDAM bombs and they were totally useless against the launched Chinese missile.

As the lock-on alarm continued booming in the ears of the two pilots, they both realized that there was only one thing left to do. Each aircraft unloaded their bombs to get rid of the weight as each pilot took evasive action going to afterburners to avoid the SAMs. White Two opened his radio channel and said, "Bulldog... I want the missile... you take out the fucking mosque..."

"Roger that... Kingfish"

In an instant, Bulldog dove down toward the mosque, yelling a Texas "HEE HAWW" as the SAMs followed. Five seconds later, the mosque exploded as the F-22 and six SAMs rammed into the structure. Kingfish pulled up on the HOTAS, hands-on throttle and stick. The F-22 responded as he went to afterburners and pulled away from the six SAMs that gave chase. Kingfish could see the orange flames of the missile clearly now as he got closer and closer. He was crossing through 39,000 feet as he opened his radio channel and said, "Tell my wife and kids that I love them very much... Tell them that I am sorry, but I had to play the hand I was dealt... I hope that they will understand." Kingfish reached for the picture of his wife and children that he had secured to the right of the PMFD LCD and screamed, "DIE YOU MUTHA F... !" Suddenly the F-22, six SAMs and the missile became one and exploded in a ball of fire. The image of the explosion was recorded by the birds and relayed to the Nimitz and Bunker. Everyone stood in silence looking at the video screen.

JERUSALEM – 1205 HOURS

The President of Israel was speaking as the President and First Lady looked on. In a few moments, he would be asked to eulogize Prime Minister Cane. He nervously looked at his watch. It was estimated that the entire operation would only take two to three minutes.

It had now been five minutes since he had received the word that the attack had begun. Could it be that they were not going to tell him that the mission had failed? He looked up at the sky. If the missile came in, he was told to expect to hear the sound of an explosion and then the fireball would eviscerate his body in a nuclear holocaust. Beads of sweat formed over his lip and on his forehead. Linda was watching him nervously drumming her fingers lightly on her thigh. Suddenly, the President heard the voice of the secret service agent in Air Force One, "Mr. President... OPERATION THUNDERBALL is over. All three missiles have been destroyed. One of our pilots took out the last missile that was actually in the air. He took his F-22 and six SAMs with him into the target."

Looking up at the sky, the President replied, "Thank God...". Reaching over to his wife, he took her hand and gave it a squeeze. She looked at him as he mouthed the words, "It's OK."

The Chief Army Rabbi approached the podium as the President of Israel returned to his seat. Pausing briefly he said, "And now, words from the President of the United States."

The President walked slowly to the podium. In his suit pocket was a speech he had prepared earlier. He decided not to read it. Placing his hands on each side of the podium, the President said, "President of Israel and Acting Prime Minister Hochberg, members of the Israeli government and the Knesset, distinguished leaders from the Middle East and around the world and to the people of Israel, the American people and I mourn with you in the loss of your leader... Prime Minister Cane."

The President was not thinking about Prime Minister Cane as he spoke, but rather the brave American pilots that had just sacrificed their lives over Iraq. Slowly he looked around the gathering and continued, "Prime Minister Cane represented Israel in a time of intense difficulties and as the Prime Ministers before him David Ben-Gurion, Moshe Sharett, Levi Eshkol, Golda Meir, Yitzhak Rabin, Menachem Begin, Yitzhak Shamir, Shimon Peres and Benjamin Netanyahu... These leaders of Israel had what it took and gave freely of their lives to serve, protect and lead Israel. Often times, many of these leaders gave up their lives to keep Israel strong.

Today, we are assembled here in the remains of the Holy Temple, the Western Wall. Built by King David, this Temple was and still is the Temple of all nations. Looking around at this gathering today, the leaders of all nations have come here to pay their respects to Prime Minister Cane. Prime Minister Cane was my friend as well as the leader of Israel... During his last visit to the White House, Prime Minister Cane was reading a poem by Robert Frost that hangs in the Oval Office, "The Road Not Taken." I would like to recite that poem to you today because it sums up what I believe to be the leadership, bravery and devotion to Israel that was the hallmark of Prime Minister Cane.

THE ROAD NOT TAKEN

Two roads diverged in a yellow wood,
And sorry I could not travel both
And be one traveler, long I stood
And looked down one as far as I could
To where it bent in the undergrowth;

Then took the other, as just as fair,
and having perhaps the better claim,
because it was grassy and wanted wear;
Though as for that the passing there
Had worn them really about the same,

And both that morning equally lay
In leaves no step had trodden black.
Oh, I kept the first for another day!
Yet knowing how way leads on to way,
I doubted if I should ever come back.

I shall be telling this with a sigh
Somewhere ages and ages hence:
Two roads diverged in a wood, and I –
I took the one less traveled by,
And has made all the difference.

After reading the poem that night, Prime Minister Cane said to me that to find peace, one must often times take the road not taken… a road that is clearly a lonely road… and sometimes a very dangerous road.

People of Israel, fear not… for the people of the United States and the free world will not forsake you in your quest for peace. As the President of the United States, I speak for all of the people of the United States of America… and I pledge to you that you will not travel down the road to peace alone, for we will be with you. On this very spot where God tested Abraham and instructed him to kill his only son Yitzhak, Abraham's faith and devotion to God… made God change his mind and allow Abraham's son to live. In this case however, God's plan has taken Prime Minister Cane away from us.

Things do not happen in this world without a reason. Only God knows the reason for the tragic death of Prime Minister Joshua Cane. Perhaps, the reason is to test our faith and determination for the cause of peace. If that is the reason… then today the people of the world must renew their covenant with God and swear that they will never give up in their quest for peace. This is the covenant Prime Minister Cane made with God and with the people of Israel… may God bless and keep him. Prime Minister Cane is no longer with us, but he is not dead if we keep him in our hearts… and if we keep the cause of peace in our hearts… it too will be eternal."

Thirty minutes later, the lone F-22 touched down on the flight deck of the USS Nimitz. Five minutes after that, the two carrier groups began to launch a barrage of cruise missiles toward Iraq and in the United States, Stealth bombers took off heading on their round trip bombing mission.

BETHESDA NAVAL HOSPITAL – 0535 HOURS

The television set in the Presidential suite was following the memorial services in Jerusalem. Both Joshua and Jacky were sitting in their beds quietly watching the speeches being given by the leaders of the free world. Joshua looked at Jacky and said, "This is somewhat embarrassing… to listen to these people talk about me."

"Embarrassing… but nice don't you think?"

There was a soft knock on the door as the head nurse entered the room, "Col. Allan and Admiral Potter are outside and wish to speak with you… Do you feel up to having visitors at this early hour?"

Jacky looked at Joshua and said, "It's OK with me…"

Joshua said, "Please show them in…"

Col. Allan and Admiral Potter entered the room and stood silently. Joshua motioned to the chairs and said, "Please…"

Col. Allan pulled his chair between the two beds and said, "The President has asked that I give you an update… I have good news… the attack on the mosques went as planned. The missiles were there and we got them all."

Joshua replied, "Were there any causalities on your part?"

"Yes… they were much better prepared than we thought, we lost 14 men… one survived and has landed safely on the USS Nimitz. We are starting our 72 hour bombing blitz as we speak…"

Suddenly, the television image of the face of the anchorperson replaced the images of the memorial service in Jerusalem, "We interrupt the coverage of the memorial service for the late Prime Minister Cane to bring you this breaking story from Iraq. We take you now to the Pentagon where a press conference is about to begin…" Joshua reached for the remote and increased the volume as the image of blue drapes with the round seal of the Pentagon prominently displayed on a round plaque hung in the center. The seal displayed the image of the Pentagon building and the words Washington, D.C. were printed beneath it. A naval officer dressed in whites approached the brown wooden podium. His face was stern as he adjusted his glasses. The name Rear Admiral Briggs, Pentagon Spokesperson appeared across the bottom of the TV screen. Rear Admiral Briggs looked up and said, "At 0500 hours Washington time, the combined air squadrons of the carrier groups from the USS Nimitz and USS George Washington launched a surgical air attack against targets in Iraq. The objective of this attack was to destroy offensive weapons in Iraq. The surgical air strike was successful and the targets were destroyed." Briggs paused and began to address the questions that were now being hurled at him. Pointing to someone off camera he said, "Yes..."

"How long was the attack... were there any casualties..."

"The entire duration of the attack was approximately three minutes..."

"Were there any casualties?"

"Yes... fourteen of our pilots were shot down."

"Are the pilots that were shot down alive and in enemy hands?"

"All fourteen pilots are presumed lost and missing in action... we are hopeful for their safe return, but as you know, Sadaam has put a price on our pilots heads."

"Is the President aware of the attack?"

"Yes... he was informed..."

"Did the President authorize the strike?"

"Yes..."

"Did the US inform any other head of state about the attack?"

"No comment."

"Will the President be returning prematurely from Israel?"

"No comment."

"We are just now receiving information over the wire services that Iraq is being attacked as we speak... can you comment on these reports?

"No comment."

"Are elements of the two carrier battle groups involved in this continued attack?"

"No comment... Gentlemen, there will be another briefing at 0900 hours today." Briggs abruptly left the podium as the correspondents shouted countless questions. The image of the anchorperson appeared again saying, "That was a live news briefing from the Pentagon in Washington D.C.... Pentagon spokesperson, Rear Admiral Briggs. It would appear that the United States launched, what was described, as a surgical strike against three targets in Iraq. These targets were described to be offensive weapons targets." Turning to her left, the anchorperson remarked, "Tom... do you have any information regarding any continued attack against Iraq?"

"Yes Paula... ZNN has just received reports from other wire services abroad that Baghdad, Irbil and Al Basrah are under heavy attack by cruise missiles. Iraq is claiming that hundreds... if not thousands of innocent men, women and children are being killed by these missile attacks... about two minutes ago; we received a report that Iraq, Iran, Libya, Syria, China and Russia are demanding an immediate halt to the attack and are also demanding an immediate emergency session of the UN Security Council. We have also received information that the targets for the air strike in Iraq were three mosques. There are also reports that leaders of the Arab community are calling for an immediate Holy War... Jihad... against the United States in retaliation for bombings of these mosques..." Placing his hand on his ear, he paused and then continued, "I have just been informed that Israel has just gone into a state of full military alert...". Paula reappeared on the screen and remarked, "Looking at the memorial service in Jerusalem... I can tell you that there is no sign that the people attending the memorial service know anything about the attack..."

Joshua hit the mute button on the television set and threw back the bed sheets saying, "I need to talk with my people immediately... I cannot continue this charade any longer... my country will be at war with Iraq very soon."

Admiral Potter leaned forward and replied, "The President has instructed us to ask you to be patient a while longer. He will return home immediately after the memorial service and wants to meet with you immediately upon his return to Washington."

Joshua glared back and said, "What does he have in mind now... may I ask?"

"I do not know, but he will explain it to you himself I assure you. He is due back at Andrews by 3 PM today..."

Joshua waited several seconds before he made his reply, "I will wait and meet with him this afternoon, but after that... I must talk with my people... my country is about to go to war and I will not allow that to happen without me being at her side."

Both Allan and Potter stood as Col. Allan replied, "I understand...". Walking out of the Presidential suite, Allan approached a guard posted in the hallway and said, "Make sure that he sees and talks with no one until I return."

The guard snapped to attention and replied, "Yes Sir!"

NEW YORK CITY, EAST SIDE – 0545 HOURS

The telephone rang softly in the darkened bedroom of John Mc Kinney, Secretary General of the United Nations. Rubbing his eyes and reaching for the phone, he turned on the light and looked at the clock, "Hello..."

"Your Excellency... sorry to wake you up at this hour but there is a crisis in Iraq."

"What is it now?"

"The United States has attacked several mosques in Iraq and are now attacking other areas with cruise missiles. The United States has made an announcement through the Pentagon that they were attacking offensive military targets."

McKinney immediately sat up in bed and replied, "When did this start?"

"About an hour ago... Iraq, Iran, Libya, Syria, China and Russia are calling for an immediate cessation of the bombing and an immediate emergency meeting of the Security Council..."

"Has the President of the Security Council been notified?"

"Yes..."

"Give me an hour and I will meet you in my office." McKinney hung up the phone and immediately showered, dressed and left for his office.

ANDREWS AIR FORCE BASE – 1523 HOURS

The tires of Air Force One scorched the runway as the President returned from Israel. Inside his private quarters, he was completing a telephone conversation with the Secretary General, John McKinney. "Yes John… I understand completely the implications of our attack against Iraq and I understand what is being said about our attack by Iraq and other countries. World opinion is not in our favor at this time, but it soon will be when the truth is known."

"Mr. President, Iraq and others are demanding an emergency session of the Security Council and demanding that the United States immediately stop the attack against Iraq."

"I am well aware of their demands John, but we will not stop our attack until we have completely destroyed Iraq's ability to launch an attack against their enemies… to hell with world opinion… and to hell with Iraq and their friends."

"Mr. President… the die is cast. The emergency session of the Security Council will begin tomorrow morning at 9:00 AM…"

"Good… we have made a request that the venue be changed from the Security Council chambers to the General Assembly Hall. What will be exposed tomorrow will be something that the world will not believe. I want this emergency session to be held in General Assembly… the Security Council can do its job in the General Assembly in front of the world."

"I will arrange for it to be so Mr. President…"

"Thank you John… see you in the morning."

The President and First Lady left Air Force One and immediately entered the helicopter that would return them to the White House. As the helicopter approached the mall and the Washington Monument, the President looked down at the people that had gathered around the White House. Riot police had placed themselves between the mob and the White House fence. The angry people below were carrying signs of protest against the US and were shouting slogans against the American aggression in Iraq. Moments later, the helicopter landed on the White House lawn. Shouts of anger rose sharply as the President and First Lady exited the helicopter and walked across the lawn and entered the White House. The President immediately entered the elevator that would take him to the bunker 400 feet below. As the President entered the bunker, the Joint Chiefs of Staff saluted. The large screens around the room were displaying images of Iraq. The President sat down and replied, "How are we doing?"

Admiral Sheppard replied, "Not as good as we had hoped. Iraq has elaborate radar and anti-aircraft batteries that are shooting down 60% of the cruise missiles before they reach their targets. The stealth bombers are just arriving and they are using smart bombs to eliminate the radar dishes... we have lost several of them as well. It would appear that Iraq has at least a hundred dishes protecting each target area. These dishes are elaborately connected to an Ethernet backbone that allows their computers to alternate the use of the dishes and confusing our anti-radar weapons. That is why we lost 14 aircraft during the first attack. We were very lucky to get that last missile."

"Tell me about it..."

Sheppard continued, "As we successfully eliminate the dishes, we are slowly inactivating the anti-aircraft cannons. At this rate, I am afraid that the attack window may need to be extended by 24 hours."

"Do whatever it takes..."

The President looked at the images on the screens as the cruise missiles flew toward their targets. Four out of ten were completing their missions as their targets exploded upon their arrival. The others were being shot down by 20 mm and 40 mm cannons and either exploding in mid air or flying apart as the wall of steel tore them apart. The stealth bombers were arriving and could be seen on the situation screen. Small blue triangles representing the stealth bombers moved silently across the map. Looking from one screen to another, the President watched as the smart bombs exploded, taking out the radar dish targets and SAMs were taking out the Stealth bombers.

The President looked at Secretary of State Scrivanich and said, "I want the Prime Minister brought to the bunker ASAP. We have to bring him up to speed and then get him to New York for tomorrows emergency Security Council meeting."

BETHESDA HOSPITAL – 1545 HOURS

Col. Allan and Admiral Potter returned to the Presidential suite, knocked softly on the door and entered; both Joshua and Jacky were watching the news reports. Col. Allan approached the Prime Minister and said, "Mr. Prime Minister, the President has asked that you join him in the White House."

"I would be delighted."

Jacky looked at Joshua and replied, "I am going with you…"

Joshua looked concerned, "You must stay… you are not well enough to travel."

"I am your wife and my place is at your side… in sickness and in health… remember?"

"I understand that… but your eyes and burns…"

"I can see well enough and I can walk…"

Allan looked at Potter and said, "Get Dr. Greene and tell her to join us…."

Joshua looked at Potter and said, "How are we getting to the White House?"

"The same way you got here by helicopter. We will put both of you on a stretcher and carry you out. From there we will fly to the CIA and transfer you to the underground transportation system and shuttle both of you to the White House. Once you are ready to go, you will be in the White House within the hour."

Dr. Greene entered the suite and marched up to Allan and said, "What is the meaning of this... you can't just take my patient out of here."

Allan looked at Dr. Greene, his eyes were glaring as he said, "Can and will doctor... now get your things together on the double. You will be taking care of The Prime Minister and Mrs. Cane in the White House tonight... That's an order!"

Dr. Greene stood silently for several seconds as she regained control of her anger and said, "Yes Sir..."

Two gurneys were rolled into the Presidential suite. Both Joshua and Jacky were placed on the gurneys, covered with sheets and a blanket, and their faces were draped with a towel leaving only their noses exposed. Dr. Greene took the IV pole and followed as Jacky was rolled out of the suite toward the elevator. The secret service and CIA agents had closed off the route to the awaiting helicopter. Within five minutes, the helicopter took off toward the CIA. From there, Joshua and Jacky were transported to the White House via the network of underground tunnels. Upon their arrival at the White House, Jacky was taken to the President's quarters where the First Lady greeted Jacky and Dr. Greene. The Prime Minister was taken immediately to the bunker.

The elevator door opened and two secret service agents and the Prime Minister entered the bunker. The President immediately stood and approached Joshua. Joshua looked at the President and extended his hand saying, "I am glad that you made it back safely Mr. President."

"Me too Mr. Prime Minister." Gesturing with his hand, the President continued, "Please follow me... we have a great deal to talk about and very little time remaining before we go to New York."

Joshua raised his eyebrow and said, "New York?"

The President and Prime Minister sat together as his staff was introduced. Joshua could not keep his eyes from the large screens that were showing the attack against Iraq. The President looked at Joshua and said, "Here's the story. Sadaam has heavily fortified his military installations throughout Iraq. We are currently bombing each site with cruise missiles and stealth bombers. Unfortunately, 60% of our cruise missiles are being shot down along with 20% of our Stealth bombers. It looks like we can complete our mission, but it will take an additional 24 to 48 hours to do so. Iraq, Iran, Libya, Syria, China and Russia are demanding an immediate cessation of all hostilities and want an emergency meeting of the Security Council held tomorrow morning."

Joshua listened closely and replied, "I understand..."

"I have demanded that the emergency Security Council meeting be held in the General Assembly Hall rather than the Security Council so that the eyes of the world can watch you return from the dead."

"It sounds a little melodramatic don't you think?"

"Yes, but it is the only way to prove to the world that Iraq attempted to assassinate not only you, but the leaders of the free world. I understand that your wife came with you."

"That is correct Mr. President."

"With your permission, I would appreciate it if she comes to the UN with us tomorrow."

"Mr. President, my wife is badly burned and blind in one eye."

"Exactly... the people of the world will never forget the story that you will tell or sight of both of you standing before the them telling your story about the brainwashing of your wife, the sinking of the Titanic and the missiles in Iraq. World opinion is against the United States and Israel right now. We have been painted as the warmongers and killers of innocent men, women and children. They must be made to realize that if we had not attacked Iraq, millions of innocent Jewish men, women and children would have been eviscerated in a nuclear holocaust. I need a favor from you. I put my life on the line to smoke out Sadaam... please allow your wife to finish the job and drive a stake into his heart."

Joshua looked at the screens watching the cruise missiles and stealth bombers. The carrier battle groups USS Nimitz and USS George Washington had now committed their remaining F-22s and

F-16s to the fight. Looking like swarms of attacking bees, the situation map displayed the attacking aircraft and cruise missiles. The explosions shown on the main screens increased in frequency as the attack increased in tempo. Countless targets were being destroyed as several F-22s and F-16s were taken out by the remaining 20mm and 40mm cannons. The images on the screens were hypnotic as Joshua watched silently for several seconds. Finally he looked at the President and said, "I am sure that my wife would have it no other way Mr. President."

CHAPTER 17

APRIL 24, 2002

UNITED NATIONS – 0800 HOURS

The United Nations was formed on June 26, 1945 by the representatives of 50 countries and officially came into existence on October 24, 1945. The world headquarters for the United Nations is located on an 18-acre site located on the East side of Manhattan on First Avenue between 42nd and 48th streets. The headquarters complex consists of four main buildings, the General Assembly building, Conference Building, 39-story Secretariat building and the Dag Hammarsjold Library. A sweeping driveway entrance flanks the front of the UN complex that is lined with the flags of the 189 Member States.

The General Assembly hall has a seating capacity of 1,800 people and is crowned with a domed ceiling. In the front of the General Assembly Hall hangs the UN emblem that consists of a map of the world and flanked by olive wreaths. Directly in front of the UN emblem on the main floor is a row of stairs that leads up to the Secretary General's seat and desk, which is prominently positioned above the main speaking podium that faces the 189 Member States and visitor's gallery. Flanking the UN emblem are two large projection screens that are used to project the image of the person addressing the UN or to display important videos or slides during the meeting. To the right of the main podium are two elevated rows of windows that are observation rooms for television cameras and other supportive UN staff services.

The General Assembly hall was alive with Member State delegates arriving for the emergency Security Council meeting. UN security forces were actively checking the hall with dogs sniffing for explosives. Each Member State delegate entered the hall through metal detectors.

A few Member State delegates were checked by the security force using a hand held wand and still others had the contents of their briefcases inspected. Security was unbelievably tight.

The President, First Lady, Joshua and Jacky landed at Newark International Airport and were immediately driven in the Presidential limo to the UN in a long motorcade of secret service and police. The Presidential motorcade approached New York City through the Holland Tunnel and then proceeded up the East side to the UN complex. At the United Nations, the President and First Lady were escorted into the General Assembly hall by the secret service and taken to a private meeting room. When the time came, the President would enter the General Assembly hall to the left of the podium. Joshua and Jacky remained in a second limo and were driven to a different remote location behind the UN. Joshua was wearing a black suit and blond wig. He had been worked over by the secret service makeup department and sported a pair of horn rimed glasses and beard. Jacky was placed in a wheel chair and Dr. Greene pushed her gently into the building. Within five minutes, they joined the President and First Lady.

The Secretary General approached the meeting room and was stopped by the secret service agents. One of the men spoke into a hidden radio microphone and then gestured for the Secretary General to enter. As the door opened, Joshua turned toward the door, removing his wig and beard. McKinney froze in his tracks as he looked at Joshua. Another secret service agent closed the door behind the Secretary General as Joshua smiled and said, "You look surprised to see me."

The stunned Secretary General stood motionless and finely said, "Good God… I thought that you were dead."

"As does everyone else in the world."

The President remarked, "I wanted you to know first John… We are about to pull the plug on Sadaam. When the Prime Minister walks out there, the world is not going to believe what this man will tell them. I need another favor… you will open the meeting, but before the session starts, I want you to allow me to address the General Assembly and introduce the Prime Minister."

"That will be highly irregular... but I don't see why I can't do it... the world will be stunned when the Prime Minister walks up to the podium... stunned... absolutely stunned."

"That's exactly what I want to happen..."

McKinney nervously looked at his watch and said, "We only have five minutes..."

The President looked at McKinney and said, "Well... let's do it."

McKinney left the conference room and entered the General Assembly. The Member State delegates had assembled and were seated as he slowly climbed the chairs to his seat. The delegates immediately placed their interpreter headsets onto there heads and sat back silently awaiting the start of the meeting. McKinney looked out at the delegates and began, "There has been a request for an emergency meeting of the Security Council by the following Member States; Iraq, Iran, Libya, Syria, China and Russia. At the request of the United States, the meeting is being held in the General Assembly Hall. The rules of the Security Council will prevail during the meeting and any discussions of any motions made by the Security Council will be entertained only by the members of the Security Council. All others will refrain from any comments during the proceedings."

McKinney paused as he looked to his right and saw that the President was waiting in the wings and continued, "Before we begin the emergency Security Council meeting, I have agreed to allow the President of the United States of America to address the General Assembly." There was a loud murmuring from the delegates as the President approached the podium. His larger than life image was being displayed on the large viewing screens as the cameraman followed his steps from his vantage point above the Assembly Hall in the television room. Looking at the audience the President began, "Your Excellency, Member States of the United Nations and people of the world... as you know, the armed forces of the United States has attacked the country of Iraq. The purpose for this attack was to destroy offensive nuclear missiles that were targeted at Israel... to be specific ... Jerusalem." As he spoke, the images of the three Iraqi mosques with their missiles inside appeared on the viewing screens as the President continued, "These missiles were intended to be launched during the memorial services for Prime Minister Joshua Cane to kill all leaders of the free world who were attending the his memorial service..."

The delegate from Iraq stood up and yelled, "Mr. Secretary... I object to these lies..."

McKinney replied, "You are out of order... please take your seat."

The delegates from Syria, Libya, and Russia immediately joined the Iraqi delegate in his protest as they too voiced their opposition to charges made by the President. The delegate from China sat quietly watching the outburst as the General Assemble Hall erupted with voices of the other delegates. McKinney banged his gavel demanding silence and said, "If this outburst does not stop immediately, I will have the offending Member State delegates removed from the proceedings." Immediately, several armed UN security men began to approach the delegates from Iraq, Syria, Libya and Russia. As they approached, each protesting delegate sat down and remained silent.

The President continued, "I assure the honorable delegate from Iraq that I speak the truth and I would like to have someone else continue this discussion... someone who knows exactly what happened prior to his attempted assassination on board the Titanic as well as the plans for the attempted assassination of the rest of the leaders of the free world. Member delegates... I give you Prime Minister Joshua Cane..."

The General Assembly erupted into chaos and then deafening silence as Joshua approached the podium. Dr. Greene followed behind pushing Jacky in her wheel chair. The giant screens displayed them both as they approached the podium. The President stood back, allowing Joshua access to the podium and Jacky was positioned by his side, to his left. Joshua looked out over the General Assembly and said, "Thank you Mr. President. Your Excellency, Member Delegates and citizens of the world... as you can see, the news of my demise has been greatly exaggerated... I am very much alive. The words spoken by the President of the United States are true..."

The UN cameraman positioned in the second row television room slowly inched his right hand toward a storage compartment in the camera mount and removed a 9 mm automatic pistol that was fitted with a small telescopic site. He continued to train the camera on Joshua as his fingers found the cold steel and encircled the pistol grip and slowly stepped away from the camera. The image of Joshua was being displayed perfectly on the two viewing screens in the General Assembly hall as the cameraman slowly began to raise the pistol. As the image of Joshua appeared in the site, the gunman carefully lined up Joshua's head between the crosshairs and opened fire. The General Assembly erupted into a state of panic as return fire erupted from UN security guards. There was the sound of shattering glass and screams filling the General Assembly hall as the security guards returned fire and emptied their clips at the lone assassin. Seconds later, his bullet riddled body fell through the shattered window onto the delegates below.

EPILOG

ARLINGTON NATIONAL CEMETARY

The flag draped coffin of fourteen American pilots lay silently above their final resting place in Arlington National Cemetery. The sound of a 21-gun salute filled the air as a Marine bugle man played Taps. The wives and families of the 14 airmen wept as they watched the honor guardsmen snap to attention and fold each of the fourteen American flags. The President and First Lady watched silently as the flags were given to each of the widows. Overhead, the sound of jets filled the air as a formation of F-22s made a flyby with one F-22 pealing out, streaking alone across the sky to form the missing man formation, a final tribute to a fallen aviator.

JERUSALEM

A single coffin, draped with an Israeli flag rested silently above its final resting place. The army's chief rabbi chanted the Kaddish. When the Kaddish was finished the sounds of sirens filled the air across Israel in a final tribute as a 21-gun salute was fired over the grave. The Israeli honor guard snapped to attention and folded the Israeli flag. Carrying the flag gently in his hands, the honor guardsman glided across the cemetery, his hands outstretched holding the flag and stopped before Prime Minister Cane. As the sirens continued to wail, Joshua accepted the flag, tears welling in his eyes and rolling down his cheek. The honor guardsman turned and silently glided away as Joshua closed his eyes, returning in his mind to those last terrible seconds in the United Nations.

Jacky had been sitting silently listening to her husband. The grandeur of the General Assembly Hall had impressed her. She had performed in many great theaters throughout the world, but the General Assembly Hall with its beautiful dome had taken her by surprise. She quietly looked at Joshua and then at the two rows of windows wondering about the people that sat silently listening. Her eyes wandered down the row of glass and noticed the television camera room. A lone camera was looking at her husband. Suddenly, she watched as the cameraman stepped away from the camera, raising his hand. In it was a gun. "NO…" Her reaction was automatic and instinctive as she raised herself up out of the wheelchair and tried to push Joshua away from the podium. Five bullets struck her in the back, propelling her into Joshua's arms. She looked at Joshua with a startled expression, as blood began to slowly trickle from the corner of her mouth. Joshua was horror stricken as he lowered her to the floor. Looking up at Joshua, Jacky whispered softly, "I love you…" Her hand trembled as she placed it softly against his cheek before it fell limply across her breast. Joshua embraced Jacky in his arms and wept repeating the words, "Jacky… don't go… NO… NO… Jacky… Jacky, don't leave me."

The tears fell softly onto the flag as Joshua stood silently at the graveside remembering the past. A feeling of loneliness filled his heart as he looked down at the coffin. For Jacky, there would now be eternal peace and yet, as the sound of a distant jet fighter rumbled across the sky, he realized that a lasting peace for his country and the world was still as elusive as it had always been. Jacky's voice filled his mind, "If you run away and hide, you will soon learn to hate yourself… and me. I did not marry a man that runs away… Remember Joshua… you can never run away from yourself… you can never run away from yourself… you can never run away from yourself… you can never run away from yourself."

Joshua wiped away the tears from his eyes, as he looked at the grave of his son, to the right of his mother's freshly dug grave. Jacky would spend eternity next to David and when his time came, he would rest eternally with his family. He looked back fondly on the memory of his son, the short period of time they had together, and now he had lost Jacky. Looking across the cemetery, he wondered what more had to be done, what more could be done to put an end to senseless wars and the death of so many innocent people? He had lost his family. What more did he have left to give? He knew the answer all to well. There was no answer. He knelt and filled his hand with the soil from Jacky's grave. As it slipped through his fingers and fell softly on Jacky's casket, he closed his eyes and whispered, "Yes my love... rest in peace... Shalom."

In the months that followed the UN tragedy, the world returned to its normal state of organized confusion. There was an uneasy feeling that somewhere in the world, another countdown was beginning and what it would bring was the topic of endless discussion by news commentators and newspaper editors around the world.

The relationship between the United States and China was of great concern and the feeling was that Washington and Beijing were headed toward confrontation as China continued to emerge as an economic and military power in Asia. It was believed that conflict between the two would be inevitable. Russia was leaning toward the old days of communism after their failed attempt at capitalism. More than once they rattled their rusty sabers at the United States as dark clouds of another cold war became visible on the distant horizon. In the Middle East, it was business as usual. Iraq once again began to rebuild and rearm since Sadaam had once again survived. In Israel, the Palestine situation continued to fester with no solution in sight.

As the world went about its business, there was the oppressive feeling lurking in the minds of everyone that one day, something else would happen and the evildoers would once again bring the world to the brink of destruction. The only question that remained was when? Feeding on the global paranoia, television evangelists preached Armageddon and cable networks once again, as they had done for the Millennium, revisited the topic of the "end of the world" and produced new documentaries loosely based on prophecies of ancient civilizations and Nostradamus. As one commentator put it, perhaps the world would end at dawn on December 22, 2012. After all, the Mayan calendar that was started in 3113 BC suddenly stopped on December 22, 2012, the dawn of a new Solar Age. Did the Mayans know something that we didn't? Only time would tell.

THE END

Printed in the United States
5922

9 781588 320506